RHINEGOLD

WORLD CONSERVA

S

AN INTERNATIONAL GUIDE TO MUSIC ST

2010

RHINEGOLD DIRECTORIES

First published in 2010 in Great Britain by
Rhinegold Publishing Ltd
241 Shaftesbury Avenue
London WC2H 8TF
United Kingdom
+44 (0)20 7333 1761

British Library Cataloguing in Publication Data.
A catalogue record for this book is available from the British Library.
ISBN 978-1-907447-06-8
ISSN 2040-2449

Printed in Great Britain by Headley Brothers Ltd, The Invicta Press, Queens Road, Ashford, Kent TN24 8HH

CONTENTS

Tom Woods
FINE STRINGED INSTRUMENTS
LONDON
Fine Italian, French & English
cellos from 17th - 20th century
Telephone: 0207 362 1812
Online cello gallery at: www.tomwoodscellos.com

EDITOR'S FOREWORD

Welcome to the 2010 edition of *Rhinegold World Conservatoires: An international guide to music study*, brought to you by the UK's leading publisher of music magazines, reference books and educational study guides, Rhinegold Publishing Ltd.

Music has often been associated with itinerancy, whether in history (the medieval troubadours and trobairitz), tradition (west African griots), myth (Orpheus) or 21st century life (the globe-trotting concert artist). It goes for musical training too. As an illustration, try working out your musical family tree – find out who taught your teacher, who taught them and so on. Before too long you're likely to find a Russian pianist, American violinist, French singer or similar, someone to give your music education an international flavour.

There is something about music which makes it mobile in this way. Even if music is not the universal language some like to claim, you certainly don't need to speak the language of your recital partner or your audience to make yourself understood musically, and there are not many professions where that is the case. So perhaps it is only natural that musicians are drawn to travel, to take their art to foreign places, to look for inspiration in faraway lands and musical traditions.

It is against this background that we at Rhinegold firmly believe that spending at least some time studying abroad is one of the most positive steps a student musician can take. So we have produced this book, partly to whet the appetite of those who might be considering it, partly to provide information to help them through the process. It includes listings for the major professional training establishments around the world (including a selection of opera studios on page 282) along with snapshots of the towns and cities, and their musical and cultural life, where they are found. There is also advice on choosing your course, on preparing to travel to and settling in a new country (we asked a number of students who have spent time abroad for their experiences), and on learning languages. And for those who may be looking beyond the western classical tradition, we have an introduction to the study of Indian classical music (it's on page 274).

If you have spent time abroad, we'd love to hear your experiences; wherever you have been let us know how you got on by emailing us: directories@rhinegold.co.uk

Toby Deller

London, February 2010.

Contributors:

Hannah Beynon, Toby Deller, Chris Elcombe, Felicity Hayward, Ashutosh Khandekar, Owen Mortimer, Alex Stevens, Clare Stevens

Special thanks to Dr Suvarnalata Rao and N Ramanathan

WHY SPECIALIST STUDY?

WHY STUDY AT A SPECIALIST INSTITUTION?

So your high school course is going well; your instrumental studies are in good shape; holiday courses with a youth orchestra or choir are the highlights of your year; or perhaps your compositions have been performed by a school ensemble or used as incidental music for a play. You have decided that music is the most important thing in your life, and you want to make it the basis of a career. What happens next? How do you choose between the myriad options for studying music at degree level?

UNIVERSITY OR CONSERVATOIRE?

For previous generations, the difference between a university and a conservatoire course was clear-cut: if your interest in the subject was primarily academic, you went to university and emerged with a degree; if you knew you wanted to be a full-time performer, you went to a conservatoire, where the focus of your time would be on your principal study and your schedule would consist of little more than tutorial sessions with an eminent teacher and hours and hours of practice, culminating in the award of a performance diploma.

Now, however, all UK conservatoires offer BMus degrees and a range of other undergraduate and postgraduate qualifications. So what is the difference between the two pathways?

You could say it is a question of balance between the vocational and academic content of the courses. A singer, for example, studying at a London conservatoire might find that the compulsory elements of their course included extended exercises in Schenkerian analysis, previously a hallmark of university courses. The aim is to nurture more rounded musicians than in

COMPOSITION

If at all possible, try to arrange a meeting with potential tutors. Open days may be a good time to do this, but they are relatively hectic so do not be afraid to sound out institutions over the possibility of a one-to-one consultation. It is not necessary for you and your tutor to share every tenet of a musical philosophy, but you should take steps to ensure you will not be at loggerheads from the outset.

Composers often find themselves struggling to mobilise fellow musicians to play their work, something dictated to a large extent by the institution's general attitude to contemporary music. Attend an open day and look for evidence of a contemporary music society or ask the department how easily composers organise performances. Your cultivated cajoling may not be so effective in a different country and/or language, so try to ensure there is a good scene before you arrive.

Competitions remain the favoured way to get noticed, but you may ask about local festivals, formal or informal links with performing institutions, or the typical career paths of recent graduates. As with other disciplines, if there are eminent, well-connected faculty members in your department who you are able to impress, you may get opportunities.

The technical/creative balance of composition being different to that of instrumental players, you should also seriously think about academic study at a university – certainly for undergraduate level. Less emphasis on composing techniques and more on broad musical knowledge could be more beneficial to your musical development, perhaps to be followed by a more technical approach in future study (this does not only apply to composers). Of course, the opposite may be true: if you feel you need sharpening, then go for a conservatoire.

Many composers have trained only in universities, or have undertaken very little training at all. It is not a formalised career and there are many more ways of reaching competency than with the rigid training and techniques of instrumental playing. Composers should choose carefully where and how to practise.

Jazz

Some differences between institutions are not specific to jazz courses, such as the number of students on the course, the amount of solo tuition time, links with visiting professionals (masterclasses etc).

Jazz-specific variations include: the degree of emphasis on standards/traditional American repertoire – some courses see this as the bedrock, while others offer more contemporary options, or let students explore their own interests to a greater extent; opportunities for composition/arrangement, and whether it is at all integrated with other composition courses (jazz composition increasingly explores orchestral/classical chamber sounds and structures); chances to collaborate with other departments such as brass and percussion; options such as professional development/promotion; the availability of group-sized rehearsal rooms, plus recording studio facilities (see below).

Opportunities to perform in external venues are invaluable – what's the local scene like, and does the conservatoire have links with any venues?

Regular, organised ensemble work and coaching is important, as is the size of the student group, in an area in which group creativity and interaction is especially important: the opportunity to work closely with a small number and develop intimate relationships could be vital, although some students might prefer to be exposed to a wider range of contacts.

Good jazz musicians who are also good teachers are relatively thin on the ground so it's worth asking around and probably having a trial lesson with members of the department.

Look for decent facilities – large practice rooms for vital ensemble work and good production/recording facilities (and, ideally, tuition) too.

Open days are always a good opportunity to get more details about amount of tuition/performance opportunities, details of which are usually rather general in prospectuses, as well as finding out if any of the staff are specialists in anything you're interested in (such as Latin music, or free jazz). Also take the opportunity to ask about provision for any particular interests you may have – learning a second instrument (percussion/singing/piano/bass) for example, can really improve your understanding of the component parts of a jazz ensemble, and enhance rhythmic/compositional skills.

It might also be worth finding out how many students of your instrument the conservatoire usually takes to give you an idea of your chances of successful application, especially if you're a rhythm section member.

You should aim to have a firm grasp of jazz language in a range of common styles and a strong technique on your instrument – you'll need to be able to play in a number of styles, often at short notice, to get known, either at jam sessions or filling in in other people's bands. Strong aural and rhythmic skills are a prerequisite, as is the ability to build and shape strong improvisations, and an understanding of group ensemble is vital. Good notation skills, plenty of performance experience and some contacts with contemporaries and perhaps also professionals are also vital. Graduates should also have developed a fairly extensive knowledge of standard repertoire (from memory).

Above all, students should aim to be well on the way to having an individual, creative voice that can communicate original ideas in a coherent way.

the past and give students a deeper understanding of their subject. Some conservatoire students will relish this opportunity; others may struggle to fulfil the course requirements. Ultimately, unless they are composition or conducting students it is probably not a priority for them; they will be much more concerned about their relationships with their teachers and about the performance opportunities or competition successes that will help to boost their future careers.

University students can expect to find core elements of their undergraduate courses such as music history and analysis taken much more seriously by their contemporaries and by teaching staff. In most music departments they will be extremely well taught and progress through to final assessments or examinations will depend on successful results in earlier years. Performance skills, on the other hand, will carry much less weight and may not even be assessed at all.

Performing opportunities

Opportunities to play in symphony orchestras or chamber ensembles, sing in choirs or perform in operas abound in both conservatoires and universities. However, for a promising student who is accustomed to being principal oboe in a county youth orchestra, for example, or singing the solos in an oratorio, it may be hard to accept the realities of life in a conservatoire where everyone is of an equal standard or better. Solo or principal player opportunities may never come their way; they may never even get to play in the college's first orchestra. The first lesson many conservatoire students learn is that competition is fierce and the music profession is even tougher than they had been led to believe. Those who opt for university, where ensembles will include non-music students, may have a more enjoyable experience even if the overall standard of the orchestra is lower.

At both university and conservatoire, the best performance opportunities may turn out to be those created by students themselves. If you have a burning desire to conduct a particular symphony or opera, or form a string quartet or vocal consort, this is the place to do it; you may never again have such a pool of talent at your disposal. Many ensembles that are household names today have their origins in experimental concerts put on in Cambridge college chapels or a university recital hall. Other established groups owe their existence

SINGING

Most places have links with certain opera companies – some formal, but most informal. The differences between these are quite major – it's hard to know without knowing people already on the courses.

Course options vary from place to place but generally each institution will offer a similar range of classes (eg acting/movement) for a similar length of time - these can vary a lot in quality.

The quality of fellow students will obviously vary, and the best institution doesn't always produce the best singers. It may just be a case of which place had the most scholarship money in one year, or just naturally gifted singers, or a good match of singers to teachers.

The personnel associated with each place is far more important than the structure of the course, and your teacher is paramount. You have to decide before you go exactly who you want to be noticed by, staff-wise. This is particularly pertinent if you are interested in a certain style of singing. Who the visiting opera coaches are is also important if you are looking at opera as a specialism.

Performance opportunities, such as opera scenes, are important, and the

to coaching residencies by distinguished mentors from which they benefitted as conservatoire students.

THE IMPORTANCE OF YOUR TEACHER

Inspirational lecturers and good relationships with your academic and personal tutors are important components of a rewarding university course, but your success and happiness will probably not stand or fall on relationships with teaching staff to the same extent as it does at conservatoire. It is still the case for anyone aspiring to a career as a solo performer that their relationship with their principal study teacher is crucial. Many will choose to study at a particular college because a certain performer is on the staff, and this outweighs any other considerations.

This is where students with prior knowledge through their existing teachers or through family connections are at a real advantage. Attending the junior department of one of the conservatoires will also help to form impressions of the tutors for their instrument, through talking to older students or attending masterclasses by conservatoire staff. Those whose experience is more limited may be able to enrol on a summer school taught by a conservatoire professor, or arrange a consultation lesson, in order to test a relationship.

Otherwise, new arrivals will simply be allocated to a professor for their discipline, perhaps with a smaller number of additional lessons from other tutors on the same instrument. Bear in mind that it is sometimes possible to change the number of lessons you receive from each tutor if one relationship works out particularly well or badly.

LOCATION, LOCATION, LOCATION

Another important factor in the choice of conservatoire is its location. A teenager from a rural village may find living in London overwhelming; the Royal Welsh College of Music and Drama in Cardiff or the Royal Scottish Academy of Music and Drama (RSAMD) in Glasgow might be a better bet for them. Travelling in London is expensive and time-consuming; students may find themselves living an hour's bus ride or more from college. The flip side of that is the opportunity to take advantage of all the top flight concerts that take place in the capital every night of the week, often offering cheap or free tickets for music students, ▶

quality of the theatre and opera productions could be relevant – it is worth making the effort to see one while you are choosing.

The number of people in your year can have a significant impact – a large number leads to not enough performance opportunities in class and coaches being spread very thinly; conversely, too few of the same voice type can restrict chances to hear others singing your repertoire, or to hear new repertoire from them.

Enquire after any relevant information that isn't given on the prospectus – extra visiting professors for example, or how often those mentioned actually come; and details of contact time/nature of classes/what actually goes on in a class. Answers will be cagey if there are weaknesses in that institution, but you could ask to be put in touch with ex-students: every singing student thinks his/her teacher is brilliant/awful while they're being taught by them. It's only afterwards that you can properly assess what was good/bad about them. This could be all the more valuable as some institutions don't offer enough guidance to their students on entry as to who would be best, and some charge for each consultation lesson, which may be prohibitive to a new student.

If, following these enquiries/consultation lessons, you have serious doubts about all possible teachers, it may not be the right course for you. Also avoid courses with particular emphases on certain periods (such as early music) or styles (opera) if this isn't your thing.

Don't necessarily expect to have a better technique after a postgrad course – and don't overstretch yourself by attempting repertoire that is beyond you. You should come out knowing plenty of repertoire well, and 5 arias/songs inside out, knowing that you can take them into an audition without risk.

and to savour the experience of studying in historic buildings such as Trinity's Old Royal Naval College in Greenwich.

Preparation for the Profession

Whereas the guidance that university careers departments can offer to music graduates is usually limited, all UK conservatoires are now geared to equipping their students for life beyond college. They are given opportunities to teach or take part in outreach activities, to develop skills such as sound engineering, and to attend seminars on marketing themselves, managing their finances or preparing for auditions. Nevertheless, too many students do still emerge from conservatoire with a naive view of their futures, partly because they have not taken advantage of the help that is on offer. The fact that instrumental or vocal tutors are rarely involved in aspects of students' professional training beyond the development of technique and musicianship has been identified as one reason for this. On the other hand, many music graduates say that the best aspect of their conservatoire experience was the opportunity to pick up their first professional engagements on the recommendation of their tutors.

Assessing the Options

There has never been a better time for prospective students to compare and contrast a variety of institutions and courses. University and conservatoire websites provide a wealth of information about individual departments and facilities – you can watch video interviews with current students and staff, have a look at the concert diaries of recital halls and find out about fees and bursaries. But there is no substitute for attending an open day, which will provide a much better impression than scrolling through an online prospectus.

Over to You

Wherever you end up studying, don't forget it is up to you to make the most of the opportunity you have been given. The music graduates who look back most fondly on their college days are those who spent hours playing a neglected collection of early keyboard instruments, seized the chance to have their new compositions performed by willing volunteers, or unexpectedly discovered that their real passion was for accompanying. Despite the best effort

BRASS AND WOODWIND

For ambitious soloists, getting to learn with a prestige concert player may mean you have to be fairly prestigious yourself. Still, high-profile figures are attainable. If you do admire a particular performer, see if they are teaching anywhere and find out the likelihood of them teaching you by asking the department administrator.

Orchestral students are likely to be in a good position to check up on their potential teachers and this is something that you should certainly do: which bands do they perform with, what recordings have they made? If they are well-connected the likelihood is that you soon will be as well.

Remember that, for wind and brass players, there is always the danger of a paucity of orchestral performing opportunities – at least in the conservatoire's main bands. Find out the depth of orchestral opportunities, and be prepared for a lot of chamber music. You may need to be proactive and arrange your own groups and concerts.

Your second study instrument is an important consideration – be careful not to have your heart set on recorder lessons, only to find that you must study the piccolo. Some conservatoires may not have the facility for certain instruments – bagpipers, for instance, should probably go to the RSAMD or consider a forces career.

Be sure of details, such as different styles of instrument. Bassoonists may need to take care of the Buffet/Heckel divide if planning to study on the continent. Brass players may find surprises of clef and transposition; though these can only add to the rich tapestry of a musical education. And details of tuition: check the hours of contact time and who they will be with.

of college administrators, conservatoires and university music departments often tend to be chaotic places where students are expected to be self-directing and self-motivating to a large extent. So do your research, choose your destination carefully, but be prepared for surprises and to forge your own pathway to success. Good luck!

STRINGS

For instrumental students, teaching is probably paramount: if your one-to-one tuition is letting you down, there is little point in being at a conservatoire at all. Make the effort to find out about the faculty and do your research on possible teachers. If any stand out, explore your options with the institution – can they guarantee your preference? What do you have to do to ensure it?

Know what you want to get out of the course. Talented young soloists travel the world to turn heroes into mentors, while orchestral musicians should think about local professional orchestras and chamber groups: do they have desk-sharing schemes for local students, or could you find yourself getting onto their lists?

In a similar vein, be aware that the relationships you make at a conservatoire will form the basis of your professional network, so it may be sensible to think about staying in the same place after graduation. Don't be naïve about where work is going to come from later.

Consider whether you want to be extensively involved in chamber performance. Perhaps you have decided that solo playing is the only thing for you, in which case you should concentrate on finding the right teacher. Others believe ensemble playing is an essential part of a musician's make-up – although taking part in chamber groups is compulsory at many conservatoires. Having chosen to specialise by choosing a conservatoire over university it may be sensible to broaden your horizons as much as possible. Make your decision and check out the options.

If you have a history of injuries, you might wish to study at an institution which has research interests, or at least makes general noises, on the subject. The Rotterdam Conservatoire runs a scheme called 'Health Platform' which acts to prevent, find treatment for and contribute research about students' injuries. Check for elective modules in Alexander technique or physiotherapy. If your problems are chronic, raise the issue – it is bound to become apparent at some stage of your studies.

Do not forget to check the basics: how many hours of one-to-one tuition time you will receive, and with whom. Many conservatoires will employ a teacher's assistant who will give you secondary tuition, and you should check the time allotted to each. Finally, your current teacher should be able to give you guidance, even about foreign study. Do not forget to ask their opinion.

STUDYING ABROAD?

Why study abroad? Well, if travel broadens the mind, then a period of studying overseas can blow your mental horizons wide open. For a musician, studying abroad offers many opportunities for professional and personal development. String players, for instance, may want to head to Vienna and pianists to Moscow to immerse themselves in an approach to technique and style that's quite different from anything they will encounter in British conservatoires. Brass and wind players, too, will find Germanic and Scandinavian musical cultures have a lot to offer in exploring different, often enlightening approaches to teaching and performance. Few singers will be able to make a good career if they stick purely to home territory, and the networking opportunities offered by taking courses overseas will stand them in good stead for developing future strands of professional work in different areas of the world.

Studying overseas helps musicians to connect to areas of the music industry that are not easily accessed from the UK. Promoters, artist managements, auditioning panels and casting directors all operate differently in different areas of the world, and some familiarity with how other cultures go about their business can be an invaluable asset to any musical career.

For some, studying abroad will be merely an adjunct to getting to know another culture and being immersed in a totally new tradition. It's unlikely that a classical musician who has trained in earnest in the UK will gain much in the way of professional career development by going to areas of the world where interest in western classical music is either or non-existent at best nascent. However, for encounters with other musical traditions, and an opportunity to exchange experiences and skills with musicians from very different backgrounds, a stint of studying music in places such as India or Africa can be extremely rewarding at a personal and creative level. You can read more about studying Indian classical music on page 274.

Using study as a means of engineering an extended recreational visit to another country is a risky tactic. A genuine interest in the chosen course of study is usually a prerequisite to building towards a career in music. Otherwise, staying motivated while coping with an unfamiliar culture might be difficult. Often this motivation will come from connecting with a respected teacher or being given opportunities to become involved in a professional forum such as a renowned orchestra or opera house.

To get the most out of studying abroad, careful preparation is vital. Unrealistic expectations at the planning stage can lead to misery and money down the drain further down the line. On the whole, studying music abroad involves the same rigours that go into becoming a professional musician in the UK, but with added challenges such as cultural unfamiliarity and the need to be unusually self-sufficient. Below are some of the factors you should consider if you are planning to embark on such an endeavour.

STUDYING ABROAD?

What is your motive for studying abroad?

If you want to go purely in order to advance your instrumental (or vocal) skills, then your priority should be to vet the institutions you will be applying for thoroughly. Look at who is on the faculty and make enquiries as to their professional reputation and their teaching methodology. If you are at a UK conservatoire, there may well be exchange schemes whereby teachers are accredited in partner organisations and the period spent abroad will contribute to your overall degree or qualification. The likelihood is that you will be going abroad because there is someone specific with whom you want to study. In this case, be aware that you will also need to be comfortable with the culture around you and well prepared for your new surroundings. Russia and the former Soviet states, for example, may have fine traditions of music teaching, but local languages are difficult to learn and teaching methods are often prescriptive and disciplined to an extreme degree.

How will you survive financially?

Studying is one thing, but how do you keep body and soul together in a context where you have no support system? First, you must research the costs of living in your chosen destination thoroughly. A scholarship or grant may look decent on paper, but big, international cities can be exorbitantly expensive to live in anywhere in the world, and finding decent accommodation can take time and effort. As far as possible, do a recce to set things up before you start your course and to get a realistic idea of how much your living expenses will be. Pump the locals for information as much as possible and take advantage of any resources and connections that your new place of study can put your way.

A few things to consider when it comes to finances:

- Transferring money and setting up bank accounts overseas can be much more complicated than you expect. Make sure that you have easy access to your bank account at home (hole-in-the-wall cards are very useful) as it could take a long time to set up accounts abroad. The US is especially notorious for this.
- Always have contingency funds to cope with unexpected events. There's nothing worse that feeling stuck miles from home without the wherewithal to return whenever you need to. Book air tickets that give you flexibility on return dates.
- UK passport holders studying in the EU can take part-time employment to fund their courses (some conservatoires don't officially allow this). Remember, however, that in many countries outside the EU, UK citizens on a student visa will be forbidden to take paid jobs, so don't count on being able to work - and that includes teaching and giving concerts - to support yourself through your studies.
- Some UK conservatoires offer exchange programmes with overseas counterparts, and sometimes these include free or subsidised board and lodging. Opting to take a well-trodden institutional path will be off-putting to those who want to study overseas out of a sense of adventure; for others it provides a reassuring way of living and learning in a new context.
- One major advantage of studying in the USA is that there are a number of generous grants and scholarships available, particularly for postgraduates, many of which cover travel, accommodation and fees. Competition for places is fearsome, but once you are in, US conservatoires and music academies go out of their way to make overseas students feel welcome and well looked-after.
- There are areas of the world such as the Baltics and eastern Europe where the cost of studying and living is considerably cheaper than in the UK, but where music education exists to a high standard. As mentioned above, however, the challenges of language and cultural differences are ever present.

Before you go

- Outside the EU, most UK students will require a special visa to study abroad. In most cases, these visas are reasonably easily obtained from the relevant consulate, but often a raft of documents to support your application will need to be sent by the organisation where you will be studying. Make sure you know exactly what is required in advance, otherwise you will waste a lot of time waiting in queues only to be sent away for more documents at the final hurdle.

- Regulations for obtaining US study visas have tightened considerably since the 9/11 terrorist attacks. Anybody visiting America to pursue a study course of more than 18 hours a week is now required to travel on student visa. There is a useful and comprehensive official website at http://educationusa.state.gov/
- In most Asian and Middle Eastern countries, overseas students are required to register with the police and with their local consulate on arrival – a wise thing to do in the unlikely event of emergencies. Take print outs of scans of your passport with you, as they may be required for official purposes.
- A good, comprehensive insurance policy is vital - particularly for medical coverage and emergency repatriation. Make sure your policy covers study overseas and that coverage for your instrument is valid for abroad.
- Health issues may be of some concern to students planning extended stays in developing countries. The Foreign Office website generally has all the information you will need to take the right precautions: www.fco.gov.uk
- Consider what steps you might need to take to make sure your instrument remains in good shape if you are heading for exotic climes. Conditions such as extreme humidity in the tropics or excessive heat and dryness can have a disastrous effect on your priceless Strad.
- Taking your instrument on an aircraft needs planning. It's a good idea to discuss the airline's policy towards musical instruments when you book your ticket. If you are a cellist or a double bass player, you will almost certainly have to book an extra seat if you want to carry your instrument in the cabin. Excess baggage charges may apply to large, heavy instruments being checked in as hold luggage.

The most comprehensive source of information on studying abroad can be found in the country specific information, where you will also be able to find information on studying in particular countries. In addition, embassies are a useful source of information. Project Visa has a searchable directory of contact details for many of the embassies around the world (http://projectvisa.com).

Studying abroad is a life-changing experience which can be both challenging, and deeply rewarding. And with travel becoming ever easier and the choice of institutions in which to study increasing year on year, the world, or the musical one anyway, really is a student's oyster! However, making the choice of where to study shouldn't be made lightly, and although it is tempting to find the country with the most sunshine and widest selection of flavoured beers, it is ultimately the educational institute itself which should take precedence. Careful time and consideration should be taken over which place would provide you with the most opportunity and best standard of teaching. Indeed, it is for the teachers themselves that many international students choose to study away from home in the first place, in the hope that, through learning with some of the best tutors in the world, they will gain significantly wider experiences and, in turn, heighten their overall career prospects.

In addition to gaining the opportunity to study with a particular tutor and uncovering a plethora of opportunities, studying abroad can equip you with a wide range of other skills which can enhance any future career; confidence, language skills, attraction to employers in a global market and world of cultural diversity, for example.

And it is not just the students who benefit. Having a diverse range of international students is also an important factor for the face of many institutions. The international fees alone provide a fundamental level of financial support for the conservatoires, in the UK at least, while sporting a diverse mix of students can also help create global status and recognition for the conservatoires. 'International students are very important for us,' says Miranda Harris, public relations and international communications manager at Trinity College of Music, London. 'They add another dimension to the overall student experience – adding to the richness of our artistic

NAME Rebecca Celebuski (percussion & timpani) **FROM** USA

WHERE DID YOU GO? Royal College of Music, UK

WHY DID YOU CHOOSE THERE? It was the only study abroad program available for musicians at Boston University. I initially went on an exchange, but loved it so much that I transferred.

WHAT DID THEY DO TO HELP YOU WHEN YOU ARRIVED? Organised a tour, a meeting with all of the people we needed to know, an international students' party and, of course, Freshers Week.

HOW DID YOU ADAPT TO LIVING IN A FOREIGN CITY? The same language, but still a surprising amount of language barrier moments! The amount of travelling in London gets tiring and I found people more introverted as well.

HOW EASY WAS IT TO SETTLE IN AND MAKE FRIENDS? It was very easy for me to make friends because the percussion department is particularly friendly and tight-knit, and we all practise in the same place so we see each other a lot. There are a lot of social activities as well which help with socialising, but you do have to make an effort yourself as well. If you're shy, it forces you to come out of your shell.

WHAT ADVICE WOULD YOU GIVE SOMEONE PLANNING TO STUDY ABROAD? Don't hang out with all your friends from your home country the whole time; you won't get a real study abroad experience that way.

NAME Jung Soo Yun (tenor) **FROM** South Korea

WHERE DID YOU GO? Royal Scottish Academy of Music & Drama, London and Cardiff International Academy of Voice

WHY DID YOU CHOOSE THERE? Recommendation from a friend who studied in the UK.

WHAT DID THE INSTITUTION DO TO HELP YOU WHEN YOU ARRIVED? They held language classes and arranged student accommodation.

HOW EASY WAS IT TO SETTLE IN AND MAKE FRIENDS? Hard at first, but I started to make more friends while working on an opera involving lots of students.

WHAT ADVICE WOULD YOU GIVE SOMEONE PLANNING TO STUDY ABROAD? Remember that it's difficult for anyone to cope in a foreign country where they don't speak the language, but it does get easier as time goes on, and it is important to keep positive.

community. Through our international alumni we can develop links with artists and organisations around the world. International students also bring short and long-term economic benefits to the local economy.' As a result, many institutes strongly encourage applications from abroad and pride themselves on a high intake from non-UK residents. Indeed, some of the highest profile conservatoires in London boast an annual intake of over 70% non-UK students, while others have students from over 60 different countries.

In order to encourage international students to apply and assist those who have already secured a place, most, if not all higher education institutes provide a significant level of help and support for their prospective students. A good starting point for information is the conservatoire's prospectus, which will usually have a dedicated section providing information for international students. Additionally, each conservatoire is likely to have further information and contact details to their international correspondents via their websites.

In order to secure a place at a conservatoire, most students will have to enrol for an audition. The physical distance of many of these can put some people off – although this situation doesn't apply to those wanting to study composition. Therefore, for those unable to make the trip or long-haul flight to the relevant venues, auditions can often be completed through a number of alternative means. This includes conservatoires themselves hosting auditions abroad, or allowing the submission of auditions through specific audio recordings.

Following the audition process, those fortunate enough to secure a place are subsequently provided with further support and advice prior to their enrolment. The student handbook (most institutes produce their own) is an important guidebook for students, and although each one differs and is tailored specifically to the institutes own schemes of work and level of support provided, the content remains largely alike and is very often the first port of call for any international-related queries. At the Royal Scottish Academy for Music and Drama (RSAMD), for example, the international student handbook 'contains information on common pre-arrival queries, such as immigration and visas, fees and funding, cost of living, accommodation and medical services provided for students in UK as well as practical information relating to their course of study.' Similarly, at the Guildhall School of Music and Drama, 'once applicants have been accepted, students are offered a variety of welcome packs, guidebooks and information packs to help them prepare for their arrival. All

NAME Felipe Oliveira (baritone) **FROM** Brazil

WHERE DID YOU GO? Royal Scottish Academy of Music & Drama, UK

WHY DID YOU CHOOSE THERE? I wanted to come to the UK because the schools are all very prestigious, but I chose not to audition in London because it was more expensive to live there than other cities. I also thought that in a smaller school I would get more performance opportunities.

HOW DID YOU ARRANGE YOUR STUDY ABROAD? I organised it via the internet, but I knew that I was more likely to get a scholarship if I did an audition in person, so I came to the UK to audition at several places and chose the best offer.

WHAT DID THE INSTITUTION DO TO HELP YOU WHEN YOU ARRIVED? They helped a lot. They put me in touch with my landlady, gave me extra English lessons and were very friendly.

HOW DID YOU ADAPT TO LIVING IN A FOREIGN CITY? I found the Glaswegian accent hard at first. Some day-to-day things, such as the transport system, took time to understand. But the secret is not to be shy, because people will recognise that you are a foreigner and will try to help. If you ask you will get an answer!

HOW EASY WAS IT TO SETTLE IN AND MAKE FRIENDS? It was quite easy because my classmates were from all over the world, so many of us were in the same situation. After a year, I had an international social network!

WHAT ADVICE WOULD YOU GIVE SOMEONE PLANNING TO STUDY ABROAD? Remember why you are there; this will help if you feel insecure or lonely. The internet has made the world smaller, so do stay in touch with your friends at home but don't stay in front of your computer all the time – make sure you enjoy the new experiences.

international students are supplied with an "Accommodation and Living Costs Booklet" and a "Before you Leave Home Handbook" which contains specific information for international students. In addition, students are provided with guidance on visas applications.' Both are available for download at: www.gsmd.ac.uk/fileadmin/user_upload/files/Applications/Before_you_leave_handbook.pdf

Taking into account that the cost of living in many of the conservatoires' home cities can be expensive for all students there, especially those from abroad, a number of scholarships and bursaries specifically designed for international students are occasionally awarded, and information about these will be provided upon request at specific institutes. Alternatively, some institutions offer the security of student accommodation to all their international students in their main halls of residence. With so many things to sort out and prepare before you arrive, knowing your accommodation is guaranteed can prove to be a huge weight off your shoulders.

Further to the support provided by the teams of staff at the conservatoires, institutes frequently encourage a high level of interaction from the students themselves. Buddy schemes, for example, and student affairs departments commit themselves to achieving a general well-being of all their fellow students, especially those from abroad, and to helping them fulfil their potential during their studies. From matriculation stage and throughout the introductory weeks, international students are encouraged to meet, chat and socialise with peers, teaching staff and support staff. At the RSAMD new students are also offered the opportunity to take part in a social programme of events which is designed to offer all students the chance to experience local and national culture and the opportunity to mix and bond with other RSAMD students. RSAMD is also a participating institution in the Glasgow International Student Welcome Programme which supports new international students upon their arrival in Glasgow, offering a meet and greet, a free transport service at the airport and

NAME Karen Gibbard (oboe)

FROM UK

WHERE DID YOU GO? Il Conservatorio Statale di Musica 'EF Dall'Abaco' in Verona, Italy

WHY DID YOU CHOOSE THERE? It was one of 5 or 6 European conservatoires that my university provided links with.

HOW DID YOU ARRANGE YOUR STUDY ABROAD? Through the University of Leeds Erasmus scheme. The study year abroad in a conservatoire was a compulsory part of the BMus course.

WHAT DID THE INSTITUTION DO TO HELP YOU WHEN YOU ARRIVED? Not a great deal; Italy isn't known for its organisation so it took a while to work out my timetable and I often felt like I had to take the initiative in order to work anything out.

HOW DID YOU ADAPT TO LIVING IN A FOREIGN CITY? I knew no Italian when I arrived in Verona and soon realised I couldn't just get away with speaking Spanish! Their academic year didn't start until November, but I arrived in September to do an intensive language course, so when term started I had already begun to settle in. Most Italians were shy of speaking English so I was thrown in at the deep end, which is a good way to learn.

HOW EASY WAS IT TO SETTLE IN AND MAKE FRIENDS? I met other international students through the university language course, and made friends at the local English-speaking church. As my grasp of Italian improved I made more friends at the conservatoire. There were many times when I felt I stood out as 'the foreigner' and longed for home, but by the end of the year I felt completely settled and distraught at having to leave.

WHAT ADVICE WOULD YOU GIVE SOMEONE PLANNING TO STUDY ABROAD? People sometimes make it sound like we can easily pick up a language if we're immersed in it, however as adults it still requires some effort and study. Try to learn the basics before you arrive and don't be afraid to make a fool of yourself, as you will improve far more quickly if you have the courage to make mistakes! There are bound to be moments when you feel homesick, but this is completely normal, so don't let it rob you of the fun of exploring a new place and culture.

information on accommodation, transport and other issues from volunteer students in the centrally-located Welcome Office. For students at the Guildhall School, their student life officer provides information and guidance for international students at the fresher's fair and weekly road shows, and supports the international student body in all areas, including applications for the 'Shine! International Student Awards'.

Apart from the many administrative and practical issues international students are faced with prior to moving and studying abroad, there is one, more day–to–day practicality that many international students have to deal with: a foreign language. In countries where the language is different to your own, it is paramount that you have a substantial grasp of the language. For example, you will need to know how to get around and sort things out from your finances to food shopping – let alone understand your classes and seminars – and without a good level of knowledge of the country's language, it can be very difficult to incorporate yourself in various activities and social groups. With this in mind, and if your first language is not English, you will be required to provide evidence of your language ability before you begin your studies through a set of pre-entry tests. At each institute, the English language requirements will vary slightly according to the programme of study. The International English Language Testing System (IELTS) is the most recognised system by which international students are measured and for those needing to take the test, arrangements can be made through your chosen conservatoire prior to your enrolment. Philip White, registrar and head of international affairs at the Royal Academy of Music explains: 'We have adopted IELTS – depending on programme we demand 5.5 or 6.0. We will accept 5.0 under certain conditions. Other language qualifications will be considered on a case by case basis. We also provide special induction and acclimatisation courses as well as English language for those in particular need.'

In addition to the information supplied by the relevant institutions themselves, many organisations, set up specifically to provide information to those studying, working or living abroad can prove be a great help. For instance, the British Council offers invaluable advice for people from the UK wishing to travel abroad. Via their website (www.britishcouncil.org) you can find a wealth of information and suggestions about how to make the most of your time while

NAME Morwenna Del Mar (cello) **FROM** UK

WHERE DID YOU GO? Eastman School of Music, Rochester, USA

WHY DID YOU CHOOSE THERE? I went to study with a specific teacher who I'd had master classes with when he'd visited England.

HOW DID YOU ARRANGE YOUR STUDY ABROAD? I sent my application form whilst studying at my previous institution. I flew there to audition in February but didn't hear whether or not I'd been accepted for a few months. Then I had to organise my visa, travel documents, accommodation and finances.

WHAT DID THE INSTITUTION DO TO HELP YOU WHEN YOU ARRIVED? International students received a specially designed booklet in advance, explaining US immigration policies, documents needed and facilities on offer. It was also possible to email the international students' office for help. All international students were invited to attend events such as pizza and film nights, barbeques, bar crawls etc. so that we could meet one another.

HOW DID YOU ADAPT TO LIVING IN A FOREIGN CITY? Having seen Rochester when I auditioned, I had an idea of what to expect, and regular classes meant that there were plenty of opportunities to meet people. Difficulties I experienced were largely to do with administrative tasks and setting-up home: bank accounts, mobile phone contracts, phone/internet, buying furniture - all much harder when you've never heard of utility companies or shops, let alone know which ones have a good reputation.

HOW EASY WAS IT TO SETTLE IN AND MAKE FRIENDS? I was lucky, as there were a few other people who went out to study at Eastman at the same time as me who I'd known in England, which made settling in much easier. I met lots of other people, and made some very close friends.

WHAT ADVICE WOULD YOU GIVE SOMEONE PLANNING TO STUDY ABROAD? Make the most of your time abroad; don't just sit in a practice room all day long, get out there and experience as much as possible. Travel, go to concerts, play to as many different people as will listen, and make the most of any opportunities offered.

NAME Arnfinn Tobiassen (organ) **FROM** Norway

WHERE DID YOU GO? Royal Academy of Music, UK

WHY DID YOU CHOOSE THERE? The main reason is that studying the organ at university level in most European countries means doing a church music course. I wanted to focus more on the organ repertoire and therefore chose to come to the UK.

HOW DID YOU ARRANGE YOUR STUDY ABROAD? I had a loan and grant that covered most of my expenses including tuition fees and accommodation. I was sent a booklet about accommodation but I had to arrange it myself.

WHAT DID THE INSTITUTION DO TO HELP YOU WHEN YOU ARRIVED? I found my teachers extremely helpful and friendly, helping out with practical matters and checking that everything was OK. There were lots of social events both within the department and involving all the other students, and the more of those I attended the more people I got to know.

HOW DID YOU ADAPT TO LIVING IN A FOREIGN CITY? First I tried to copy the habits and routines I had at home, but gradually I started adapting things like meal times and the sort of food I was cooking. Newspapers and TV are vital to become good at small talk.

HOW EASY WAS IT TO SETTLE IN AND MAKE FRIENDS? Not too difficult. The first term is always a bit challenging because you can spend a lot of time missing the friends at home, but gradually you get over that phase and you start making new friends.

WHAT ADVICE WOULD YOU GIVE SOMEONE PLANNING TO STUDY ABROAD? Bring a couple of items with you that remind you of home. I brought a lot of books!

studying in a different country; from a list of language schools in the UK which offer English language courses and in-depth information packs on immigration procedures, to the best pubs and bars to visit. Another useful source of information can be found at the UK Council for International Student Affairs (www.ukcisa.org.uk/) which, as its website states, 'promotes and protects the needs of international students in the UK'.

Finally, as well as providing encouragement and support for students from abroad wishing to study away from their home countries, conservatoires frequently have schemes set up providing the opportunity for students resident in the country of the conservatoire to study abroad for a period of time during their studies. One main way in which this is made possible is through the well-known Erasmus scheme. The Erasmus scheme works according to the following key words: Employability, Recognition, Adventure, Student Life, Maturity, Understanding and Satisfaction. As is the case with any student studying abroad, the benefits include strengthening self-confidence, independence, developing personal and professional contacts, experiencing different methods of study, and gaining insight into the international music profession to name but a few and can be a worthwhile experience all-round.

NAME Elizabeth Borowsky (piano) **FROM** USA

WHERE DID YOU GO? Trinity College of Music, UK

WHY DID YOU CHOOSE THERE? The location of the institution; it was also part of the exchange program offered through my home university, which meant easy transfer of credits and no payment over and above my normal tuition fees.

HOW DID YOU ARRANGE YOUR STUDY ABROAD? Through my home university and my own personal planning.

WHAT DID THE INSTITUTION DO TO HELP YOU WHEN YOU ARRIVED? Assistance with registration and orientation.

HOW DID YOU ADAPT TO LIVING IN A FOREIGN CITY? Very well! The college boasts students from around the world, and London was a wonderful city to live in.

HOW EASY WAS IT TO SETTLE IN AND MAKE FRIENDS? Despite arriving in the spring semester, I found students very welcoming and made lasting friendships.

WHAT ADVICE WOULD YOU GIVE SOMEONE PLANNING TO STUDY ABROAD? Enjoy every moment ... Six months goes by very fast!

STUDENT LIFE

Most institutes work on an exchange agreement and have partnerships with countries in Europe as well as the USA, Canada and parts of Asia. So if you're a student with the travelling bug but don't want to lose out on your studies, spending time studying abroad is an avenue well worth looking in to can prove a hugely rewarding adventure and addition to your study years.

NAME Alexander Campkin (composition) **FROM** UK

WHERE DID YOU GO? Universität für Musik und Darstellende Kunst Wien, Austria

WHY DID YOU CHOOSE THERE? I received a tutorial from a professor who teaches in Vienna, and was quite inspired. I wanted to study with him, and was interested in going abroad.

HOW DID YOU ARRANGE YOUR STUDY ABROAD? I contacted the professor, but it was quite last minute and it wasn't easy finding accommodation.

WHAT DID THE INSTITUTION DO TO HELP YOU WHEN YOU ARRIVED? Virtually none. They provide a huge amount of support for Erasmus students, but I somewhat fell through the net because I was doing a more specialised course.

HOW DID YOU ADAPT TO LIVING IN A FOREIGN CITY? I went in understanding no German whatsoever. Whilst most people could speak English, German was spoken so much that there was a lot I didn't understand at the beginning. It seemed quite daunting at the outset, but I took it as a challenge and really enjoyed it.

HOW EASY WAS IT TO SETTLE IN AND MAKE FRIENDS? Very easy indeed; I was fortunate enough to be living in an enormous Studentenheim (student dormitory, like halls in the UK). It was all very sociable and I fitted in easily; my friends taught me a lot about Vienna.

WHAT ADVICE WOULD YOU GIVE SOMEONE PLANNING TO STUDY ABROAD? Plan as far in advance as possible. Select accommodation with lots of other students in the centre of the city and get it booked early. Accept that they do things a bit differently abroad; enjoy these differences. Make friends early on and have an amazing time!

NAME Benjamin Shepherd (piano) **FROM** UK

WHERE DID YOU GO? Bratislava Academy of Music and Dramatic Arts, Slovakia

WHY DID YOU CHOOSE THERE? I chose to go to Slovakia to study with a particular professor. I wanted to experience studying abroad and it gave me the opportunity to gain new ideas and experience another culture.

HOW DID YOU ARRANGE YOUR STUDY ABROAD? I spoke to the Erasmus co-ordinator at my university who presented me with a list of possible foreign institutions to study at. Since the conservatoire in Slovakia wasn't listed, I contacted them myself and helped to set up a bi-lateral agreement, allowing me to apply. After auditioning by sending a CD recording and playing to a panel at my university, I was accepted to study and could arrange the details.

WHAT DID THE INSTITUTION DO TO HELP YOU WHEN YOU ARRIVED? They made me feel very welcome. I had a tour of the building, and was given an ID card etc. I was told how to use the various facilities and was able to ask them if I had any problems. They also put me in contact with my principal study teacher.

HOW DID YOU ADAPT TO LIVING IN A FOREIGN CITY? I took a nine-month language course beforehand; the conservatoire also arranged language lessons and most people were able to converse with me in English if I got stuck. My lessons were in Slovak, which was hard at first, but I soon grasped the general concepts. At the end of my year there, I was fluent.

HOW EASY WAS IT TO SETTLE IN AND MAKE FRIENDS? I found it very easy to settle in and lots of my fellow students were curious about the UK and always wanted me to teach them English, so I always had a lot of people approaching me who then became good friends.

WHAT ADVICE WOULD YOU GIVE SOMEONE PLANNING TO STUDY ABROAD? Make sure that you ask your home institution about the transference of credits and marks from one institution to another. Since there was no way of standardising my grades from Slovakia, my previous marks ended up counting towards my degree.

LEARNING LANGUAGES

If you have the urge to spend a significant period of time living in a foreign country, particularly if you have not made your mind up where to go, the question of language is bound to crop up. Of course, if you have already studied a language, this may be one of the reasons why you are looking to travel abroad. But if not, you will need to realise that a tourist's level of knowledge will not be enough to allow you to negotiate day-to-day life in a strange country. You will need to be able to manage your finances, arrange accommodation, socialise and so on, not to mention follow classes.

Doubtless, this prospect is one thing which puts people off the idea of living abroad, or at least encourages them to choose countries which speak the same language as them. But learning a foreign language brings all kinds of benefits, certainly benefits that outweigh the difficulties.

The first thing to recognise is that being able to use a language on a daily basis, so much so that it becomes part of your everyday surroundings, is not the same as trying to learn grammar and vocabulary in a classroom. Although this is certainly helpful in enabling students to gain a deeper knowledge of how a language works, nothing compares to the practical application of it – musicians more than anyone know the difference between written analysis and actual music-making, or the relief of performing compared with the repetitiveness of technical work. You could even say that, for a music student obsessed with practice and perfection, learning a language is a way to use your brain doing something different; and having an ear for sound should help you with the aural side of communicating.

In fact, just as there are captivating performers who are more timid away from the concert platform, there are those who find they can express themselves more adventurously in a foreign language. Partly this is because, if you are a visitor making an honest effort to communicate with people in their own language, you are not only more likely to be welcomed, but your linguistic clumsiness will also be excused. This in turn will help your confidence, and you will inevitably find yourself trying to find new ways to say things ... thereby improving your language skills. And if you find yourself living or working in a small town, or in a particularly close professional community (like music), it's possible to stand out in a way you might not back home.

The various organisations promoting foreign language learning all point to the communicative aspect as being one of the main pluses. As an individual you find yourself with new people to interact with. But you also play your part in promoting understanding between cultures, in promoting a less insular outlook on the world. And if that sounds idealistic, there are other advantages that can benefit you personally, as those same organisations argue: it's an additional skill you can put on your CV; travelling overseas to learn a language can open doors in other countries; by learning on your own initiative, you are demonstrating your self-motivation.

These advantages are relevant to musicians in particular. Say you are a member of a string quartet and you are beginning the process of promoting your group, think how much wider you can spread the word if each of you could speak a second language. Or imagine you want to build up your teaching portfolio; you could offer classes in another language; indeed, it would make it easier to establish your teaching in another country. Take a third scenario: you don't want to take on any more teaching or playing (perhaps it doesn't fit with your domestic arrangements), but want to find a way to earn some income another way; if you become really proficient and are prepared to take a few more exams, there are opportunities for freelance translation and interpretation work. And with so much demographic movement, particularly within Europe, this is even more so if the language you learn is a less widely spoken one.

The final thing to realise is that most conservatoires offer assistance in language-learning, often through associated universities, but many expect non-native speakers to be able to show their abilities have reached an acceptable level as part of the application process. So make enquiries at your home institution, nearest university or college, or at the cultural office in your home country of the place you are visiting (organisations like the Goethe-Institut, for instance).

Powodzenia; or should that be boa sorte, or bonne chance, veel geluk...

CALENDAR

SEPTEMBER 2010

Mon	Tue	Wed	Thu	Fri	Sat	Sun
		1	2	3	4	5
6	7	8	9	10	11	12
13	14	15	16	17	18	19
20	21	22	23	24	25	26
27	28	29	30			

OCTOBER 2010

Mon	Tue	Wed	Thu	Fri	Sat	Sun
				1	2	3
4	5	6	7	8	9	10
11	12	13	14	15	16	17
18	19	20	21	22	23	24
25	26	27	28	29	30	31

NOVEMBER 2010

Mon	Tue	Wed	Thu	Fri	Sat	Sun
1	2	3	4	5	6	7
8	9	10	11	12	13	14
15	16	17	18	19	20	21
22	23	24	25	26	27	28
29	30					

DECEMBER 2010

Mon	Tue	Wed	Thu	Fri	Sat	Sun
		1	2	3	4	5
6	7	8	9	10	11	12
13	14	15	16	17	18	19
20	21	22	23	24	25	26
27	28	29	30	31		

JANUARY 2011

Mon	Tue	Wed	Thu	Fri	Sat	Sun
31					1	2
3	4	5	6	7	8	9
10	11	12	13	14	15	16
17	18	19	20	21	22	23
24	25	26	27	28	29	30

FEBRUARY 2011

Mon	Tue	Wed	Thu	Fri	Sat	Sun
	1	2	3	4	5	6
7	8	9	10	11	12	13
14	15	16	17	18	19	20
21	22	23	24	25	26	27
28						

MARCH 2011

Mon	Tue	Wed	Thu	Fri	Sat	Sun
	1	2	3	4	5	6
7	8	9	10	11	12	13
14	15	16	17	18	19	20
21	22	23	24	25	26	27
28	29	30	31			

APRIL 2011

Mon	Tue	Wed	Thu	Fri	Sat	Sun
				1	2	3
4	5	6	7	8	9	10
11	12	13	14	15	16	17
18	19	20	21	22	23	24
25	26	27	28	29	30	

MAY 2011

Mon	Tue	Wed	Thu	Fri	Sat	Sun
30	31					1
2	3	4	5	6	7	8
9	10	11	12	13	14	15
16	17	18	19	20	21	22
23	24	25	26	27	28	29

JUNE 2011

Mon	Tue	Wed	Thu	Fri	Sat	Sun
		1	2	3	4	5
6	7	8	9	10	11	12
13	14	15	16	17	18	19
20	21	22	23	24	25	26
27	28	29	30			

JULY 2011

Mon	Tue	Wed	Thu	Fri	Sat	Sun
				1	2	3
4	5	6	7	8	9	10
11	12	13	14	15	16	17
18	19	20	21	22	23	24
25	26	27	28	29	30	31

AUGUST 2011

Mon	Tue	Wed	Thu	Fri	Sat	Sun
1	2	3	4	5	6	7
8	9	10	11	12	13	14
15	16	17	18	19	20	21
22	23	24	25	26	27	28
29	30	31				

NATIONAL HOLIDAYS

	Sep 2010	Oct 2010	Nov 2010	Dec 2010	Jan 2011	Feb 2011	Mar 2011	Apr 2011	May 2011	Jun 2011	Jul 2011	Aug 2011
AUSTRALIA				25, 26, 27,28	1, 26		2	22, 23, 25		13		1
AUSTRIA		26	1	8, 25, 26	1, 6			25	1	2, 12, 23		15
BELGIUM			1, 11	25	1			25	1	2, 13	21	15
CANADA	6	11	11	25, 26, 27,28	1			22, 25	23		1	
DENMARK	1, 6			24,25, 26	1, 6			1,16,18, 21, 22, 24, 25	26	2, 5, 12, 13		
FINLAND			6	6, 24, 25,26	1, 6			22, 25	1	2, 12, 25		
FRANCE			1, 11	25	1			24	1, 8	2, 12	14	15
GERMANY		3		25, 26	1, 6			22, 24, 25	1	2, 13, 23		
ISRAEL	9-10, 18, 23-29, 30	1		1-9			20	19	8	8-9		
ITALY			1	8, 25, 26	1, 6			24, 25	1	2		15
IRELAND			25	25, 26	1		17	25	2	6		1
NETHERLANDS				25, 26	1			24, 25, 30	5	2, 12		
NEW ZEALAND				25, 26	1, 2	6		22, 25		6		
NORWAY				25, 26	1			21, 22, 25	1, 17	2, 13		
PORTUGAL		5	1	1, 8, 25	1		8	22, 24, 25	1	10, 13, 23, 24		15
SPAIN		12	1	6, 8, 25	1			22	1			15
SWEDEN			6	25, 26	1			22, 25	1	6, 25		
UK				25, 26	1			22, 25	2, 30			29
USA	6	11	11, 25	24, 25, 31	1, 17	21			30		4	

DIALLING CODES

Albania	335
Algeria	213
Argentina	54
Armenia	374
Australia	61
Austria	43
Bahrain	973
Bangladesh	880
Belgium	32
Belize	501
Bolivia	591
Bosnia Herzegovina	387
Brazil	55
Bulgaria	359
Cameroon	237
Canada	1
Cape Verde	238
Chad	235
Chile	56
China	86
Colombia	57
Congo	243
Costa Rica	506
Côte d'Ivoire	225
Croatia	385
Cuba	53
Cyprus	357
Czech Republic	420
Denmark	45
Dominican Republic	1809
Ecuador	593
Egypt	20
Estonia	372
Fiji	679
Finland	358
France	33
Gambia	220
Germany	49
Ghana	233
Gibraltar	350
Greece	30
Greenland	299
Guadeloupe	590
Guatemala	502
Haiti	509
Hong Kong	852
Hungary	36
Iceland	354
India	91
Indonesia	62
Iran	98
Iraq	964
Ireland	353
Israel	972
Italy	39
Japan	81
Jordan	962
Kenya	254
Korea (South)	82
Kuwait	365
Latvia	371
Lebanon	961
Libya	218
Liechtenstein	423
Lithuania	370
Luxembourg	352
Macedonia	389
Madagascar	261
Malaysia	60
Maldives	960
Malta	356
Martinique	596
Mexico	52
Micronesia	691
Moldova	373
Monaco	377
Morocco	212
Namibia	264
Nepal	977
Netherlands	31
New Zealand	64
Nicaragua	505
Nigeria	234
Norway	47
Pakistan	92
Panama	507
Paraguay	595
Peru	51
Philippines	63
Poland	48
Portugal	351
Romania	40
Russia	7
Saudi Arabia	966
Senegal	221
Sierra Leone	232
Singapore	65
Slovakia	421
Slovenia	386
South Africa	27
Spain	34
Sri Lanka	94
Sudan	249
Sweden	46
Switzerland	41
Syria	963
Taiwan	886
Thailand	66
Tunisia	216
Turkey	90
Ukraine	380
United Arab Emirates	971
UK	44
USA	1
Uruguay	598
Venezuela	58
Vietnam	84
Yemen	967
Zambia	260
Zimbabwe	263

United Kingdom and Ireland

United Kingdom

UNITED KINGDOM

For a country labelled 'the land without music' at the beginning of the 20th century, the UK has certainly developed since then into a thriving musical location. Perhaps music in Germany is more deeply embedded at a local level – outside the main UK cities, high quality performance is harder to find, although most regional orchestras devote a fair amount of time performing away from their home venues. Perhaps it has been more heavily funded in other countries, with the UK falling between the US model of private funding and the European model of central/municipal funding.

But in those cities – notably London, Glasgow, Manchester, Birmingham, Cardiff, Leeds, in other words, exactly those cities where the conservatoires are based – there is a huge range of well-organised, well-promoted concerts to hear. What is more, British orchestras manage consistently to attract high-calibre performers, many having international conductors at their helm.

In addition, the country has two other strong traditions that others may not. Perhaps because of the concentration of high profile music in a few cities, there is a wide network of local music festivals, some prominent, but others more locally orientated. Secondly, the level of music-making at an amateur level is second to none, and this includes instrumental participation as well as singing.

The UK's conservatoires all award degrees which are accredited by universities and course structure and content is conceived along university lines, albeit with a focus on practical performance. The closeness of the systems means that many students do first degrees at university, only auditioning for postgraduate courses after that. Undergraduate degrees are generally awarded after 4 years' study, with postgraduate courses (masters or postgraduate diplomas) after a further 1 or 2 years.

Conservatoires are partially funded by government and are theoretically independent when it comes to curriculum and course content, although institutions' funding is in part subject to satisfactory results in quality control exercises so there is some measure of central control. A proportion of funding is also dependent on a conservatoire demonstrating a certain percentage (75%) graduates are employable within music.

BIRMINGHAM

City in central England, sometimes known as 'England's second city' thanks to the importance it gained in country's industrial development. Although industrialisation has left its mark, this is not all unpleasant – the city is the location for one of the early model towns, Bournville, built for workers at Cadbury's cocoa and chocolate factory; also, many canals pass through it, linking city to countryside. Architecture largely reflects 18th and 19th century importance, with new developments replacing some of the uglier post-war constructions. Well connected to other cities in the UK, both north (Manchester, Glasgow) and south (Oxford, London).

CLIMATE

Warmest month July (11-22°C), coldest month January and February (0-6°C). Rainfall fairly consistent throughout the year ranging between 45mm and 65mm per month.

MUSICAL LIFE

Over the past 20 years, it has developed a strong musical identity through the City of Birmingham Symphony Orchestra (and its associated chorus). Orchestra's main venue is Symphony Hall, renowned for its good acoustics; its sister venue is the recently renovated Birmingham Town Hall (both have non-classical performances). The orchestra is based at CBSO Centre with 300-seat performance space and rehearsal facilities. Orchestra of the Swan is a chamber orchestra based in nearby Stratford with frequent concerts in Birmingham and surrounding counties. Contemporary music from Birmingham Contemporary Music Group. Adrian Boult Hall is conservatoire's hall but public concerts are held there. Ballet at Birmingham Hippodrome (English National Ballet); no city opera house, but Birmingham Opera Company performs opera in unusual places. Concerts at Birmingham Cathedral and Barber Institute of Fine Arts; close to Warwick Arts Centre in Coventry for further classical concerts.

OTHER CULTURAL INFORMATION

Birmingham Repertory Theatre and Old Rep Theatre are main venues for drama; also the Alexandra and Hippodrome receiving venues. Several galleries and exhibitions – the main city museum and gallery has a large collection of pre-Raphaelite paintings; art deco Barber Institute for early 20th century art; jewellery quarter has its own museum. Also botanical gardens.

FESTIVALS AND EVENTS

Early music festival in autumn, jazz festival in July. ArtsFest is a weekend in September of free performing arts events across the city. City's multicultural population reflected in various community festivals.

LOCAL PUBLICATIONS

Birmingham Mail (www.birminghammail.net) is the city's main daily paper

TOURIST INFORMATION

www.visitbirmingham.com, +44 121 202 5115

BIRMINGHAM CONSERVATOIRE

Paradise Place, Birmingham, B3 3HG, United Kingdom
t: +44 121 331 5901 *f:* +44 121 331 5906
e: conservatoire@bcu.ac.uk *w:* www.conservatoire.bcu.ac.uk

Course information Undergrad courses in music and jazz, both with option to include PGCE; bespoke undergrad, conversion and postgrad jazz courses; postgrad performance-only courses (inc part time, intensive and professional level). Postgraduate diploma and MMus combine advanced study in performance, jazz, composition, community music or musicology with academic programme. MPhil/PhD offered full-time, part-time or distance learning. Joint courses offered in popular music, music tech and digital arts in performance.

Admissions information *Term dates* Late Sep-mid Dec (autumn term); mid Jan-mid Mar (spring term); mid Apr-end Jun (summer term). *Application requirements* All candidates: English language skills equivalent to IELTS 6.0, except PGCert (specialist performance) (IELTS 5.5) and MMus (IELTS 6.5). All applicants auditioned and/or interviewed. Undergrad: practical skills equivalent to ABRSM gr 8 (distinction), plus academic qualifications suitable for entry into higher education in home country. Postgrad: first degree plus practical skills. *Application deadline* 1 Oct via www.cukas.ac.uk; late applications accepted until 31 Aug for courses/areas with vacancies (please contact if applying after 1 Feb). *Fees* Fees for 2010 are on website. *Scholarships* Variety of scholarships available, awarded on merit. Further details available on website. *No of students* Around 600 students, of whom 60 from EU countries, and 40 from outside EU. *Language requirements* English (as per entrance requirements).

Facilities *Music facilities* 520 seat Adrian Boult Hall, Recital Hall (set up for performance with live

electronics), 6 recording studios, music library. Extensive events run by the conservatoire as well as other organisations. *Performance opportunities* A wide variety of performance opportunities, from in house productions to external engagements; the conservatoire supports students pursuing indepentdent performance projects. *Accommodation* Some assistance available through Birmingham City University accommodation services dept; see www.bcu.ac.uk/accommodation for full details.

CARDIFF

Welsh capital on the south coast of the country with a population of over 300,000. Developed as a port, particularly servicing the once dominant Welsh coal industry. Although that industry has declined, the city has remained prosperous, with recent redevelopments on Cardiff Bay (including the Welsh Assembly building) and city centre giving it the appearance of a smart modern place. This has helped give the city a lively nightlife, popular among students and young people.

CLIMATE

Warmest month July (13-22°C), coldest month January (-2-8°C). Wettest month December (130mm), driest months April-July (around 60mm).

MUSICAL LIFE

Centre for musical activity is the dramatic sea-front Wales Millennium Centre. Includes opera house, home to Welsh National Opera (main theatre and 2 smaller spaces) and the Wales's main orchestra, the BBC National Orchestra of Wales, in recently completed Hoddinott Hall (350-seat space) plus studio, practice rooms and backstage facilities. Music Theatre Wales produces range of contemporary opera and staged music for touring. Main concert hall is St David's Hall, staging a range of live entertainment apart from classical music. University's concert hall has regular classical performances from visiting soloists and ensembles as well as student performances. National Museum Wales had various music projects alongside its art exhibitions. Wales (though not Cardiff in particular) has strong choral tradition, especially male voice choirs. Also lively rock scene: International Arena venue for large-scale rock and pop.

OTHER CULTURAL INFORMATION

Chapter is a modern arts venue focusing on film and theatre/dance performance (there are 3 theatre spaces), plus workshop spaces. The Gate is a smaller venue based around a 350-seat performance space. National Museum covers art, history and archaeology, especially focusing on Wales. Sherman Theatre for standard theatrical productions. For many in Wales, the main national cultural activity is rugby, and the national stadium (the Millennium Stadium) is close to city centre.

FESTIVALS AND EVENTS

Cardiff Singer of the World one of the most important international events (biennial, odd years). Annual Welsh Proms at St David's Hall features orchestras from Wales and beyond.

TOURIST INFORMATION

www.visitcardiff.com, visitor@cardiff.gov.uk, +44 870 1211 258

ROYAL WELSH COLLEGE OF MUSIC & DRAMA

Castle Grounds, Cathays Park, Cardiff, CF10 3ER, United Kingdom
t: 02920 391361 *f:* 02920 391305 *e:* music.admissions@rwcmd.ac.uk *w:* www.rwcmd.ac.uk
Contact Jennifer Grey, admission officer.
Course information BMus (Hons) music, PGDip in music, MA in music performance, MMus, MMus in creative technology (by distance learning), MPhil/PhD; also MA in music therapy.
Admissions information *Term dates* Sep-Jul *Application requirements* For PGDip a good honours degree or equivalent (not necessarily in music). For MMus and MA, upper second class degree in music with significant practical or creative component, or university degree plus significant practical diploma in music. *Application deadline* 1 Oct. *Fees* £2680-5130 (UK and EU students), depending on course (MMus in creative music tech, to be confirmed); £2030 for MA in music therapy. *Scholarships* A number of scholarships available to outstanding applicants on the basis of audition. Worth up to full value of tuition. *No of students* 640 students in total (inc overseas students). *Language requirements* Overseas students require appropriate level of English proficiency (see website for details).
Facilities *Music facilities* Open-air courtyard performance space, 3 recital rooms, 50 practice/teaching studios containing a large number of upright and grand pianos; collection of period instruments; recording studio; library including internet, audio-visual facilities, Sibelius score-writing workstations. *Accommodation* Halls of residence nearby; student services dept provides one-to-one service to help all students find suitable accommodation.

UNITED KINGDOM

GLASGOW

Scotland's largest city, though not its capital, on river Clyde towards the country's west coast. Formerly a major shipbuilding city (further downriver at the city's port) and trading port. From 1960s onwards, decline in traditional industries led to downturn in fortunes, but from 1980s on, investment brought about significant regeneration. Now shipbuilding still active, alongside service, high tech and research industries. City is birthplace of art nouveau designer, architect and artist Charles Rennie Mackintosh; many examples of his distinctive buildings are spread across city in among numerous other Victorian buildings. In general, local sandstone of buildings give a distinctive character to the place.

CLIMATE

Warmest months July and August (10-18°C), coldest months December-February (1-6°C).Wettest between October and January (85mm), driest months May and June (under 40mm).

MUSICAL LIFE

Although not the Scottish capital, it has many advantages over Edinburgh as far as classical music goes. Well-regarded Scottish Opera housed at Theatre Royal. The 2 main national symphony orchestras based there: Royal Scottish National Orchestra has Royal Concert Hall as its home; BBC Scottish Symphony Orchestra based at renovated City Halls and has radio studios for broadcasts. Scottish Ensemble is smaller group; city also receives visits from Edinburgh-based Scottish Chamber Orchestra; contemporary music from Paragon Ensemble. All perform in venues around Scotland.

OTHER CULTURAL INFORMATION

Centre for Contemporary Arts is home to the Scottish Ensemble, but has a wider cultural remit to promote new and experimental performance and film. Various places where Charles Rennie Mackintosh's work (buildings and interiors as well as artefacts) is on display. One of these buildings, the Lighthouse, now a centre for architecture and design. Kelvingrove gallery and museum and Hunterian museum are 2 major institutions.

FESTIVALS AND EVENTS

Celtic Connections a major celebration across the city at the start of the year of Scottish music in its various forms. Jazz festival in June; comedy festival in March.

LOCAL PUBLICATIONS

Various newspapers, The Herald (www.heraldscotland.com) being the main daily broadsheet covering Scottish news and affairs (its main rival The Scotsman is published in Edinburgh); i-on magazine (http://ionmagazine.co.uk) has 2 editions, one covering events and entertainment in Glasgow, the other the same for Edinburgh.

TOURIST INFORMATION

www.visitscotland.com, +0845 22 55 121

ROYAL SCOTTISH ACADEMY OF MUSIC AND DRAMA

100 Renfrew St, Glasgow G2 3DB
t: +44 141 332 4101 *f:* +44 141 332 8909 *e:* registry@rsamd.ac.uk; j.carberry@rsamd.ac.uk
Contact Jill Carberry, welfare & international student advisor

Course information Undergrad courses inc bachelor of music with honours, BEd (Music) with honours, BA (Scottish Music) with honours, BA acting, BA musical theatre, BA contemporary performance practice, BA technical & production arts, BA digital film & TV, BA modern ballet. Postgrad courses inc master of music, postgraduate diploma, master of opera, MA musical theatre, MA classical & contemporary text, research degrees, MA arts in social contexts.

Admissions information *Term dates* 28 Sep 2010-1 Jul 2011. *Applications requirements* General undergrad entry requirements: passes in 3 subjects at Higher, passes in 2 subjects at Advanced Higher or an appropriate Scottish Group award at Higher level, or passes in 2 subjects at A level (where appropriate AS level results will be taken into account); or recognised equivalences inc overseas qualifications. General postgrad entry requirements: applicants will normally be graduates or diplomats who have already undertaken extensive study in the area of specialisation. *Application deadline* School of music: 1 Oct for entry in subsequent year; school of drama: 31 Mar (undergrad), 31 May (postgrad) for entry in subsequent year. *Fees* £1775 (home students)-£13,824 (international); figures for guidance only. *Scholarships* A number of entrance scholarships awarded as part of the audition/selection process on the basis of merit. *No of students* 785, inc 85 overseas students. *Language requirements* Non-native speakers must submit evidence of their English language level; see www.rsamd.ac.uk/international/english for more information.

Facilities *Music facilities* Wide range of fully equipped teaching facilities, rehearsal and practice rooms, organ room, classrooms and lecture theatre, recording studio, dance studio, concert hall (355 seats), recital room (108 seats), theatre (344 seats) and opera studio. *Performance opportunities* Range of opportunities are available inc performance in student productions of operas, pantomimes, recitals, orchestral and cabaret-style events. *Accommodation* Halls of residence are situtated a 10 min walk from RSAMD. Places available on application. RSAMD is part of the Private Accommodation Database for students of institutions in Glasgow, see www.accom.gla.ac.uk/pad for further details. Contact welfare & international student advisor for more information on private rented accommodation.

LEEDS

West Yorkshire city which grew into importance due to the range of industries based there in 17-19th centuries. Prosperity of the city at this time reflected in monumental buildings such as town hall, but also its characteristic ornate shopping arcades in the city centre. Now home to several higher education institutions and a popular city for students to stay.

CLIMATE

Warmest months July and August (12-22°C), coldest months December and January (0-6°C). Rainfall ranges between 45mm (February) and 70mm (August), but is fairly consistent throughout the year.

MUSICAL LIFE

Principal music performing organisation is Opera North, based at the Grand Theatre and Opera House. Acts as 2 organisations in one as the opera orchestra also performs widely at concert series in the city (Leeds International Concert Season) and the region. Howard Assembly Room features a wide range of music from classical to folk. Classical and contemporary dance at Northern Ballet Theatre (tours widely).

OTHER CULTURAL INFORMATION

Henry Moore Institute sculpture centre includes collections and changing exhibitions; City Art Gallery also has substantial sculpture collection among its collections. The Leeds City Museum is a recently re-opened institution with exhibitions, interactive displays and so on. Saltaire, just outside city, is Unesco world heritage site, includes art gallery (Salt's Mill). For theatre, West Yorkshire Playhouse very highly regarded.

FESTIVALS AND EVENTS

Leeds piano, conducting and Lieder competitions (one a year in rotation) are major events in musical calendar. Shakespeare Festival in July; annual film festival in November. Leeds Festival weekend of rock at end of August.

LOCAL PUBLICATIONS

The dailies Yorkshire Post and Yorkshire Evening Post (www.yorkshirepost.co.uk) cover national news from a Yorkshire perspective. For what's on information, The Leeds Guide (www.leedsguide.co.uk) is produced fortnightly

TOURIST INFORMATION

www.leedsliveitloveit.com, tourinfo@leeds.gov.uk, +44 113 242 5242

LEEDS COLLEGE OF MUSIC

3 Quarry Hill, Leeds, LS2 7PD, United Kingdom
t: +44 113 222 3400; +44 113 222 3416 (course enquiries) *f:* +44 113 243 8798
e: enquiries@lcm.ac.uk *w:* www.lcm.ac.uk

Course information Foundation degrees in music production for film and TV, and commercial music production; bachelor's in music, jazz, popular music studies, music production; PGDip or MA in performance, composition, music production and musicology.

Admissions information *Application requirements* Applications through CUKAS. Audition for performance courses; overseas auditions possible in China, Hong Kong, Japan, Norway, USA. *Fees* £1615-4290 (home/EU), £1832-10,290 (international), depending on course level. *Scholarships* Various awards available; see website for details.

Facilities *Music facilities* 350-seat concert venue, extensive library, 24-track digital recording studios and edit suites, computer composition studio, Cubase lab, learning resource centre, large collection of instruments (including Indian and Caribbean), archive of jazz and pop. *Performance opportunities* Links with local concerts, events and festivals and such as FuseLeeds, Leeds International Concert Season and Leeds Lieder+; frequent local concerts featuring students and alumni. Student ensembles include symphony orchestra, big band, Omar Puente's Latin Jazz Band, jazz groups and combos, choral society and chamber choir. *Accommodation* Accommodation

UK & IRELAND

for new students provided; accommodation office advises on housing for others.

LONDON

Capital city whose importance dates back to Roman times. Location on river Thames gave it great significance as trading port, and this in turn attracted people from around the world to work there. Today has become one of the most international cities, not only in terms of business and trade, but the variety of nationalities and cultures represented. Conurbation itself (Greater London) is home to over 8 million people and spreads over a number of local districts many of which have distinctive character. A large number of students (approx 200,000) from all over the world attend its various institutions.

CLIMATE

Warmest months July and August (13-22°C), coolest month January (2-7°C). Rainfall is modest but relatively uniform throughout the year.

MUSICAL LIFE

5 major symphony orchestras based there (London Symphony, London Philharmonic, Philharmonia, Royal Philharmonic, BBC Symphony Orchestra), 2 opera houses (Royal Opera and English National Opera), and various venues. Barbican Centre and Southbank Centre are all-round arts centres, the latter with 3 concert halls of different sizes; Royal Albert Hall stages large-scale popular classical music and opera as well as orchestral concerts; medium sized venues such as Cadogan Hall and St John's Smith Square, plus smaller halls for prestigious recitals and chamber music, eg Wigmore Hall, LSO St Lukes and newly opened Kings Place; regular performances of music in churches, especially in City of London, but also West End (eg St James's Piccadilly) and in local districts.

OTHER CULTURAL INFORMATION

Theatre and dance events at the Southbank (National Theatre) and Barbican, and the West End is an area of central London with large concentration of theatres covering range of styles from new writing to musicals. Large range of galleries: National Gallery for all-round collection, riverside Tate galleries (one focusing on modern, one on British art); Royal Academy for high-profile changing exhibitions. Also museums focusing on various subjects from London history, British and world culture (British Museum) to design (Victoria and Albert), science and nature.

FESTIVALS AND EVENTS

BBC Proms (throughout summer) is one of world's largest classical music events; Spitalfields Festival (June and December) and City of London Festivals (June) both in historic centre of the capital. Various specialist events, eg Lufthansa Festival of Baroque Music (May); chamber music at London String Quartet Week; KlezFest for various aspects of Jewish music. Festivals in different boroughs: Hampstead and Highgate Festival in north (May); Chelsea Festival in west (June); Dulwich Festival in south (May). Many events arranged celebrating different cultures living in London.

LOCAL PUBLICATIONS

Evening Standard (www.thisislondon.co.uk) is the city's main local paper, covering news, what's on etc. Time Out the main, weekly, listings magazine.

TOURIST INFORMATION

www.visitlondon.com

GUILDHALL SCHOOL OF MUSIC & DRAMA

Silk St, London, EC2Y 8DT, United Kingdom
t: +44 20 7628 2571 *f:* +44 20 7256 9438 *e:* music@gsmd.ac.uk *w:* www.gsmd.ac.uk

Course information BMus, MPerf, MComp, MMus, PGDip, MLead, DMus, MMA/DMA, MA in music therapy. *Instrumental* Principal study at BMus and PG level *Vocal* Principal study at BMus and PG level *Conducting* Available as BMus elective only *Historical performance* Available as elective at BMus level, MComp and DMus at PG level. *Contemporary* Principal study or elective at BMus level; specialism at PG level. *Composition* Available as principal study or elective at BMus; DMus or MComp. *Orchestral* Included in BMus course; specialism at PG level. *Chamber music* Included in BMus course; specialism at PG level. *Opera* Opera studies available as part of BMus vocal studies programme; specialist PG opera course offered. *Jazz/world* Principal study at BMus or PG level. *Other* Music therapy offered as BMus elective, or MA at postgraduate level.

Admissions information *Term dates* Mid Sep-early Dec; mid Jan-early Apr; late Apr-mid Jul. *Application requirements* See website for full application details and course content. *Application deadline* 1 Oct. *Fees* See website for details. *Scholarships* See website. *No of students* Approx 40% of total students from overseas. *Language requirements* See website

Facilities *Music facilities* Practice facilities within school, plus annexe with 46 further practice studios;

fully equipped theatre for opera productions. The school has developed links with London Symphony Orchestra and Barbican Centre, with opportunities for school's performers to give concerts in the hall and LSO St Luke's. *Performance opportunities* Extensive programme of outside engagements plus a large number of music ensembles within the school. *Accommodation* 177 places in school's hall of residence; advice on other accommodation available.

LONDON COLLEGE OF MUSIC, THAMES VALLEY UNIVERSITY
t: +44 20 8231 2304; +44 20 8231 2706 (international office) *f:* +44 20 8231 5646
e: music@tvu.ac.uk *w:* http://music.tvu.ac.uk
Course information Courses in music (performance/composition), Sikh/Indian classical music, popular music performance, music technology, sound engineering and production, composing for theatre, composing for film/TV, artist management, media health, audio technology.

ROYAL ACADEMY OF MUSIC
Marylebone Rd, London NW1H 5HT, United Kingdom
t: +44 20 7873 7373 *f:* +44 20 7873 7374
e: registry@ram.ac.uk *w:* www.ram.ac.uk
Contact Edward Kemp-Luck, international admissions officer.
Course information BMus (undergrad), MA, MMus, PhD.
Admissions information *Term dates* Early Sep-late Nov; early Jan-mid Mar; mid Apr-end Jun. *Application requirements* RAM is not member of CUKAS; see website for full application details. *Application deadline* 1 Oct, except 7 Jan for MPhil, conducting, choral conducting, and for N America auditions. *Fees* BMus: £3145 (home/EU), £15,500 (international); MA: £7600 (home/EU), £16,200 (international); MMus: £7600 (home/EU), £16,500 (international). For other fees, see website. *Scholarships* Many scholarships available; see website for details. *No of students* Approx 650 students, inc about 50% from overseas. *Language requirements* If English is not your first language, you are required to demonstrate your proficiency. See website for details.
Facilities *Music facilities* 100 teaching and practice rooms, Sir Jack Lyons Theatre, concert room, recital room, electronic studios, creative technology lab, well-stocked library. Main concert hall is Duke's Hall (seats 400). *Performance opportunities* Busy schedule of chamber music, ensemble and orchestral concerts. Full listings on website. *Accommodation* Student accommodation primarily for 1st year students

ROYAL COLLEGE OF MUSIC
Prince Consort Rd, London SW7 2BS, United Kingdom
t: 020 7589 3643 *f:* 020 7589 7740 *e:* info@rcm.ac.uk; international@rcm.ac.uk *w:* www.rcm.ac.uk
Contact Darren Clark.
Course information BMus(Hons), integrated masters programme (including Masters and PG Dip), artist diploma in opera studies, graduate diploma (singer), artist diploma, DMus.
Admissions information *Term dates* Mid Sep-mid Dec (autumn term); mid Jan-late Mar (spring term); mid Apr-mid Jul 2010 (summer term). *Application requirements* Extremely high standard of performance at audition. A Level (or equivalent) music at grade C or higher plus one other subject; for EU/overseas students, equivalent home qualifications accepted. For grad dip/masters programmes, bachelors degree or equivalent required; for artist diploma, postgrad qualification with distinction. For DMus, taught masters required. *Application deadline* 1 Oct . *Fees* £3145-8726 pa depending on course (home/EU students); £8665-15780 pa depending on course (overseas students). *Scholarships* All applicants who audition in person will be considered for a scholarship; scholarships (up to full value of tuition fees) awarded based on standard of performance. *No of students* 340 national and 349 international students. ***Language requierements*** EU/overseas students whose first language is not English must gain IELTS at Level 6 (or acceptable equivalent) before beginning studies.***Facilities*** *Music facilities* 2 concert halls, opera theatre, electroacoustic and recording studio, museum housing and displaying college's collection of historical instruments, large number of teaching studios and practice rooms, 3-manual Walker organ; library and reading room, listening facilities. *Accommodation* 180 places in hall of residence; student services advise on other accommodation available.

TRINITY COLLEGE OF MUSIC
King Charles Court, Old Royal Naval College, Greenwich, London, SE10 9JF United Kingdom
t: +44 20 8305 4444 *f:* +44 20 8305 9444
e: enquiries@tcm.ac.uk *w:* www.tcm.ac.uk
Course information Foundation degree in musical theatre; bachelor of music performance; bachelor

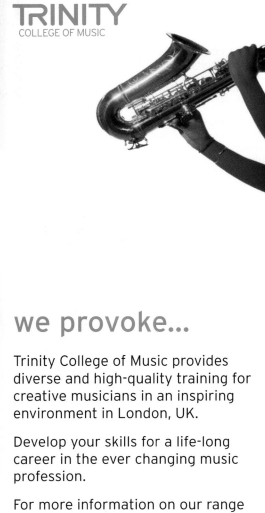

Why Trinity?

As a student at Trinity you become part of an exciting, vibrant and supportive community of musicians. In its unique setting at the Old Royal Naval College, Greenwich, students enjoy beautiful surroundings and are only 20 minutes away from central London.

We offer a range of undergraduate and postgraduate level courses which focus on developing our students' core skills to the highest possible standard whilst helping them develop the skills they need to succeed as music professionals.

Our success stems from our unique approach to education. We know that students need to attain the highest level of technical ability in their chosen instrument and to this end we employ an exceptional team of highly qualified teachers from the London music profession. This is to be expected but it doesn't alone ensure graduate employability. At Trinity, alongside rigorous technical training we provide our students with the skills they need to succeed in the professional world where engagement with both communities and other artists is essential.

"Trinity College of Music will help you become the very best musician you can be. Whether you aspire to be a soloist, chamber musician, member of an orchestra or a portfolio musician, our experienced teachers and coaches will guide and nurture your musical development in what is surely one of the most beautiful locations in the world. This combination provides our students with a truly inspirational environment in which to study; a vibrant, supportive and above all encouraging musical community."

Nic Pendlebury, Head of String Faculty at Trinity College of Music

To find out more, please visit our website **www.tcm.ac.uk**

of music, Indian music; various flexible courses possible from pre-undergrad to postgrad level, tailored to personal interests and needs of individuals; PGCE 'Musicians in Education'; master of music performance/composition/creative practice; postgrad advanced diploma.
Admissions information *Application requirements* Most courses available for online application via CUKAS. *Application deadline* 1 Oct. *Fees* £700-7200 (home/EU), £700-14,700 (overseas), depending on course. *No of students* Approx 600 students.
Facilities *Music facilities* Practice facilities; Blackheath Halls college's own concert venue. Library and resource centre, audio-visual facilities, Sibelius software. *Accommodation* Guaranteed place in halls of residence for all 1st year students; warden's office and students' union provide advice on finding private accommodation.

MANCHESTER

Vies with Birmingham for the unofficial title of England's 'second city'; located in north west of England. Like most major UK cities, its history linked to industrial revolution; in Manchester's case, the city was a centre for the country's textile industry, and city linked closely to political development of the country from then on. Also as with other cities, it went into decline only to undergo significant regeneration projects. Large number of students attracted to its major higher educational establishments not to mention its legendary nightlife.

CLIMATE

Warmest months July and August (12-20°C), coldest month January (1-6°C). Rainfall fairly uniform throughout the year (60-80mm).

MUSICAL LIFE

Very active city musically. 3 major orchestras: Hallé, based at Bridgewater Hall (over 2300 seats), is one of Britain's most respected groups; BBC Philharmonic is the broadcaster's northern England orchestra, based in the city and performing at Studio 7 concert hall studio; Manchester Camerata a chamber orchestra giving concerts in various venues in the city and the region more widely. Opera comes mostly through tours, particularly from Opera North, to the Lowry Lyric Theatre in nearby Salford. Various concert and recital series at these and other venues (eg Manchester Cathedral). As well as to the senior music college, city is home to specialist music school, Chetham's, whose students give regular performances in and around the city.

OTHER CULTURAL INFORMATION

Royal Exchange Theatre for drama (unusual in that the main theatre is in the round venue; also 2 smaller spaces). Cube is city-based museum exploring Manchester's architectural history; Whitworth Art Gallery has a substantial collection of British watercolours among other artworks, and received numerous changing exhibitions; Manchester Art Gallery located in a distinctive Victorian building. The Lowry is an arts centre in nearby Salford, with 2 theatres and performing arts studio alongside art exhibitions.

FESTIVALS AND EVENTS

Features a wide range of events with musical side. Manchester International Festival is a broad arts festival consisting entirely of new work (biennial, odd years). Manchester International Piano Competition an annual event combining competitive element with showcase for young performers.

LOCAL PUBLICATIONS

Manchester Evening News is the city's main daily newspaper.

TOURIST INFORMATION

www.visitmanchester.com, touristinformation@marketing-manchester.co.uk, +44 871 222 8223

ROYAL NORTHERN COLLEGE OF MUSIC
124 Oxford Rd, Manchester, M13 9RD, United Kingdom
t: +44 161 907 5200 *f:* +44 161 273 7611
e: admissions@rncm.ac.uk; international@rncm.ac.uk *w:* www.rncm.ac.uk
Contact Tatyana Yekimova, international officer.
Course information Bachelor degree in music, foundation degree in popular music practice (session musician); postgrad masters degrees and diplomas in performance and composition;

professional courses leading to RNCM International Artist Diploma (solo course, chamber music course, opera studio); MPhil and DPhil; PGCE in music with specialist instrumental teaching; PGDip in instrumental teaching and postgraduate certificate in performing arts education (PGCertPAE)

Admissions information *Term dates* Mid Sep-mid Dec (autumn term); early Jan-end Mar (spring term); mid Apr-early Jul (summer term). *Application requirements* High level of performing/composing ability; for overseas students, standard of general education comparable to UK candidates, and high enough

standard of English. *Application deadline* 1 Oct, but some flexibility for international students in particular. *Fees* £3145-8495 (UK & EU students, depending on course); £13,895-17,695 (Isle of Man, Channel Islands and non-EU students) in 2009-2010 year (reviewed annually). *Scholarships* Some scholarships available to those demonstrating outstanding ability and potential at audition. Postgrad and non-EU applicants may apply for limited number of bursaries towards fees and maintenance, made on the basis of need; students expected to undertake activities for benefit of the college. *No of students* 550 UK students, 54 EU students, 126 overseas students, 8 from islands.

Facilities *Music facilities* Opera theatre; concert hall with Hradetsky organ; extensive library with IT, listening and video facilities; over 80 tutorial spaces and practice rooms; over 120 pianos. *Performance opportunities* Extensive performance programme. Professional development dept arranges external work for students. *Accommodation* 316 rooms in halls of residence; help available finding private accommodation.

MUSIC FESTIVALS

5th British International Male Voice Choral Festival Cornwall 47 Deeping St James Rd, Northborough, Peterborough PE6 9BT *t:* 01778 347381 *e:* peter.davies@abcd.org.uk *w:* www.cimvcf.org.uk Peter Davies, festival dir. The largest male voice choral festival in Europe with competitions, symposia and workshops. Over 60 male voice choirs from the UK and across the world participate in concerts and festival activities all across Cornwall, at Truro Cathedral and at the Hall for Cornwall.

Abbotsbury Music Festival PO Box 5968, Abbotsbury, Weymouth DT3 4JR *t:* 01305 871475 *e:* info@abbmusic.org.uk *w:* www.abbmusic.org.uk; www.st-catherine.org.uk Barbara Laurie. Charity providing professional music/theatrical performances for W Dorset and villages along the heritage Jurassic coast in W Dorset.

Aberdeen International Youth Festival Custom House, 35 Regent Quay, Aberdeen AB11 5BE *t:* 01224 213800 *f:* 01224 641122 *e:* info@aiyf.org *w:* www.aiyf.org Stewart Aitken, artistic dir. One of the world's largest young people's multi-arts festivals with perfs and w/shops attracting up to 1000 participants from the UK and around the world. Participation is through application; all art forms and music genres considered. Events in Aberdeen city, Aberdeenshire and across the NE of Scotland.

Aberystwyth Musicfest - International Festival and Summer School Aberystwyth Arts Centre, Penglais, Aberystwyth SY23 3DE *t:* 01970 622338 *f:* 01970 622883 *e:* musicfest@aber.ac.uk *w:* www.abermusicfest.org Sophie Bennett, co-ord Bursaries available for summer school, applications by Jul.

acoustICA Series at the ICA London c/o CAE/L, PO Box 27838, London SE24 9YL *t:* 07962 521330 *f:* 0870 051 7527 *e:* info@caelondon.org *w:* www.caelondon.org Rachel McCarthy, admin; Sinan Savaskan, artistic dir.

Adur Festival Adur District Council, Civic Centre, Ham Rd, Shoreham-by-the-Sea BN43 6PR *t:* 01273 263274 *f:* 01273 263027 *e:* pamela.driscoll@adur.gov.uk *w:* www.adurfestival.com Pamela Driscoll, artistic dir. Community-based with a balance of high quality professional and amateur performances and events.

Aldeburgh Easter Festival Aldeburgh Music, Snape Maltings Concert Hall, Snape, Saxmundham IP17 1 SP *t:* 01728 687100 *f:* 01728 687120 *e:* enquiries@aldeburgh.co.uk *w:* www.aldeburgh.co.uk Hettie Hope, artistic admin; Marc Ernesti, head of mktg & media. Offers a variety of classical music, all in the world-famous Snape Maltings Concert Hall and new creative campus at Snape.

Aldeburgh Festival Aldeburgh Music, Snape Maltings Concert Hall, Snape, Saxmundham IP17 1SP *t:* 01728 687100 *f:* 01728 687120 *e:* enquiries@aldeburgh.co.uk *w:* www.aldeburgh.co.uk Hettie Hope, artistic admin; Marc Ernesti, head of mktg & media. Offers a variety of classical music, all in the world-famous Snape Maltings Concert Hall and new creative campus at Snape.

Amersham Festival of Music Ranmoor, Croft Rd, Chalfont St Peter SL9 9AF *t:* 01753 884628 *w:* www.amershamfestival.org Iain Ledingham, artistic dir; Lynda Weiss, chair.

Annual Festival of New Organ Music *w:* www.afnom.org Festival for composers to submit compositions for performance, discussion and sale.

ArtsFest Environment & Culture - Events Section, House of Sport, 300 Broad St, Birmingham B1 2DR *t:* 0121 464 5678 *e:* Elise_duncan@birmingham.gov.uk *w:* www.artsfest.org.uk Elise Duncan, festival co-ord Annual event produced by Birmingham City Council. All activity within city centre, indoors and outdoors. To help break down barriers to the arts, all events free, with no pre-booking, usually lasting only 30 mins.

Ashbourne Festival St John's Community Hall, King St, Ashbourne DE6 1EA *t:* 01335 348707 *e:* info@ashbournefestival.org *w:* http://ashbournefestival.org Ann Rosser, vice chair, Ashbourne Arts. An eclectic mix of performances and exhibitions.

Autumn in Malvern Festival 42 Worcester Rd, Great Malvern WR14 4AA *t:* 01684 569721 *e:* petersmith@malvernmusic.co.uk *w:* www.malvernfestival.co.uk Peter Smith, artistic dir. Classical music-based with strong literary and visual arts element. Features established and emerging artists.

Bangor New Music Festival The School of Music, University of Wales, Bangor LL57 2DG *t:* 01248 382181 *e:* info@bnmf.co.uk *w:* www.bnmf.co.uk Mirain Evans, admin. Festival of contemporary classical music.

Banstead Arts Festival Little Hilden, Park Rd, Banstead SM7 3EL *t:* 01737 352098 *w:* www.bansteadarts.co.uk Stephen Oliver, artistic dir, chair; EA Smith, sec; Gerald Baines, treas. Annual festival featuring lunchtime concerts, exhibitions, walks, talks, coach visits and a wide variety of evening events and music from jazz to chmbr music.

Barmouth Arts Festival 1 Epworth Terrace, Barmouth, Gwynedd LL42 1PN *t:* 01341 280392 *w:* www.barmouthartsfestival.co.uk Mair Jones, sec. Annual festival of varied programme.

Bath International Music Festival Bath Festivals Trust, Abbey Chambers, Kingston Buildings, Bath BA1 1NT *t:* 01225 462231 *f:* 01225 445551 *e:* info@bathfestivals.org.uk *w:* www.bathmusicfest.org.uk Joanna MacGregor, artistic dir; Nod Knowles, CEO. International festival of classical, jazz, world, contemporary, traditional and electronic music, featuring collaborations and commissions.

Bath Mozartfest 110 Gloucester Ave, London NW1 8HX *t:* 020 7483 2681 *f:* 020 7586 5343 *e:* sarah.gordon@easynet.co.uk *w:* www.bathmozartfest.org.uk Emma Cross, admin; Amelia Freedman, artistic dir. 10 day annual festival of classical, chmbr, orch and choral music.

BBC Proms Room 1045, Broadcasting House, Portland Place, London W1A 1AA *t:* 020 7765 5575 *f:* 020 7765 2031 *e:* proms@bbc.co.uk *w:* www.bbc.co.uk/proms Roger Wright, artistic dir; Rosemary Gent, artistic admin. Takes place over 2 months every summer at London's Royal Albert Hall. For every concert, up to 1400 'Promming' (standing) tickets are held back for sale on the day at £5 each.

Beaminster Festival The Yarn Barton Centre, Fleet St, Beaminster DT8 8DR *t:* 01308 862943 *e:* beamfest@btinternet.com *w:* www.beamfest.org.uk Tanya Bruce-Lockhart, festival dir. Festival of music and the visual arts: classical, jazz, folk, swing, theatre, paintings, photography, literature plus open-air events.

Beaumaris Festival 6 Lon-y-Celyn, Cardiff CF14 7BW *t:* 01248 810134 *e:* ahose@stetson.edu *w:* www.beaumarisfestival.com Anthony Hose, artistic dir; Ann Lock, sec. Orch and choral concerts, recitals, chmbr music, poetry, art exhibitions.

Beverley & East Riding Early Music Festival National Centre for Early Music, St Margaret's Church, Walmgate, York YO1 9TL *t:* 01904 632220 *f:* 01904 612631 *e:* info@ncem.co.uk *w:* www.ncem.co.uk Delma Tomlin, dir.

Beverley Chamber Music Festival Springfield, Colton, Ulverston LA12 8HE *t:* 01229 861325 *e:* gaildudson@colton2.demon.co.uk Martin Roscoe, artistic dir; Gail Dudson, mgr.

Beverley Folk, Acoustic and Roots Festival Beverley Leisure Complex, Flemingate, Beverley HU17 0LT *t:* 01377 217569 *f:* 01377 217754 *e:* info@beverleyfestival.com *w:* www.beverleyfestival.com Chris Wade, artistic dir. 3 nights and 2 days of international music, dance, comedy, spoken word, events for all ages, w/shops, camping, craft and food stalls, plus real ale. Main events at Leisure Complex and adjacent area; other events at the minster and friary.

Birmingham Early Music Festival PO Box 9442, Birmingham B15 3QA *t:* 0121 427 1509 *f:* 0121 427 1511 *e:* info@bemf.net *w:* www.bemf.net Dina Ahmad, festival admin. Brings internationally renowned period music specialists into venues across the city, staging concerts based on an annual theme.

Birmingham International Jazz Festival PO Box 944, Birmingham B16 8UT *t:* 0121 454 7020 *f:* 0121 454 9996 *e:* festival@bigbearmusic.com *w:* www.birminghamjazzfestival.com Jim Simpson, artistic dir; Tim Jennings, asst dir; Steve Kelly, mktg mgr.

Blackthorpe Barn International Summer Music Estate Office, Rougham, Bury St Edmunds IP30 9LZ *t:* 01359 270091 *e:* events@blackthorpebarn.com *w:* www.blackthorpebarn.com George Agnew, arts dir.

Bledington Music Festival 9 Jackson Rd, Bledington, Chipping Norton OX7 6XN *t:* 01608 658669 *e:* enquiries@bledingtonmusicfestival.co.uk *w:* www.bledingtonmusicfestival.co.uk Rodney Beacham, festival org; Thomas Trotter, pres; Catrin Finch, vice pres. At St Leonard's Church, Bledington.

Blyth Valley Chamber Music The Box Office, Marshwinds, 32 Saxmundham Rd, Aldeburgh IP15 5JE *t:* 01728 453193 *e:* info@concertsatcratfield.org.uk *w:* www.concertsatcratfield.org.uk

Brancaster Midsummer Music *t:* 01485 210527 *w:* www.brancaster.net/midsummer

Brecon Jazz Lion House, Bethel Sq, Brecon LD3 7EF *t:* 01874 625511, also fax *e:* info@breconjazz.co.uk *w:* www.breconjazz.co.uk Catrin Slater, festival admin.

Brighton Early Music Festival Ham Cottage, Albourne Rd, Hurstpierpoint BN6 9ES *t:* 01273 833746 *e:* mike@bremf.org.uk *w:* www.bremf.org.uk Mike Clemens, festival chair. Annual festival of professional concerts and w/shops in the Brighton and Hove area.

Brighton Festival Festival Office, 12a Pavilion Buildings, Castle Square, Brighton BN1 1EE *t:* 01273 700747 *f:* 01273 707505 *e:* info@brightonfestival.org *w:* www.brightonfestival.org

Brinkburn Music Summer Festival Foundry Lane Studios, Foundry Lane, Newcastle upon Tyne NE6 1LH *t:* 0191 265 7777 *e:* contact@brinkburnmusic.org *w:* www.brinkburnmusic.org Alison Robson, gen mgr; Paul McCreesh, artistic dir. Classical music ranging from early to contemporary performed by world class musicians in the beautiful setting of a 12th C priory.

Bromsgrove Festival 10 Evertons Close, Droitwich WR9 8AE *t:* 01905 779852 (home); 01527 575441 (work) *f:* 01527 575366; 01527 574651 *e:* andrewh@lgharris.co.uk *w:* www.bromsgrovefestival.co.uk AD Harris, hon sec.

Buckingham Summer Festival 1 Poplars Close, Preston Bissett MK18 4LR *t:* 01280 848275 *e:* robert_secret@fastmail.fm Robert Secret, artistic dir. Festival of chmbr music, inst and vocal recitals. Fully professional morning and lunchtime recitals with evening celebrity concerts.

Bude Jazz Festival PO Box 32, Bude EX23 9YW *t:* 01594 516834, also fax *e:* information@budejazzfestival.co.uk *w:* www.budejazzfestival.co.uk Rachel Hayward, artistic dir; Jean Manuel, Diana Ohlson, admin.

Bury St Edmunds Festival West Suffolk House, Western Way, Bury St Edmunds IP33 3YU *t:* 01284 757630 *f:* 01284 757631 *e:* nick.wells@stedsbc.gov.uk *w:* www.buryfestival.co.uk Nick Wells, artistic dir. Takes place in a variety of locations. Festival has strong music focus, esp classical and jazz; the programme covers a wide range of art forms inc dance, drama, comedy, walks, talks and exhibitions.

Buxton Festival 3 The Square, Buxton SK17 6AZ *t:* 01298 70395 *f:* 01298 72289 *e:* info@buxtonfestival.co.uk *w:* www.buxtonfestival.co.uk Andrew Greenwood, artistic dir; Glyn Foley, chief exec. Opera, music and literature in a stunning Peak District setting.

Cambridge Music Festival *e:* director@cammusic.co.uk *w:* www.cammusic.co.uk Paul Gudgin, festival dir. Theme of music and evolution.

Cambridge Summer Music Festival (Cambridge Summer Recitals) 8 Horn Lane, Linton, Cambridge CB21 4HT *t:* 01223 894161 *f:* 01223 892945 *e:* info@cambridgesummermusic.com *w:* www.cambridgesummermusic.com Juliet Abrahamson, artistic dir. About 50 concerts in many historic venues, inc Music for the Kids series. Also runs other concerts during the year, and Spring Concert Series in May.

Camerata Ireland Clandeboye Festival Hibernia House, 99-101 High St, Holywood, Co Down BT18 9AG *t:* 028 9042 7600 *f:* 028 9042 8011 *e:* info@camerata-ireland.com *w:* www.camerata-ireland.com Gavin O'Sullivan, festival dir. Festival of classical music set in the Clandeboye Estate, featuring established and the next generation of Irish musicians and Camerata Ireland.

Canterbury Festival Festival Office, Christ Church Gate, The Precincts, Canterbury CT1 2EE *t:* 01227

canterburyfestival.co.uk *w:* www.canterburyfestival.co.uk Rosie Turner, festival dir. International arts festival offering 200 events in 2 wks across the art forms of music, theatre and visual arts.

Carducci Festival Elmwood, Southwood Rd, Shalden, Alton GU34 4DX *t:* 01420 86267 *e:* carduccitrust@gmail.com *w:* www.carducciquartet.co.uk Cathy Boyes, admin. Annual festival of the Carducci String Quartet in Highnam.

Carlisle International Summer Festival 6 The Abbey, Carlisle CA3 8TZ *f:* 01228 547049 *e:* miccarlisle@btinternet.com *w:* www.carlislefestival.org.uk Jeremy Suter, chair of Carlisle Festival Ltd Brings musicians of international repute to Carlisle, encourages local professional and amateur artists and involves the wider community in classical music.

Castleward Opera Festival Unit A, 280 Comber Rd, Lisburn BT27 6TA *t:* 028 9263 9545 *f:* 028 9263 9588 *e:* info@castlewardopera.com *w:* www.castlewardopera.com

Celtic Connections The Glasgow Royal Concert Hall, 2 Sauchiehall St, Glasgow G2 3NY *t:* 0141 353 8080 *f:* 0141 353 8026 *w:* www.celticconections.com Over 300 concerts, ceilidhs, talks, free events, late night sessions and workshops in 14 venues across the city.

Charleston Manor Festival 15 Birchwood Ave, London N10 3BE *t:* 020 8444 1065 *e:* admin@charlestonmanorfestival.com *w:* www.charlestonmanorfestival.com Robert Cohen, artistic dir. Annual festival; Robert Cohen invites friends and colleagues, some of the most outstanding classical musicians, to join him for intense yet congenial music-making.

Chelsea Arts Festival The Crypt, St Luke's Church, Sydney St, London SW3 6NH *t:* 020 7349 8101 *e:* info@chelseafestival.org *w:* www.chelseafestival.org.uk Stewart Collins, festival dir.

Cheltenham Jazz Festival 109-111 Bath Rd, Cheltenham GL53 7LS *t:* 01242 774400 *f:* 01242 256457 *w:* www.cheltenhamfestivals.com Philip Woods, festival organiser. In association with Radio 2.

Cheltenham Music Festival Cheltenham Festivals, 109-11 Bath Rd, Cheltenham GL53 7LS *t:* 01242 774400 *f:* 01242 256457 *e:* music@cheltenhamfestivals.com *w:* www.cheltenhamfestivals.com

Chester Festivals Ltd Visit Chester & Cheshire, Chester Railway Station, 1st Floor, West Wing Offices, Station Rd, Chester CH1 3NT *t:* 01244 405631 *f:* 01244 405601 *w:* www.chesterfestivals.co.uk Kate Sawallisch, festival mgr. 2 wk festival with classical music at its core, focusing on the voice.

Chetham's International Summer School and Festival for Pianists Chetham's School of Music, Long Millgate, Manchester M3 1SB *t:* 01625 266899, also fax *e:* info@pianosummerschool.com *w:* www.pianosummerschool.com Murray McLachlan, artistic dir; Kathryn Page, admin. Recitals, lectures, intensive tuition, m/classes by world-class concert pianists.

Chichester Festivities Canon Gate House, South St, Chichester PO19 1PU *t:* 01243 528356 *e:* info@chifest.org.uk *w:* www.chifest.org.uk Amanda Sharp, dir.

Chobham Music Festival Dingle, Castle Grove Rd, Chobham GU24 8EF *t:* 01276 858552 *w:* http://festival.chobham.org John Parry, festival dir; Dale Chamber, musical dir. Annual festival featuring classical music, jazz, br bands, children's events etc.

Church Stretton and South Shropshire Arts Festival 3 Cunnery Terrace, Church Stretton SY6 6AL *t:* 01694 722257 *e:* gandrwalker@talktalk.net *w:* www.strettonfestival.org.uk Richard Walker, artistic dir. A fortnight of music, drama, lectures and art in the heart of Shropshire.

City of Derry Jazz and Big Band Festival Derry City Council, 98 Strand Rd, Derry BT48 7NN *t:* 028 7137 6545 *f:* 028 7137 0080 *e:* jazz@derrycity.gov.uk *w:* www.cityofderryjazzfestival.com Johnny Murray, contact.

City of London Festival Fitz Eylwin House, 25 Holborn Viaduct, London EC1A 2BP *t:* 020 7583 3585 *f:* 020 7353 0455 *e:* admin@colf.org *w:* www.colf.org Lindsey Dear, gen mgr. Concerts in various venues throughout the square mile; also free outdoor events in the City's open spaces and Hampstead Heath.

Cleckheaton Folk Festival 84 Pyenot Hall Lane, Cleckheaton BD19 5BA *t:* 01274 879761 *e:* dave@cleckheatonfolkfestival.org *w:* www.cleckheatonfolkfestival.org Dave Minich, festival dir. Friendly w/end of folk music and entertainment for all ages.

Corbridge Chamber Music Festival 44 Radipole Rd, London SW6 5DL *t:* 020 7736 5268 *e:* penny@mneary.co.uk *w:* www.gouldpianotrio.com Penny Neary, sec. Chmbr music performed in St Andrew's church by the Gould Piano Trio, Robert Plane (cl) and friends. Festival service, family concert.

Corsham Festival The Pound Arts Centre, Pound Pill, Corsham SN13 9HX *t:* 01249 701628 *f:* 01249 712618 *e:* info@corshamfestival.org.uk *w:* www.corshamfestival.org.uk Michael Cainen, mktg & programming co-ord. A leading small contemporary arts festival, featuring over 20 different events over 8 days.

Cotswold Early Music Festival Atkyns Manor, South Cerney, Cirencester GL7 5TT *t:* 01285 860395 *f:* 01285 862449 *e:* info@cotswold-emf.co.uk *w:* www.cotswold-emf.co.uk Mark Venn, festival dir.

Coventry Jazz Festival c/o CV One Ltd, 1 Castle Yard, off Hay Lane, Coventry CV1 5RF *t:* 024 7660 7020 *f:* 024 7660 7001 *e:* jazz@cvone.co.uk *w:* www.coventryjazzfestival.com

Dante Summer Festival Jopes Park Cottage, Luckett, Callington PL17 8LN *t:* 01579 370589 *e:* dandm@seward.eclipse.co.uk *w:* www.dantefestival.org David Seward, festival admin. Festival run by the internationally renowned Dante String Quartet with guest artists. Quartet concerts, w/shops and special events for children in ancient churches and traditional barns. Theme for 2010: Intimate Voices, with music by Haydn, Beethoven, Brahms, Sibelius, Smetana.

Dartington International Summer School The Barn, Dartington Hall, Totnes TQ9 6DE *t:* 01803 847080 *f:* 01803 847087 *e:* summerschool@dartington.org *w:* www.dartington.org/summer-school Gavin Henderson CBE, artistic dir; Emily Hoare, creative producer; Clê Morse-Privett, admin; Sam Macaulay, operations mgr. 3 concerts every day, plus w/shops and m/classes.

Deal Festival of Music and the Arts Festival Office, The Pines, St Andrew's Gdns, Shepherdswell CT15 7LP *t:* 01304 830443 *e:* irondraw@btinternet.com *w:* http://dealfestival.co.uk Mrs Willie Cooper. Concerts in Deal, Sandwich and Dover.

Denbigh Midsummer Festival The Glass Onion Cafe, Back Row, Denbigh LL16 3TE *t:* 01745 816080; 01745 813125 *e:* festival@visitdenbigh.co.uk *w:* www.visitdenbigh.co.uk/midsummer2.html Sue Muse.

Devizes Festival Bachelor's Mead, Horton, Devizes SN10 3NB *w:* www.devizesfestival.co.uk James Harrison, chair. International artists from a wide spectrum of arts.

Dorset Opera Witchampton, Dorset BH21 5AU *t:* 01258 840000 *f:* 01258 840946 *e:* info@dorsetopera.com *w:* www.dorsetopera.com Roderick Kennedy, gen & artistic dir. Residential opera summer school and festival where choristers and technical theatre students of all ages get to work alongside famous international opera stars. Full professional orch, cond, dir, chorus master etc.

Dulwich Festival PO Box 26999, London SE21 8YX *e:* info@dulwichfestival.co.uk *w:* www.dulwichfestival.co.uk

Dumfries and Galloway Arts Festival Gracefield Arts Centre, 28 Edinburgh Rd, Dumfries DG1 1JQ *t:* 01387 260447 *e:* info@dgartsfestival.org.uk *w:* www.dgartsfestival.org.uk Annette Rogers, admin. A multi-genre festival with national and international performers.

East Neuk Festival 29 Regent St, Edinburgh EH15 2AY *t:* 0131 669 1750, also fax *e:* info@eastneukfestival.co.uk *w:* www.eastneukfestival.com Svend Brown, artistic dir. Music and readings in intimate venues.

Edinburgh & Glasgow - Festival of British Youth Orchestras NAYO, Central Hall, West Tollcross, Edinburgh EH3 9BP *t:* 0131 221 1927 *f:* 0131 229 2921 *e:* info@nayofestival.com *w:* www.nayo.org.uk Susan White, gen mgr. No event in 2010; details of future events tbc.

Edinburgh International Festival The Hub, Castlehill, Edinburgh EH1 2NE *t:* 0131 473 2099 *f:* 0131 473 2002 *e:* eif@eif.co.uk *w:* www.eif.co.uk Jonathan Mills, festival dir. 3 weeks of world class theatre, dance, opera and music in Scotland's capital city.

Edinburgh International Harp Festival Unit 10, 78 Albion Rd, Edinburgh EH7 5QZ *t:* 0131 652 0585, also fax *e:* harp.festival@hotmail.com *w:* www.harpfestival.co.uk Alex Johnston, admin. 6 day festival devoted to all harps and their music - traditional Scottish, Irish and Welsh, classical, Paraguayan, jazz and much more. Classes for everyone from complete beginners to advanced players.

Edinburgh International Jazz and Blues Festival 89 Giles St, Edinburgh EH6 6BZ *t:* 0131 467 5200 *w:* www.edinburghjazzfestival.co.uk

Egerton Festival The Granary, Newland Green, Egerton, Ashford TN27 9EP *t:* 01233 840630 *e:* ljanecarr@btinternet.com *w:* www.egertonmusicfestival.co.uk Triennial festival; other musical events held each year throughout the year.

English Haydn Festival, Bridgnorth *t:* 01746 763591 *e:* info@englishhaydn.com *w:* www.haydn.org.uk MC Proudman, treas. Orch concerts, chmbr music, choral music, recitals and opera. Period insts.

English Heritage Picnic Concerts IMG, Pier House, Strand on the Green, London W4 3NN *t:* 020 8223 5000; 0845 658 6960 (information) *f:* 020 8233 5001 *e:* concerts@imgworld.com *w:* www.picnicconcerts.com Tomas Lane, mktg co-ord. Concerts take place against the stunning backdrop of Audley End House, Saffron Walden.

English Heritage Picnic Concerts Series IMG, Pier House, Strand on the Green, London W4 3NN *t:* 020 8233 5000; 0845 658 6960 (information) *f:* 020 8233 5001 *e:* concerts@imgworld.com *w:* www.picnicconcerts.com Tomas Lane, mktg co-ord. Concerts take place against the stunning backdrop of Kenwood House.

English Music Festival, The The Red House, Lanchards Lane, Shillingstone DT11 0QU *t:* 07808 473889 *e:* em.marshall@btinternet.com *w:* www.englishmusicfestival.org.uk Em Marshall, mgr & artistic dir. Annual festival featuring works by British composers of all periods, focusing on the early 20th C. World class artists and a range of events from solo recitals through to full orch concerts.

Exeter Autumn Festival 4.46, Civic Centre, Paris St, Exeter EX1 1JJ *t:* 01392 265205 *f:* 01392 265366 *e:* general.festivals@exeter.gov.uk *w:* www.exeter.gov.uk/festival Val Wilson, festival mgr.

Exon Singers Festival (Tavistock & Buckfast) 6 Ashlake Rd, London SW16 2BB *t:* 020 8677 0882 *e:* secretary@exonsingers.org.uk *w:* www.exonsingers.org.uk Graham Wood, sec. Recitals, concerts and services (inc compline) in Tavistock's 13th C parish church; broadcast of choral evening prayer from Buckfast Abbey

Finchcocks Festival Finchcocks Musical Museum, Goudhurst TN17 1HH *t:* 01580 211702 *f:* 01580 211007 *e:* info@finchcocks.co.uk *w:* www.finchcocks.co.uk Katrina Burnett, dir; Richard Burnett MBE, artistic dir.

Fishguard International Music Festival Hafan Deg, Panteg, Manorowen, Fishguard SA65 9QD *t:* 01348 875538 *w:* www.fishguardmusicfestival.co.uk

Florestan Festival c/o Florestan Festival at Peasmarsh, Strawberry Hole Oast, Ewhurst Lane, Northiam TN31 6XJ *t:* 01491 874210 *e:* enquiries@florestantrio.com *w:* www.florestantrio.com Imogen Smart. Annual chmbr music festival curated by The Florestan Trio. Includes perfs by The Florestan Trio, invited guests, and a major concerto concert at St Mary's church Rye.

Garsington Opera Garsington OX44 9DH *t:* 01865 368201 *f:* 01865 361545 *e:* office@garsingtonopera.org *w:* www.garsingtonopera.org

Gateway International Roots Music Festival Brewery Arts Centre, Highgate, Kendal LA9 4HE *t:* 01539 722833 *e:* admin@breweryarts.co.uk *w:* www.breweryarts.co.uk Mike Chadwick. Primarily features new roots musics (trad non-classical music forms) from around the world, for which it is a national showcase. Features established and emerging artists.

Glasgow International Jazz Festival 81 High St, Glasgow G1 1NB *t:* 0141 552 3552 *f:* 0141 552 3592 *w:* www.jazzfest.co.uk Events in venues across the city.

Glyndebourne Festival Opera Glyndebourne, Lewes BN8 5UU *t:* 01273 812321; 01273 815000 (info) *f:* 01273 812783 *e:* info@glyndebourne.com *w:* www.glyndebourne.com David Pickard, gen dir. New productions and revivals.

Gower Festival Cruachen, Reynoldston, Swansea SA3 1BR *t:* 01792 390404, also fax *e:* gwylgwyr@googlemail.com *w:* www.gowerfestival.org Gareth Walters, artistic dir. International festival of classical music, esp chmbr music, in historic venues across the Gower peninsula.

Grassington Festival Riverbank House, Threshfield, nr Skipton BD23 5BS *t:* 01756 753357 *e:* arts@grassington-festival.org.uk *w:* www.grassington-festival.org.uk Amelia Vyvyan, festival dir.

Greenwich + Docklands Festivals The Borough Hall, Royal Hill, London SE10 8RE *t:* 020 8305 1818 *f:* 020 8305 1188 *e:* admin@festival.org *w:* www.festival.org Bradley Hemmings, artistic dir. Arts festival and event producing organisation.

Greenwich International Festival & Exhibition The Old Royal Naval College, Greenwich, London SE10 9LW *t:* 01274 288100 *f:* 01274 596226 *e:* enquiries@earlymusicfestival.com *w:* www.earlymusicfestival.com Peter Booth, dir. Major international early music exhibition held at the Old Royal Naval College, Greenwich, London. Around 100 exhibitors over 3 days. Concerts, m/classes, w/shops, demonstration recitals.

Gregynog Festival Gregynog, Tregynon, Newtown, Powys SY16 3PW *t:* 01686 207100 *f:* 01686 650656 *e:* post@gwylgregynogfestival.org *w:* www.gwylgregynogfestival.org Rhian Davies, artistic dir; Sarah Yeomans, admin. International arts event in the magnificent setting of Gregynog Hall's intimate and historic music room. 2010 theme: Pleasure Gardens.

Grimsby St Hughs Festival 24 Bradford Ave, Cleethorpes DN35 0BD *e:* david.power3@virgin.net *w:* www.grimsby-st-hughs-festival.org.uk David Power, artistic dir. 5 concerts of mainly 20th C chmbr mus.

Guildford International Music Festival c/o Dept of Music & Sound Recording, University of Surrey, Guildford GU2 7XH *t:* 01483 689690 *f:* 01483 686501 *e:* p.b.johnson@surrey.ac.uk *w:* www.guildfordinternationalmusicfestival.co.uk Pauline Johnson, artistic dir; Patricia Grayburn, exec dir.

UNITED KINGDOM

Professional and community festival with established and emerging artists, covering a wide range of musical genres.

Guildford Spring Music Festival *e:* performance@gsmf.org.uk *w:* www.gsmf.co.uk Tony Hennessey-Brown, festival co-ord. Biennial festival. All performers have strong Guildford connections, through birth, education, work or residency. Musicians wishing to be considered for future festivals should email for more information.

Guiting Festival Langley Lodge, Langley, Winchcombe GL54 5AB *t:* 01242 603912 *e:* guitingfestival@talktalk.net *w:* www.guitingfestival.org Duncan Westerman, artistic dir. Classical music and jazz in a rural Cotswold setting.

Hampstead and Highgate Festival PO Box 11845, London NW3 9FH *t:* 020 8761 6565 *e:* music@gbz.demon.co.uk *w:* www.hamandhighfest.co.uk Danny Driver, artistic dir; Gwenneth Bransby-Zachary, festival dir. Annual arts festival, including broad range of classical music, literature and visual art in venues in around Hampstead & Highgate. 2010 celebrates centenary 1st performance in Paris of the Firebird

Hampton Court Palace Festival IMG Arts & Entertainment, Pier House, Strand on the Green, London W4 3NN *t:* 020 8233 5000 *f:* 020 8233 5001 *e:* concerts@imgworld.com *w:* www.hamptoncourtfestival.com

Harrogate International Festival Raglan House, Raglan St, Harrogate HG1 1LE *t:* 01423 562303 *f:* 01423 521264 *e:* info@harrogate-festival.org.uk *w:* www.harrogate-festival.org.uk Sharon Canavar, chief exec.

Harrogate International Youth Music Festival Perform Europe, One Jubilee St, Brighton BN1 1GE *t:* 01273 810742 *f:* 01273 693148 *e:* sales@performeurope.co.uk *w:* www.performeurope.co.uk

Haslemere Festival Haslemere Hall, Bridge Rd, Haslemere GU27 2AS *t:* 01418 644473 *e:* donaldson@haslemere.com *w:* www.haslemerefestival.org.uk H Donaldson, chair. Broadly based festival with concerts, weekday talks and weekend family events.

Hebden Bridge Arts Festival New Oxford House, Albert St, Hebden Bridge HX7 8AH *t:* 01422 842684 *e:* hbfestival@gmail.com *w:* www.hebdenbridgeartsfestival.co.uk Rebecca Yorke, festival co-ord. Annual 2-week event celebrating art, literature, drama, music and all other art forms.

Henley Festival 14 Friday St, Henley-on-Thames RG9 1AH *t:* 01491 843400 *f:* 01491 410482 *e:* info@henley-festival.co.uk *w:* www.henley-festival.co.uk Stewart Collins, artistic dir. Showcases world-class performers in classical, jazz, pop, world and folk music from its floating stage built on the river.

Hexham Abbey Festival Hexham Abbey Parish Centre, Beaumont St, Hexham NE46 3NB *t:* 07979 866303 *f:* 01434 606116 *e:* festival@hexhamabbey.org.uk *w:* www.hexhamabbey.org.uk/festival Graham Coatman, artistic dir. 10 days of classical, early, choral, contemporary, jazz, world and folk music, supplemented by Young Artist Platford; commissions, community & educ projects, exhibitions, film, street theatre etc.

Honiton Festival Hollick, Yarnscombe EX31 3LQ *t:* 01271 858249 *f:* 01271 858375 *e:* eucorch1@aol.com Ambrose Miller, mus dir.

Huddersfield Contemporary Music Festival Room TC/09, University of Huddersfield, Huddersfield HD1 3DH *t:* 01484 472900 *e:* hcmfinfo@hud.ac.uk *w:* www.hcmf.co.uk 50 events over 10 days, inc jazz, classical, electronic and improvised music, music theatre, film and multimedia events, installations, free workshops, drop-in events and a diverse educ programme. Attracts composers, performers and an audience from across the UK and around the world.

Iford Festival Iford Arts Ltd, The Gatehouse, Iford, nr Bath BA15 2BA *t:* 01225 868124 *f:* 01225 867471 *e:* music@ifordarts.co.uk *w:* www.ifordarts.co.uk Judy Eglington, artistic dir; Deborah Heyden, gen mgr; Jonelle Daniels, mktg mgr. Site-specific opera productions in the Italianate cloister at Iford Manor; jazz and world music promenades.

International Choir Festival of Jersey Le Catel Farm, La Rue de la Falaise, Trinity, Jersey JE3 5BQ *t:* 01534 864014 *e:* nickcabot@localdial.com *w:* www.internationalchoirfestivalofjersey.com Nick Cabot, musical dir. Biennial festival.

International East Anglian Summer Music Festival 3-5 Bridge St, Hadleigh IP7 6BY *t:* 01473 822596, also fax *e:* thomas.mcintosh@minstrelmusic.co.uk *w:* www.minstrelmusic.co.uk Thomas McIntosh, artistic dir; MHV Reckitt, admin. Classical chmbr music. All concerts at The Old School, Hadleigh.

International Guitar Foundation and Festivals Newton Park, Newton St Loe, Bath BA2 9BN *t:* 01225 875522 *f:* 01225 875495 *e:* phil@igf.org.uk *w:* www.igf.org.uk

International Organ Festival at St Albans PO Box 80, St Albans AL3 4HR *t:* 01727 844765 *f:* 01727 868941 *e:* info@organfestival.com *w:* www.organfestival.com David Titterington, artistic dir; Hilary Crook, admin sec. Biennial international music festival with org competitions for interpretation and improvisation at its heart. Also concerts, recitals, an exhibition of small orgs and an awayday visit to Eton College, Reading Town Hall and Douai Abbey.

International Ralph Vaughan Williams Festival Music at Woodhouse, Woodhouse Copse, Holmbury St Mary, Dorking RH5 6NL *t:* 01306 730956 *e:* info@woodhousesounds.com *w:* www.woodhousesounds.com

Jennings Keswick Jazz Festival Theatre by the Lake, Lakeside, Keswick CA12 5DJ *t:* 01768 772282; 01768 781123 (jazz office) *f:* 01768 774698 *w:* www.keswickjazzfestival.co.uk John Minnion, programmer; Sophie Curtis, admin.

Jewish Culture Day at the Southbank Centre Jewish Music Institute, SOAS, University of London, PO Box 232, Harrow HA1 2NN *t:* 020 8909 2445 *f:* 020 8909 1030 *e:* jewishmusic@jmi.org.uk *w:* www.jmi.org.uk Geraldine Auerbach MBE, festival dir. Centred around a day at Southbank Centre, the festival includes music of the Jewish diaspora from Klezmer to cabaret, classical, cantorical, choral and the music of Oriental communities, with exotic insts and songs in many languages.

Jewish Song Summer School JMI, SOAS, University of London, Thornhaugh St, Russell Sq, London WC1H 0XG *t:* 020 8909 2445 *f:* 020 8909 1030 *e:* jewishmusic@jmi.org.uk *w:* www.jmi.org.uk Yvonne Glass, event co-ord. Exploration of the repertoire, interpretation, style and pronunciation of Jewish songs in Jewish languages of Yiddish and Ladino in w/shops and m/classes for professional and amateur singers. Directed by Shura Lipovsky of Amsterdam with an international faculty inc Polina Shepherd. Runs parallel with JMI Klezfest London.

King's Lynn Festival 5 Thoresby College, Queen St, King's Lynn PE30 1HX *t:* 01553 767557 *f:* 01553 767688 *w:* www.kingslynnfestival.org.uk Ambrose Miller, artistic dir; Joanne Mawson, admin. General arts festival featuring orch and choral concerts, classical recitals, talks, literature and exhibitions.

Kingston and Richmond Early Music Festival 10 Viking Court, Beaver Close, Hampton TW12 2BZ *t:* 020 8941 4917 *e:* williamsummers@uwclub.net *w:* www.lokimusic.co.uk William Summers.

KlezFest London JMI, SOAS, University of London, Thornhaugh St, Russell Sq, London WC1H 0XG *t:* 020 8909 2445 *f:* 020 8909 1030 *e:* jewishmusic@jmi.org.uk *w:* www.jmi.org.uk Yvonne Glass, event co-ord. Hands-on learning experience with luminaries of the Klezmer revival from Europe and America, focusing on the style, ornamentation, rhythm and repertoire of eastern European Jewish music, song and dance in w/shops, ens playing and m/classes. For amateur and professional instrumentalists, singers and dancers. Presented by the Jewish Music Institute.

Lake District Summer Music International Festival Stricklandgate House, 92 Stricklandgate, Kendal LA9 4PU *t:* 0845 644 2505 *f:* 0845 644 2506 *e:* info@ldsm.org.uk *w:* www.ldsm.org.uk Renna Kellaway, artistic dir; Garfield Jackson, artistic assoc; Andrew Lucas, exec organiser. Widely spread music festival offering chmbr mus, opera, orchs, m/classes, talks and exhibitions in over 50 events against the backdrop of the Lake District.

Lanercost Festival Lanercost Priory, Brampton CA8 2HQ *t:* 0845 257 3401 *e:* info@lanercostfestival.co.uk *w:* www.lanercostfestival.co.uk Festival at Lanercost Priory.

Leamington Music Festival Weekend Northgate, Warwick CV34 4JL *t:* 01926 497000 *e:* richard@leamingtonmusic.org *w:* www.leamingtonmusic.org Richard Phillips. 2010: early romantic composers performed by various artists. Theme for 2011: later romantic composers.

Leeds Lieder+ Festival Office, Leeds College of Music, 3 Quarry Hill, Leeds LS2 7PD *t:* 0113 234 6956 *e:* info@leedslieder.org.uk *w:* www.leedslieder.org.uk Jane Anthony, founder & festival dir; David Hoult, chair; Lord Harewood, pres; Elly Ameling, hon patron; Malcolm Martineau, artistic dir. Biennial festival of art song in central Leeds venues. Recitals and other events inc m/classes, w/shops, world premieres, talks, composers and poets forum.

Leicester Early Music Festival 126 Shanklin Drive, Leicester LE2 3QB *t:* 0116 270 9984, also fax *e:* mail@earlymusicleicester.co.uk *w:* www.earlymusicleicester.co.uk John Bence, dir. Festival has a strong family target and associated events such as guided walks, wine tasting, dance choral and jnr w/shops.

Leicester International Music Festival New Walk Museum, 53 New Walk, Leicester LE1 7EA *t:* 0116 225 4916, also fax *e:* musicfest@btconnect.com *w:* www.musicfestival.co.uk Peter Baker, chair of festival board & festival mgr. Classical chmbr music festival with an ens of international soloists playing chmbr music, inc contemporary and commissioned works. Different composer in residence each year; 2010 composer John Woolrich.

Leith Hill Musical Festival 59 Eastwick Park Ave,

Great Bookham KT23 3LZ *t:* 01372 458811, also fax *w:* www.lhmf.co.uk Brian Kay, artistic dir; Liz May, hon sec. Festival in Dorking with strong links to Ralph Vaughan Williams, its conductor for nearly 50 yrs. Morning competitions for member choirs followed by evening perf with professional orch and soloists.

Leominster Festival 8 Westgate, Leominster HR6 8SA *e:* leominster-festival@yahoo.co.uk *w:* www.leominster-festival.co.uk Donald Millar, chair.

Liberation - Jersey International Music Festival Beechwood House, La Rue du Crocquet, St Brelade, Jersey JE3 8BZ *t:* 01534 767547 *e:* info@musicjersey.com *w:* www.musicjersey.com James Mews, chair. Internationally acclaimed artists performing in various settings inc heritage sites and castles, at sea on a yacht, as well as in the Jersey Opera House and Jersey Arts Centre; also community and educ events.

Lichfield Festival 7 The Close, Lichfield WS13 7LD *t:* 01543 306270 *f:* 01543 306274 *e:* info@lichfieldfestival.org *w:* www.lichfieldfestival.org Fiona Stuart, artistic dir. Multi-arts festival with strong classical music content plus jazz, world, folk, centred on Lichfield Cathedral, Lichfield Garrick Theatre and small church and other venues around Staffs.

Life Force Festival *t:* 01420 592200 *e:* community@altoncollege.ac.uk *w:* www.altoncollege.ac.uk/music Martin Read, head of mus. Series of concerts and educ w/shops. Concerts prefaced by short talk from the performers; w/shops open to young musicians, offering opportunity for students to work with the musicians to experience and explore their individual genre.

Lincoln and Lincolnshire International Chamber Music Festival Counterpoint, Grantham St, Lincoln LN2 1LW *t:* 07757 708858 *e:* licmfoffice@ntlworld.com *w:* www.licmf.org.uk Cathy Platt, sec. Chmbr music festival of 6 concerts in Lincoln and around the county's market towns. Details of the theme, exact dates and venues available on website

Little Missenden Festival 3 Mill End Cottages, Little Missenden HP7 0RG *t:* 01494 864686 *e:* contact@little-missenden.org *w:* www.little-missenden.org

Liverpool Summer Pops CMP Entertainment, 08 Place, 36-38 Whitechapel, Liverpool L1 6DZ *t:* 0151 708 6050 *f:* 0151 707 0400 *e:* info@cmplive.com *w:* www.summerpops.com Chas Cole, mgr dir. Held at Liverpool Echo Arena.

Llandeilo Fawr Festival of Music 129 Rhosmaen St, Llandeilo, Carmarthenshire SA19 6EN *t:* 01558 823294 *e:* juliajones.heelappeal@tesco.net *w:* www.llandeilofawr.net Julia Jones, festival dir. Internationally renowned singers, instrumentalists and choirs visit one of Wales's loveliest towns for a week of intensive music-making.

Llangollen International Musical Eisteddfod Eisteddfod Office, 1st Floor, Royal International Pavilion, Llangollen LL20 8SW *t:* 01978 862000 *f:* 01978 862002 *e:* info@international-eisteddfod.co.uk *w:* www.international-eisteddfod.co.uk; www.llangollen2010.co.uk Mervyn Cousins, exec dir. World-renowned festival of music, song and dance. Competitors from more than 50 countries; concerts each evening by world-class artists.

Llantilio Crossenny Festival of Music and Drama Treadam Farm, Llantillio Crossenny, Abergavenney, Monmouthshire NP7 8TA *t:* 01600 780233 *e:* llantilio@btinternet.com Robyn Sevastos, mus dir; Eleanor Farncombe, artistic dir.

London Bach Society's Bachfest Bach House, 73 High St, Old Oxted RH8 9LN *t:* 01883 717372 *f:* 01883 715851 *e:* lbs@lonbachsoc.demon.co.uk *w:* www.bachlive.co.uk Margaret Steinitz, artistic dir. Annual festival. Participation by invitation, but artist info/biographical material welcome (professional forces only).

London Festival of Contemporary Church Music St Pancras Church, Euston Rd, London NW1 2BA *t:* 020 7388 1461, also fax *e:* office@stpancraschurch.org *w:* www.stpancraschurch.org Christopher Batchelor, artistic dir. Principal aim is to showcase perfs of recent and contemporary liturgical music and org music at the very highest levels, both in the context of services and concerts.

London Handel Festival Horton House, 8 Ditton St, Ilminster *t:* 01460 53500, also fax *e:* c-hodgson@btconnect.com *w:* www.london-handel-festival.com Laurence Cummings, mus dir; Denys Darlow, founder cond; Catherine Hodgson, festival dir. Performances of the works of Handel and his contemporaries.

London International Festival of Exploratory Music 76 Kestrel House, Pickard St, London EC1V 8EL *t:* 020 7490 2497 *e:* info@lifem.org.uk *w:* www.lifem.org.uk Miguel Santos, festival dir. Festival of boundary-expanding music explorations committed to the world of life and music of all sorts of genres and origins. Also free programme of music-related films.

London Jazz Festival in association with Radio 3 51 Kingsway Place, Sans Walk, London EC1R 0LU *t:* 020 7324 1880 *f:* 020 7324 1881 *w:* www.londonjazzfestival.org.uk John Cumming, David

Jones, Claire Whitaker, artistic dirs.

London New Wind Festival c/o Catherine Pluygers, 119 Woolstone Rd, London SE23 2TQ *t:* 020 8699 1101 *f:* 020 8699 2219 *e:* catherinepluygers@hotmail.com *w:* www.londonnewwindfestival.org Catherine Pluygers, artistic dir. 8-10 concerts. Specialises in promoting new music for ww insts.

London Song Festival Flat 1, 42 The Crescent, London SW19 8AN *t:* 020 8879 0323; 07973 292992 *e:* nigelfoster@londonsongfestival.org *w:* www.londonsongfestival.org Nigel Foster, dir. Promotes the song repertoire through an annual series of concerts and m/classes. Each year a different theme is explored; well-known and rare repertoire presented in innovative programmes featuring the finest UK recitalists.

London String Quartet Week 8 Woodlands Rd, Romford RM1 4HD *t:* 01708 761423 *e:* info@playquartet.com *w:* www.playquartet.com Ruth Wheal, gen mgr. Various diverse events celebrating the art of the string quartet. Includes London International String Quartet Competition.

Longborough Festival Opera Longborough, Moreton-in-Marsh GL56 0QF *t:* 01451 830292 *f:* 01451 830605 *e:* admin@lfo.org.uk *w:* www.lfo.org.uk Lizzie Graham, dir; Amanda Laidler, pres. 3 operas produced.

Lower Machen Festival 29 Fisher Hill Way, Cardiff CF15 8DR *t:* 07831 300617 *e:* info@lowermachenfestival.co.uk *w:* www.lowermachenfestival.co.uk Alison Mears & Peter Esswood, artistic dirs.

Ludlow Festival The Festival Office, Castle Sq, Ludlow SY8 1AY *t:* 01584 875070 *f:* 01584 877673 *e:* admin@ludlowfestival.co.uk *w:* www.ludlowfestival.co.uk

Lufthansa Festival of Baroque Music PO Box 526, Harpenden AL5 9FA *e:* info@lufthansafestival.org.uk *w:* www.lufthansafestival.org.uk Lindsay Kemp, artistic dir; Lucy Bending, mgr. International festival featuring 17th-18th C music performed by the world's leading artists and ensembles at St John's Smith Square, Westminster Abbey and other venues in the Westminster area. Approx 10 fully professional concerts.

Machynlleth Festival Y Tabernacl, Heol Penrallt, Machynlleth, Powys SY20 8AJ *t:* 01654 703355 *f:* 01654 702160 *e:* info@momawales.org.uk *w:* www.momawales.org.uk Raymond Jones, admin. Takes place annually in late Aug. Eminent perfs take part in a wide range of events from choral singing and jazz to chmbr music and poetry readings.

Mananan International Festival of Music and the Arts Mananan Festival Office, Erin Arts Centre, Victoria Sq, Port Erin, Isle of Man IM9 6LD *t:* 01624 835858 *f:* 01624 836658 *e:* information@erinartscentre.com *w:* www.erinartscentre.com John Bethell MBE, artistic dir. Annual music festival, in association with BBC R3.

Manchester International Festival 3rd Floor, 81 King St, Manchester M2 4AH *t:* 0161 238 7300 *f:* 0161 832 7047 *e:* info@mif.co.uk *w:* www.mif.co.uk International festival of original, new work and special events.

Manchester Jazz Festival 226 Ducie House, Ducie St, Manchester M1 2JW *t:* 0161 228 0662, also fax *e:* fanny@manchesterjazz.com *w:* www.manchesterjazz.com Steve Mead, artistic dir; Mick Waterfield, producer. Contemporary jazz festival featuring primarily new work by NW-based artists.

Marsden Jazz Festival 10 Peel St, Marsden, Huddersfield HD7 6BW *t:* 01484 846969, also fax *e:* mjfoffice@tiscali.co.uk *w:* www.marsdenjazzfestival.com Barney Stevenson, festival chair. International stars from the world of jazz; around 60 live music events, over 40 of which are free of charge. Takes place over 3 days each Oct in the picturesque Pennine village of Marsden.

Mary Wakefield Westmorland Festival 6 Summerhill, Kendal LA9 4JU *t:* 01539 736193 *e:* rosemary.howell@virgin.net *w:* www.mwwf.co.uk R Howell, sec. Biennial festival with full range of adjudicated classes for all ages, schools w/shops, presentation days and concerts, culminating with a major choral concert.

Mayfield Festival of Music and the Arts *e:* info@mayfieldfestival.co.uk *w:* www.mayfieldfestival.co.uk

Mendelssohn on Mull Festival Druimfin, Tobermory, Isle of Mull PA75 6QB *t:* 01688 302828 *e:* administrator@mullfest.org.uk *w:* www.mullfest.org.uk Trish Haworth, admin; Levon Chilingirian, artistic dir; Marilyn Jeffcoat, chair.

Midsummer Music 56 Severalls Ave, Chesham HP5 3EL *t:* 01494 783643 *e:* madeleine.mattar@hotmail.co.uk *w:* www.midsummermusic.org.uk Madeleine Mattar, festival dir; Paul Lewis, Bjørg Lewis, artistic dirs. International chmbr musicians performing at St Mary Magdalene Church, Latimer, Bucks.

Milton Abbey Music Festival 22 Binghams Rd, Crossways, Dorchester DT2 8BW *t:* 01305 852489 *e:* fatmangre6br@tiscali.co.uk *w:* www.milton-abbey-music-festival.co.uk F Greenslade.

Minehead and Exmoor 'Sidella', Whitegate Rd,

Minehead TA24 5SP *t:* 01643 702353 *e:* minehead.festival@virgin.net David Yates, chair. The Festival Orchestra is made up of professional musicians from all over the country, providing W Somerset with 3 different programmes in a week. Artistic dir & cond: Richard Dickins, dir of music at Imperial College, London and principal cond at RCM jnr dept.

Music at Leasowes Bank Leasowes Bank Farm, Ratlinghope, nr Shrewsbury SY5 0SW *t:* 01743 790769, also fax *e:* musicatleasowes@googlemail.com *w:* www.leasowesmusicfestival.co.uk Frances Williams, festival dir. Series of concerts covering a wide range of music. New commission each season.

Music at Paxton Paxton House, Paxton, Scottish Borders TD15 1SZ *t:* 07752 570389; 01289 386291 (Paxton House) *e:* info@musicatpaxton.co.uk *w:* www.musicatpaxton.co.uk Helen Jamieson, festival mgr. 10-day festival of chmbr music featuring international musicians alongside young and locally based artists.

Music at Plush 11 Well Walk, London NW3 1BY *t:* 020 3286 1885 *e:* admin@musicatplush.net *w:* www.musicatplush.net Adrian Brendel, mus dir; Cathy Boyes, admin; Katharina Brendel, producer. Annual concert series of classical and contemporary music performed by world-class musicians in the rural setting of St John's Church in Plush.

Music at Restoration House Restoration House, Crow Lane, Rochester ME1 1RF *t:* 01634 848520 *e:* robert.tucker@restorationhouse.co.uk Robert Tucker, artistic dir. Period music on early insts in 17th C great chamber. Baroque, classical and early romantic specialities.

Music at the Priory Kingston House, Leonard Stanley, Stonehouse GL10 3NX *t:* 01453 822299, also fax *w:* www.leonardstanley.org.uk Robert A Hutchings, chair.

Music from a Foreign Land Stricklandgate House, 92 Stricklandgate, Kendal LA9 4PU *t:* 0845 644 2144 *f:* 0845 644 2506 *e:* info@ldsm.org.uk *w:* www.ldsm.org.uk Andrew Lucas, dir. Music and musicians from around the world in creative w/shops and perfs.

Nailsworth Festival Stonehill, Nympsfield GL6 0NH *t:* 01453 860671 *e:* festival@nailsworthfestival.org.uk *w:* www.nailsworthfestival.org.uk Tony Anhoury, programme co-ord. Arts, crafts, family entertainment.

National Festival of Music for Youth Music for Youth, 102 Point Pleasant, London SW18 1PP *t:* 020 8870 9624 *f:* 020 8870 9935 *e:* mfy@mfy.org.uk *w:* www.mfy.org.uk Vicky Walker, festival mgr.

Newbury Spring Festival 1 Bridge St, Newbury RG14 5BH *t:* 01635 32421; 01635 528766 *f:* 01635 528690 *e:* info@newburyspringfestival.org.uk *w:* www.newburyspringfestival.org.uk Mark Eynon, festival dir; Zoe Seenan, festival mgr; Emma O'Donnell, mkt mgr; Jane Pickering, festival sec. Fortnight of world-class music in Newbury and surrounding villages. International symphony orchs, ens and soloists, jazz legends, world music artists and the classical music stars of tomorrow.

Norfolk & Norwich Festival First Floor, Augustine Steward House, 14 Tombland, Norwich NR3 1HF *t:* 01603 877750 *f:* 01603 877766 *e:* info@nnfestival.org.uk *w:* www.nnfestival.org.uk Jonathan Holloway, festival dir; Clare Lovell, gen mgr; Daisy Turvill-Petre, communications offr. International arts festival for the east of England: classical, jazz, world and new music, theatre, dance, circus, outdoor spectaculars, children's events and visual arts.

The Northern Aldborough Festival The Festival Office, Aldborough Manor, Boroughbridge YO51 9EP *t:* 01423 324899 *f:* 01423 323761 *e:* festival@aldborough.com *w:* www.aldboroughfestival.com Dawn Seymour, festival admin; Robert Ogden, artistic dir. Music festival in the heart of N Yorks. Perfs inc 2 operas, pno recitals, quartets, cabaret night and last-night open air picnic finale. Morning concerts in stately homes in rural Yorks.

Northern Chords: The North East Chamber Music Festival *t:* 07912 375242 *e:* jonathan@northernchords.co.uk *w:* www.northernchords.co.uk Jonathan Bloxham, artistic dir & founder.

North Wales International Music Festival (St Asaph) Festival Office, Irish Sq, Upper Denbigh Rd, St Asaph LL17 0RL *t:* 01745 584508 *e:* admin@northwalesmusicfestival.co.uk *w:* www.northwalesmusicfestival.co.uk Ann Atkinson, artistic dir; Katy Morgan, festival co-ord; Sian Rackham, festival admin asst.

Norton Music Festival Festival Office, Constance House, 117a High St, Norton, Stockton on Tees *t:* 01642 355383 *f:* 01642 500400 *e:* nortonmusicfestival@btconnect.com *w:* www.nortonmusicfestival.com

Opera Holland Park Central Library, Phillimore Walk, London W8 7RX *t:* 020 7631 2049; 020 7361 2047 (audition enqs) *f:* 020 7361 2317 *e:* info@operahollandpark.com *w:* www.operahollandpark.com Michael Volpe, gen, mkt & publicity mgr; James Clutton, producer; Clarinda Chan, asst mkt & publicity offr; Katharine Camiller, asst producer. Summer festival of operas featuring

6 productions every year in Holland Park, with grade I listed Holland House as a backdrop. Resident orch is City of London Sinfonia.

Oundle International Festival 4 New St, Oundle PE8 4ED *t:* 01832 274919, also fax *e:* information@oundlefestival.org.uk *w:* www.oundlefestival.org.uk Patricia Ryan, festival dir. Mainly classical music, featuring professional chmbr, orch, choral and organ music, with some jazz, open-air theatre and occasionally community opera. Also Music in Quiet Places series of concerts in village churches.

Oxford Chamber Music Festival St Hilda's College, Oxford OX4 1DY *t:* 0845 652 0762 *e:* office@ocmf.net *w:* www.ocmf.net Clare La Roche Salter, festival dir; Priya Mitchell, artistic dir.

Oxford Early Music Festival 33 Binswood Ave, Headington, Oxford OX3 8NY *t:* 01865 751928, also fax *e:* festival@charivari.co.uk *w:* www.charivari.co.uk Kah-Ming Ng, mus dir.

Oxford May Music 48 Great Clarendon St, Oxford OX2 6AX *t:* 01865 273323 *f:* 01865 273417 *e:* info@oxfordmaymusic.co.uk *w:* www.oxfordmaymusic.co.uk Jack Liebeck, artistic dir.

Oxford Philomusica International Piano Festival & Summer Academy Templeton College, Kennington Rd, Oxford OX1 5NY *t:* 0870 606 0804 *f:* 020 8208 4239 *e:* info@oxfordphil.com *w:* www.oxfordphil.com Marios Papadopoulos, artistic dir.

Padstow Arts Festival *w:* www.padstowartsfestival.com

The Pembroke Festival Foundry House Community Centre, Orange Way, Pembroke Commons, Pembroke SA71 4DR *t:* 01646 680090 *w:* www.pembrokefestival.org.uk Elvira Adams, chair. Festival of music and the arts showcasing local talent.

Pennine Spring Music 24 Northgate, Heptonstall HX7 7ND *t:* 01422 843995 *e:* jean@richux.plus.com *w:* www.penninespringmusic.co.uk Jean Leach, chair. W/shops and rehearsals for participants; application open to all age groups, pref gr 6+. Orch/choral concerts, chmbr music or recitals performed each evening.

Perth Festival of the Arts 3-5 High St, Perth PH1 5JS *t:* 01577 862420 *f:* 01577 864519 *e:* info@perthfestival.co.uk *w:* www.perthfestival.co.uk Sandra Ralston, admin. Annual arts festival inc classical, opera, jazz, rock, folk, theatre and dance. Venues inc Perth Concert Hall, Perth Theatre and St John's Kirk.

Petersfield Musical Festival Fenns, Reservoir Lane, Petersfield GU32 2HX *t:* 01730 263539 *e:* philip._young@virgin.net *w:* www.petersfieldmusicalfestival.org.uk Philip Young, chair. In E Hampshire's premier musical event, local choirs sing in 2 major concerts with a professional orchestra and professional soloists. There are also youth concerts, an amateur orch concert and other associated events.

Petworth Festival 151 Whites Green Lodge, Lurgashall, Petworth GU28 9BD *t:* 01798 343055 *e:* info@petworthfestival.org.uk *w:* www.petworthfestival.org.uk Kate Wardle, festival mgr. Arts festival inc chmbr music, jazz, speech, drama and art among other things.

Plaxtol Music Festival PO Box 308, Sevenoaks TN15 0ZW *t:* 01732 811036, also fax *e:* mcarboni@carbonimedia.com *w:* www.plaxtolfestival.co.uk Classical chmbr and jazz concerts held in Plaxtol Church and surrounding venues every 2 yrs.

Play the Field *e:* info@playthefield.co.uk *w:* www.playthefield.co.uk Charles Hazelwood, dir.

Portsmouth Festivities 10 High St, Old Portsmouth PO1 2LN *t:* 023 9268 1390 *e:* festivities@pgs.org.uk *w:* www.portsmouth.co.uk 2009 celebrating the 500th anniversary of accession of Henry VIII; music, drama, outdoor events, family & children's events, education projects, exhibitions and more in venues across the city.

Presteigne Festival of Music and the Arts PO Box 30, Presteigne, Powys LD8 2WF *t:* 01544 267800 *e:* georgevass@presteignefestival.com *w:* www.presteignefestival.com George Vass, artistic dir; Alison Porter, festival producer; Annie Nethercott, gen mgr. Highly popular festival of music and the arts specialising in the perf of contemporary music, with a strong reputation for innovative and individual programming.

Proms at St Jude's St Jude-on-the-Hill, Central Sq, London NW11 7AH *t:* 020 8455 8687 *f:* 020 8458 3143 *e:* da.harris@which.net; y.baker@ukonline.co.uk *w:* www.promsatstjudes.org.uk David Harris, mktg & press offr; Yvonne Baker, gen enquiries. Mainly classical concerts covering orch, choral, chmbr and recitals. Also jazz; lunchtime concerts devoted to young talented musicians.

The Regis School of Music Summer Festival 46 Sudley Rd, Bognor Regis PO21 1ER *t:* 01243 866462 *e:* recital@tiscali.co.uk *w:* www.regisschoolofmusic.co.uk Alexander Levtov, artistic dir; Nina Levtov, admin. International soloists and chmbr music perfs. Competition for amateur musicians at the Recital Hall of the Regis School of Music.

Ripon International Festival Festival Office, Holly Howe, Copt Hewick, Ripon HG4 5BY *t:* 01765 605508 *e:* info@riponinternationalfestival.com *w:* www.riponinternationalfesival.com Janusz Piotrowicz, artistic dir. Symphony, choral, chmbr, world music, drama, puppetry.

RNCM Chamber Music Festival RNCM, 124 Oxford Rd, Manchester M13 9RD *t:* 07733 091771 *f:* 0161 273 7611 *e:* jane.thompson@btconnect.com *w:* www.rncm.ac.uk Alasdair Tait, artistic dir; Jane Thompson, admin.

Roman River Music Festival *e:* zelie@romanrivermusic.org.uk *w:* http://romanrivermusic.blogspot.com/ Orlando Jopling, artistic dir.

Rotherham Open Arts Festival c/o Community Arts Office, Central Library, Walker Place, Rotherham S65 1JH *t:* 01494 526052 *e:* sean.rourke@rotherham.gov.uk *w:* www.rotherhamculture.org Sean Rourke, dir; Claire Saddlington, festival admin. Featuring all perf arts in a Spiegeltent with emphasis on music: classical, world, folk, jazz and blues.

Rottingdean Spring Music Festival 1 Bazehill Rd, Rottingdean, Brighton BN2 7DB *t:* 01273 300894 *e:* britchorinst@fastnet.co.uk *w:* www.britchorinst.co.uk Roy Wales, dir. Chamber music, choral w/shop, orch and choral concerts, opera dinner, songs of musicals dinner, male voice choir concert.

Royal Tunbridge Wells International Music Festival Ockhams, Edenbridge TN8 5PS *t:* 01732 863630 *e:* info@tunbridgewellsfestival.co.uk *w:* www.tunbridgewellsfestival.co.uk

Rye Arts Festival PO Box 33, Rye TN31 7YB *t:* 01797 224442 *w:* www.ryeartsfestival.co.uk

Ryedale Festival Memorial Hall, Potter Hill, Pickering YO18 8AA *t:* 01751 475777 *e:* info@ryedalefestival.co.uk *w:* www.ryedalefestival.co.uk Classical music festival held in various venues within Ryedale, N Yorks.

Sacconi Chamber Music Festival 152 Malyons Rd, London SE13 7XG *t:* 07974 102014 *e:* rhianL2000@hotmail.com *w:* www.sacconi.com/festival Rhian Hancox, admin. Chmbr music from the Sacconi String Quartet and guests at St Eanswythe's Church.

Saddleworth Festival of the Arts Civic Hall, Lee St, Uppermill, Oldham OL3 6AE *t:* 01457 874296 *e:* info@saddleworthfestival.org.uk *w:* www.saddleworthfestival.org.uk Ken Deighton. Held every 4 yrs.

Salisbury International Arts Festival 87 Crane St, Salisbury SP1 2PU *t:* 01722 332977 *e:* info@salisburyfestival.co.uk *w:* www.salisburyfestival.co.uk Caroline Peacock, festival mgr; Maria Bota, festival dir. Multi-arts festival across the Salisbury area in venues from Salisbury Cathedral to Salisbury Arts Centre, churches, village halls and outdoor spaces, inc classical and contemporary concerts, literature, theatre and dance, community projects and street art.

Scottish International Festival of Trumpets addressall *w:* www.sift-uk.com Glenn Munro, contact. Festival in Elgin. W/shops and m/classes; recitals; concerts by local, national and international artists.

Sevenoaks Summer Festival *w:* www.sevenoaksfestival.org.uk Music, drama, dance, comedy and other events.

Shaldon Festival Greenbank, Higher Ringmore Rd, Shaldon, Teignmouth TQ14 0EZ *t:* 01626 873492 *e:* shaldonfestival@aol.com *w:* www.shaldonfestival.co.uk MC Watson, sec.

Shipley Arts Festival c/o The Plat, Thakeham Rd, Coolham RH13 8QD *t:* 01403 741685 *e:* shipleyfestival@bernardimusicgroup.com *w:* www.bernardimusicgroup.com Andrew Bernardi, artistic dir; Anne Clarke, art exhibition dir. International music and arts festival serving the community of W Sussex. Patrons: RT Hon Francis Maude MP, Gavin Henderson CBE, Mark Burrell Esq.

Sidmouth FolkWeek Tourist Information Centre, Ham Lane, Sidmouth EX10 8XR *t:* 01395 578627 *e:* info@sidmouthfolkweek.co.uk *w:* www.sidmouthfolkweek.co.uk The best of folk music, dance and song and more besides in E Devon.

Snape Proms Aldeburgh Music, Snape Maltings Concert Hall, Snape, Saxmundham IP17 1SP *t:* 01728 687100 *f:* 01728 687120 *e:* enquiries@aldeburgh.co.uk *w:* www.aldeburgh.co.uk Hettie Hope, artistic admin; Marc Ernesti, head of mktg & media. Offers everything from jazz, classical, world and folk music to comedy and poetry, all in the world-famous Snape Maltings Concert Hall.

Sonorities Festival of Contemporary Music School of Music, Queen's University, Belfast BT7 1NN *t:* 028 9097 4829 *f:* 028 9033 5053 *e:* sonorities@qub.ac.uk *w:* www.sonorities.org.uk Michael Alcorn. Established festival of new music showcasing the highest quality international artists across areas such as composition, improvisation, installation and audio-visual.

sound c/o Woodend Barn Arts Centre, Banchory, AB31 5QA *t:* 01330 825431 *e:* info@sound-scotland.co.uk *w:* www.sound-scotland.co.uk Fiona Robertson, festival co-ord. NE Scotland's festival of new music.

Sounds New 127 Shalmsford St, Chartham, Cantebury CT4 7RE *t:* 01227 731818 *e:* info@soundsnew.org.uk *w:* www.soundsnew.org.uk Festival

of contemporary music.
Soundwaves Festival 21 Preston Drove, Brighton BN1 6LA *e:* info@soundwaves-festival.org.uk *w:* www.soundwaves-festival.org.uk Festival of new music in Brighton.
Southern Cathedrals Festival Dept of Liturgy and Music, Salisbury Cathedral, 33 The Close, Salisbury SP1 2EJ *t:* 01722 555148 *f:* 01722 555117 *w:* www.southerncathedralsfestival.org.uk David Halls, artistic dir. Features sacred music in the English choral trad, sung by the cathedral choirs of Chichester, Salisbury and Winchester. 2010 festival in Chichester.
Spitalfields Music 61 Brushfield St, London E1 6AA *t:* 020 7377 0287 *f:* 020 7247 0494 *e:* info@spitalfieldsmusic.org.uk *w:* www.spitalfieldsmusic.org.uk Abigail Pogson, exec dir. Classical and new music festival with year-round learning and participation programme.
Spring Sounds Orchestra of the Swan, Civic Hall, 14 Rother St, Stratford-upon-Avon CV37 6LU *t:* 01789 267567 *e:* info@springsounds.co.uk; david@orchestraoftheswan.org *w:* www.springsounds.co.uk David Curtis, dir. Festival featuring Orchestra of the Swan, Tasmin Little, other acclaimed soloists, new commissions.
St Ceciliatide International Festival of Music Bank Cottage, Preston Capes NN11 3TD *t:* 01327 360931 *e:* festival@st-cecilatide.com *w:* www.st-ceciliatide.com Bernard Rapson, dir. Festival of chmbr music, food and wine taking place around St Cecilia's Day (22 Nov) in one of London's finest old City livery hall.s
St Cuthbert's Music Festival *t:* 01749 672611 *e:* portpubs@blueyonder.co.uk *w:* www.st.cuthbertswells.co.uk Terry Delaney. Annual event at the Church of St Cuthbert, Wells. Lunchtime and evening events covering wide range of musical tastes, with performers ranging form soloists to well-known orchs.
St Davids Cathedral Festival / Gwyl Eglwys Gadeiriol Tyddewi St Davids Cathedral, Deanery Office, St Davids SA62 6RH *t:* 01437 720057 *f:* 01437 721885 *e:* cathedralfestival@onetel.com; cathedralfestival@googlemail.com *w:* www.stdavidscathedral.org.uk Katherine Pearce, admin; Alexander Mason, artistic dir. Week of classical and contemporary professional music concerts set in the surroundings of St Davids Cathedral
St Endellion Summer Festival c/o Glebe Farmhouse, St Endellion, Port Isaac PL29 3TP *e:* sally@donegani.com; trevilley@tiscali.co.uk; spicerannie@aol.com *w:* www.endellion.org.uk Sally Donegani, artistic admin; Patrick Gale, chair; Annie Spice, PR/mailing lists. Artistic director for 2010 is Mark Padmore. The festival draws on a mixture of professionals and professional-standard amateurs to mount a sequence of opera, orch, choral and chmbr concerts and church services. Most concerts given in ancient church of St Endellion, with one in Truro Cathedral. Participation is by invitiation (send CVs to Sally Donegani). Non-performing volunteers welcome (contact Patrick Gale). Shorter festival each Easter (James Burton, mus dir).
St Magnus Festival 60 Victoria St, Kirkwall, Orkney KW15 1DN *t:* 01856 871445 *f:* 01856 871170 *e:* info@stmagnusfestival.com *w:* www.stmagnusfestival.com Angela Henderson, admin. Orkney's midsummer celebration of the arts: music, theatre, visual arts, literature, community events, excursions, Festival Club, Orkney Conducting Course and St Magnus Composers' Course.
Stour Music 2 Rural Terrace, Wye, nr Ashford TN25 5AP *t:* 01233 812267 *e:* mark.deller@virgin.net *w:* www.stourmusic.org.uk Mark Deller, festival dir. Festival of early music.
Stratford on Avon Music Festival *t:* 01274 858249 *f:* 01271 858375 *e:* eucorch1@aol.com *w:* www.stratfordmusicfestival.com Ambrose Miller.
Suffolk Villages Festival 119 Maldon Rd, Colchester CO3 3AX *t:* 01206 366603 *f:* 01206 543417 *e:* info@suffolkvillagesfestival.com *w:* www.suffolkvillagesfestival.com Peter Holman, artistic dir; Louise Jameson, admin. Early music.
Summer Music - Hallé Promenade Concerts Hallé Concerts Society, The Bridgewater Hall, Manchester M1 5HA *t:* 0161 237 7000 *f:* 0161 237 7029 *e:* info@halle.co.uk *w:* www.halle.co.uk Sir Mark Elder CBE, mus dir; John Summers, chief exec.
Sunbury and Shepperton Arts Festival Riverside Arts Centre, 59 Thames St, Sunbury-on-Thames TW16 5QF *w:* www.riversidearts.co.uk
Swaledale Festival Hudson House, Reeth, Richmond *t:* 01748 880018 *f:* 01748 880028 *e:* enquiries@swaledale-festival.org.uk *w:* www.swaledale-festival.org.uk Margaret Murphy, admin. Eclectic mix of classical, jazz, folk, world and brass along with arts, poetry and country walks. Tradition of commissioning new works.
Swanage Jazz Festival 2 Alexandra Terrace, Swanage BH19 2QQ *t:* 01929 425371 *e:* fredlindop@tiscali.co.uk Fred Lindop, artistic dir. Many bands from across the jazz spectrum, inc established names and new talents.
Swansea Festival of Music and the Arts 9 Gabalfa Rd, Sketty, Swansea SA2 8NF *t:* 01792

411570, also fax *e:* admin@swanseafestival.org *w:* www.swanseafestival.org Susan Croall, admin; Huw Tregelles Williams, chair. Range of national and international artists at city venues; symphony orchs, opera, jazz, chmbr music, recitals, contemporary dance, lectures, visual arts.

Tenby Arts Festival 24 Penally Heights, Penally, Tenby SA70 7QP *t:* 01834 845341 *w:* www.tenbyartsfest.co.uk Diana Lunn, sec.

Tetbury Music Festival PO Box 52, Long Newnton, Tetbury GL8 8ZS *t:* 07809 767574 *e:* info@tetburymusicfestival.org.uk *w:* www.tetburymusicfestival.org.uk Elise Smith, Graham Kean, co-dirs. Annual classical music festival.

Thaxted Festival Festival Office, Clarance House, Thaxted CM6 2PJ *t:* 01371 831421 *e:* thaxtedfestival@btconnect.com *w:* www.thaxtedfestival.org.uk Gareth Stainer, artistic dir; Ann Pickhaver, admin. Classical music (orch, ens, choral, pno), opera and jazz.

Three Choirs Festival 7c College Green, Gloucester GL1 2LX *t:* 01452 529819 *f:* 01452 502854 *e:* info@3choirs.org *w:* www.3choirs.org Geraint Bowen, artistic dir, Hereford; Adrian Partington, artistic dir, Gloucester; Adrian Lucas, artistic dir, Worcester; Paul Hedley, gen mgr. Oldest non-competitive festival in Europe; cycles round the 3 cathedral cities of Hereford, Gloucester and Worcester in rotation. Comprises nightly choral and orch music in one of the cathedrals, alongside a full programme of chmbr mus.

Tilford Bach Festival Fairlawne, Kiln Way, Grayshott, Hindhead GU26 6JF *t:* 01428 713338 *w:* www.tilbach.org.uk Adrian Butterfield, mus dirs; Sheila Austin, hon sec. At Farnham Castle and All Saints Church, Tilford.

Towersey Village Festival Mrs Casey Music, PO Box 296, Matlock DE4 3XU *t:* 01629 827017 *f:* 01629 821874 *e:* info@towerseyfestival.com *w:* www.towerseyfestival.com Relaxed, family-friendly festival; eclectic mix of concerts, w/shops, dances and dedicated youth and children's programmes.

Tudeley Festival Postern Park Oast, Tonbridge TN11 0QT *t:* 01732 773322 *f:* 01732 773344 *e:* tudeleyfestival@aol.com *w:* www.tudeleyfestival.org.uk Stephen Coles, artistic dir.

Two Moors Festival Barkham, Sandyway, Exmoor, South Molton EX36 3LU *t:* 01643 831370, also fax *e:* 2mf@onetel.com *w:* www.thetwomoorsfestival.com Penny Adie MBE, artistic dir; Jon Adie, chief exec.

UK Songwriting Festival Bath Spa University, Newton Park, Newton St Loe, Bath BA2 9BN *t:* 01225 875522 *f:* 01225 875495 *e:* l.endean@bathspa.ac.uk *w:* www.uksongwritingfestival.com Joe Bennett, artistic dir. Opportunity to share enthusiasm for songwriting with other songwriters; tutors available; chance to record in state-of-the-art recording studio.

Ulverston International Music Festival The Box Office, Coronation Hall, County Sq, Ulverston LA12 7LZ *t:* 0845 658 8982 *e:* ulverstonmusicfestival@googlemail.com *w:* www.ulverstonmusicfestival.co.uk Rowena Gibbons, admin. Internationally renowned musicians perform in Ulverston and surrounding area. Also autumn and winter concerts, plus educ activity programme.

Upton Jazz Festival Upton Jazz Association Ltd, 18 Riverside Close, Upton-upon-Severn WR8 0JN *t:* 01684 593254, also fax *e:* info@uptonjazz.co.uk *w:* www.uptonjazz.co.uk Deirdre Thompson, sec. International jazz festival.

Vale of Glamorgan Festival of Music Festival Office, 20 Orchard St, Llandovery, Carms SA20 0DG *t:* 01550 721565 *e:* valeofglamorgan.festival@virgin.net *w:* www.valeofglamorganfestival.org John Metcalf, artistic dir; Deborah Keyser, admin. Annual festival of living composers held at venues in and around the Vale of Glamorgan.

Voices in Paisley 21 Forbes Place, Paisley PA1 1UT *t:* 0141 849 1721 *e:* info@paisleyfestivalcompany.com *w:* www.paisleyfestivalcompany.com Fred Hay. Autumn festival incorporating Paisley Choral Festival and Fringe Voices! The festival brings professional and amateur, local, national and international choirs plus performers of vocal harmony in non-choral styles to 'Scotland's choir town'.

Wareham Music Festival Town Hall, East St, Wareham BH20 5EY *t:* 01929 550771 *f:* 01929 553521 *e:* rod@wareham-tc.gov.uk *w:* www.wareham-music.org.uk Rod Curtis, sec. Annual free music festival; all types of music, for all age groups, at pubs, cafes, town hall and Wareham Quay.

Wimbledon Music Festival *w:* www.wimbledonmusicfestival.co.uk World class artists in various venues in Wimbledon.

Winchester Festival 9 The Close, Winchester SO23 9LS *t:* 01962 857240 *e:* winchesterfestival@winchester-cathedral.org.uk *w:* www.winchesterfestival.co.uk Carol Butler, exec dir. Multi-arts festival in venues across Winchester.

Windsor Festival 3 Park St, Windsor SL4 1LU *t:* 01753 714364 *f:* 01753 866845 *e:* info@windsorfestival.com *w:* www.windsorfestival.com Martin Denny, festival dir. Over 80 events celebrating music, literature and local heritage.

International and local performers and events opportunities for children and families.

Wirksworth Festival Festival Office, Church Walk, Wirksworth DE4 4DP *t:* 01629 824003 *e:* info@wirksworthfestival.co.uk *w:* www.wirksworthfestival.co.uk Janette Hockley-Webster, operations mgr.

Wooburn Festival Sunrise, Harvest Hill, Bourne End SL8 5JJ *t:* 01628 530492 *e:* briandiana@talktalk.net *w:* www.wooburn.com Brian Johnson, chair. A music and arts festival for the Chilterns and Thames Valley.

Wycombe Arts Festival HP12 4DB *t:* 01494 528226 *f:* 01464 512000 *e:* johnw.beaumont@virgin.net *w:* www.wycombeartsfestival.org

Wymondham Music Festival The Festival Office, 9 Vimy Drive, Wymondham NR18 0PB *t:* 01953 601939 *e:* office@wymfestival.org.uk *w:* www.wymfestival.org.uk Evening concerts, daytime recitals, gigs, w/shops, jazz; town busking day, live music in the Market Place.

York Early Music Christmas Festival The National Centre for Early Music, St Margaret's Church, Walmgate, York YO1 9TL *t:* 01904 632220 *f:* 01904 612631 *e:* info@ncem.co.uk *w:* www.ncem.co.uk Delma Tomlin, admin dir.

York Early Music Festival The National Centre for Early Music, St Margaret's Church, Walmgate, York YO1 0TL *t:* 01904 632220 *f:* 01904 612631 *e:* info@ncem.co.uk *w:* www.ncem.co.uk Delma Tomlin, admin dir; John Bryan, artistic adviser; Robert Hollingworth, artistic advisor.

IRELAND

IRELAND

Ireland is famed for being both relaxed and welcoming, forward-looking as well as having a strong sense of history. And being part of the Eurozone, it is an attractive location for many visitors from Europe. In fact, the country's appeal is wider thanks to an Irish diaspora in North America and Australia that identifies closely with it.

As far as music goes, traditional Irish music, particularly when allied to dancing, has a strong presence in the country not just in the more informal settings of pubs and local community festivals but also in competitions, and it is not uncommon to find collaborations between Ireland's classical and folk musicians on the concert platform. Both classical and traditional styles are supported by dedicated organisations. The Comhaltas Ceoltóri Éirann (http://comhaltas.ie) has the aim of preserving and promoting Irish traditional music across the world which it does through laying on classes, touring music groups and running competitions; the Contemporary Music Centre, Ireland (www.cmc.ie) is focused rather on contemporary classical music, and has a variety of resources (library, archive, composer details etc) at its disposal – in truth, however, traditional styles are closely linked with contemporary musical expression, with numerous composers drawing on it in their work. Ireland's other musical strength, as a breeding ground for pop and rock bands, should not be forgotten, particularly as the resulting music so often has a traditionally Irish flavour to it. The Journal of Music is an Ireland-based publication (non-academic) which covers all these areas and more, and has an international distribution.

Ireland operates a 2-cycle system with a 4-year undergraduate period leading to bachelors degree (BMus or BA, depending on the institution and course content) followed by 1-year or 2-year postgraduate (MMus or MA).

CORK

City, with a very strong civic identity, in the south of the country linked to the coast by the river Lee. The port part of the city is located in one of the world's largest natural harbours. Ireland's tallest building (the Elysian, with a modern design) is in the city; however, the majority of architecture dates from the 19th century.

CLIMATE

Warmest month July (11-19°C), coldest month January (2-7°C). Generally, rainfall levels are high with over 100mm per month from October to March.

MUSICAL LIFE

Curtis Auditorium at Cork School of Music is a popular venue for classical music, concerts and performances by visiting artists. Cork Opera House stages a range of productions (opera is only a small part of its overall repertoire); opera also at Everyman Palace. Music at Triskel Arts Centre tends to be traditional Irish, jazz, pop etc rather than classical.

OTHER CULTURAL INFORMATION

Art gallery at University College Cork (temporary exhibitions) as well as a municipal gallery. Everyman Palace the main theatre venue, Triskel Arts Centre has a range of performance and visual arts; Cork Arts Theatre is a new venue for small-scale theatre productions (100-seat auditorium); Granary focuses on contermporary and experimental performance.

FESTIVALS AND EVENTS

Long-established annual choral festival in April-May. Jazz festival in October; Midsummer Festival is a multi-arts and entertainment event. West Cork Music in June has international classical musicians, not in the city but in Bantry (about 50km along the coast); East Cork Early Music Festival just outside the city in nearby Midleton.

TOURIST INFORMATION

www.cometocork.com, +353 21 4255100

CIT CORK SCHOOL OF MUSIC

Union Quay, Cork, Ireland
t: +353 21 480 7310
f: +353 21 454 7601
e: bmus@cit.ie *w:* www.cit.ie
Contact Gabriela Mayer (international enquiries).

Course information Bachelor of music, master of arts (performance, composition). *Other* Music technology, music therapy.

Admissions information *Term dates* Sep-Jun. *Application requirements* School leaving certificate or equivalent; audition. *Application deadline* 1st years: Feb; 2nd and 4th years: 15 Jan (BMus), 15 May (MA or Erasmus). *Fees* EUR 3819 (BMus); EUR 3379 (MA) figures for 2009/10. Erasmus students pay fees at home institution. *Scholarships* None. *No of students* 162 students.

A new, purpose-built home for the CSM provides 13,000m^2 of state-of-the-art facilities and includes a library, 60 studios (equipped with new Steinway grand pianos), a large auditorium, a drama theatre, recording studio, an electronic music studio, an Audiolab, a MusicITlab, and a postgraduate centre. CSM is Ireland's largest conservatory of music and drama and its staff includes many performers of national and international standing.

DUBLIN

Irish capital on the river Liffey where it meets the Irish sea on the east of the country. Its main period of historical development was in the 17th-18th century period of prosperity; the architecture of the city strongly reflects this period – the distinctive neo-classical riverside Custom House is a good example; more recently the city has prospered economically once more resulting in further redevelopment and building. The city is popular among students (there are 3 universities and several other educational institutions) and it attracts visitors from around the world, many of whom come for the nightlife of the Temple Bar area or the live traditional music played throughout the city and for which it is renowned.

CLIMATE

Warmest month July (11-19°C), coolest months January and February (2-8°C). Rainfall levels are relatively even throughout the year – December tends to be wettest, spring/early summer driest (although late summer rain can be heavy).

MUSICAL LIFE

Gaiety Theatre for opera (it is the base for Opera Ireland) as well as musicals; another Dublin-based company is Opera Theatre Company (it tours throughout the country). National Concert Hall is the base for the National Symphony Orchestra of Ireland, an orchestra managed by RTE broadcaster as is the RTE Concert Orchestra and the Vanbrugh Quartet. RDS Concert Hall has classical and rock concerts.

OTHER CULTURAL INFORMATION

One of the world's most renowned literary cities, counting Joyce, Beckett, Wilde, Yeats, George Bernard Shaw and Swift among its prominent figures – James Joyce Centre promotes events about the author, and there is a Shaw Birthplace Museum. Theatre is consequently a major artform: the Abbey Theatre is the national theatre and the country's most famous; there are theatre spaces at The Helix arts centre. Project Arts Centre is focused on contemporary performance and visual arts.

FESTIVALS AND EVENTS

Importance of literature reflected in the existence of the Dublin Theatre Festival and Fringe Festival (both September), and the Dublin Writers' Festival (early June). Choir and organ festival in June (triennial, next in 2011), also a triennial piano competition (next event in 2012). International film festival runs for 10 days in February. A unique tradition is Bloomsday, every 16 June, the day on which Joyce's Ulysses is set, when Dubliners recreate episodes from the novel. St Patrick's Day (17 March) a big day of national celebration that is repeated worldwide.

LOCAL PUBLICATIONS

The Dubliner (www.thedubliner.ie) covers culture, entertainment and going out in the city.

TOURIST INFORMATION

www.visitdublin.com, +353 66 979 2083

DIT CONSERVATORY OF MUSIC AND DRAMA

163-167 Rathmines Rd, Dublin 6, Ireland
t: +353 1 402 3513 *f:* +353 1 402 3512
e: conservatory@dit.ie; international@dit.ie *w:* www.dit.ie
Contact Fiona Howard

Course information Bachelor of music, bachelor in music education, foundation certificate in music (1 year); also bachelor of arts in drama (performance). Postgrad: master of music (performance), postgraduate diploma in music (performance), MPhil and PhD by research and compostion. Also Junior Conservatory, part time instrumental and vocal tuition.

Admissions information *Term dates* Sep-Jun *Application requirements* See website for details. *Application deadline* 1 Feb (EU applicants apply through Central Applications Office); Apr (non-EU applicants apply through DIT International Office). *Fees* EU applicants who are first time undergrads and resident in EU state for at least 3 of the preceding 5 years are not normally required to pay tuition fees for bachelor of music, bachelor in music education and bachelor of arts in drama (performance). For current information on fees, please see website. *No of students* Over 200 full time undergrad/postgrad students. *Language requirements* English

Facilities *Performance opportunities* Recitals, chamber music, ensemble concerts, opera productions *Accommodation* Accommodation office produces list of available living accommodation.

ROYAL IRISH ACADEMY OF MUSIC

36-38 Westland Row, Dublin 2, Ireland
t: +353 1 6764412 *f:* +353 1 6622798
e: info@riam.ie; generaloffice@riam.ie *w:* www.riam.ie

Course information Doctorate, master in music performance, BA in music performance, BA in

composition, bachelor in music education and an access course; also associate and licentiate diplomas in teaching and performance. *Instrumental* Piano, harpsichord, organ and accordion, strings, brass, woodwind, percussion. *Historical performance* Recorder ensemble. *Orchestral* Symphony and chamber orchestras *Chamber music* Wind ensembles, percussion ensemble, string chamber orchestra and quartets. *Choral* Choral groups *Jazz/world* Jazz ensemble
Facilities *Performance opportunities* A wide variety of ensembles that perform throughout the year; masterclasses.

MUSIC FESTIVALS

Cork International Choral Festival Civic Trust House, 50 Pope's Quay, Cork, Ireland *t:* +353 21 4215125 *f:* +323 21 4215192 *e:* info@corkchoral.ie *w:* www.corkchoral.ie World class festival celebrating the best of choral and vocal music. Programme includes prestigious international and national competitions, gala and fringe concerts, public performances, and an education programme.
The East Cork Early Music Festival 95 Main St, Midleton, County Cork, Ireland *t:* +353 21 463 6761 *e:* info@eastcorkearlymusic.ie *w:* www.eastcorkearlymusic.ie
Galway Early Music Festival Caherfurvaus, Craughwell, Co Galway, Ireland *t:* +353 87 930 5506 *e:* info@galwayearlymusic.com *w:* www.galwayearlymusic.com Medieval, renaissance and baroque music and dance. Imaginative programming in the medieval city of Galway includes concerts, w/shops and free public perfs. 2010 theme: Music and Madness.
Kilkenny Arts Festival 9-10 Abbey Business Centre, Abbey St, Kilkenny, Ireland *t:* +353 56 776 3663 *f:* +353 56 775 1704 *e:* info@kilkennyarts.ie *w:* www.kilkennyarts.ie Multi-arts festival covering classical, jazz, contemporary and traditional music, visual arts, literature, theatre and children's events.
Limerick International Music Festival *t:* +353 61 213 130 *e:* ico@ul.ie *w:* www.irishchamberorchestra.com
Pipeworks St Catherine's Church, Thomas St, Dublin 8, Ireland *t:* +353 85 786 8860 *e:* adminpipeworks@gmail.com *w:* www.pipeworksfestival.com Triennial festival featuring organ-playing competition.
West Cork Chamber Music Festival West Cork Music, 13 Glengarriff Rd, Bantry, Co Cork, Ireland *t:* +353 27 52788 *f:* +353 27 52797 *e:* westcorkmusic@eircom.net *w:* www.westcorkmusic.ie
Wexford Festival Opera Wexford Opera House, High St, Wexford, Ireland *t:* +353 53 9122 400 *e:* info@wexfordopera.com *w:* www.wexfordopera.com

CROSSING EUROPE TO STUDY – AN INTRODUCTION TO ERASMUS

For those interested in travelling abroad to study, there are three principal ways of doing so. The first is to apply directly to institutions that catch your eye, following whatever degree programme, diploma or other qualification is appropriate. This will mean several years' study abroad, a daunting prospect for some, one which may not be suitable for every subject – going to France to study French literature is one thing; going to study history may or may not be.

Another is to take advantage of exchange partnerships set up between individual institutions. If you are considering travelling abroad as part of your course, it is worth asking the conservatoires or colleges you are interested in whether they have such partnerships and if so, with whom.

In order to give a greater number of students the opportunity to travel abroad within Europe, the European Union set up the Erasmus scheme, the third method. Erasmus stands for European Region Action Scheme for the Mobility of University Students (it is also the name of a Dutch renaissance theologian). It is one of several educational programmes that fall under the umbrella of the EU's 'Lifelong Learning Programme 2007-2013'; others focus or have focused on activity in schools, adult education, vocational training and so on. Erasmus itself has a number of aims as well as increasing the number of exchanges and improving the quality of the experience for those undertaking them, but it is the individual students who are the obvious beneficiaries.

Under the scheme, students and teachers at one of the 2200 or so universities across the 31 participating countries who are also citizens of one of those countries can take advantage of the opportunity to spend from three months to one academic year at a European university. This kind of year abroad system has been long part of the modern language student's higher education experience, and for obvious reasons – it is surely one of the best ways to learn a foreign language, and students can pick up much about a culture through exposure to daily life there. However, for many of these students the year abroad counts little directly to their final degree results, rather like sandwich years spent working in industry for students more generally.

As with institution-to-institution exchange schemes, conservatoires and universities will have established Erasmus partners (so again, it is worth checking with whom). Although this may appear restrictive, it does mean that the two colleges in question will have developed a relationship, making it less likely that your stay there will be affected by basic lack of understanding, or a failure of expectation.

But the real advantage for Erasmus students is that the marks they earn on any courses they take while on exchange are recognised as part of their home degree course. There is another advantage, however: students are not required to pay tuition fees at the institution they are travelling to. This gives Erasmus students an advantage over those applying direct, particularly when travelling to a country with a policy of levying substantial tuition fees. Other financial help is available too. Once offered an Erasmus place, students can apply for an Erasmus grant through the institution they are visiting; this aims to help with living costs, although it is unlikely to be sufficient to cover all living costs.

THE FOLLOWING WEBSITES ARE USEFUL FOR STUDENTS WANTING TO FIND OUT MORE:

- European Commission Education & Training Detailed website covering education in the EU, including summary of Erasmus and other programmes

  http://ec.europa.eu/education

- The AEC Bologna Declaration and Music Resource run by Association of European Conservatoires (AEC)

  www.bologna-and-music.org

- IRIS – Integrated Reporting for International Students Provides information about Erasmus institutions

  http://iris.siu.no

THE BOLOGNA PROCESS

If you have already started making enquiries about travelling to study within Europe, you will probably have come across the term 'Bologna Process'. Nothing to do with making ragù, the term refers to the long-term aim of harmonising educational standards across the continent, agreed at a meeting in 1999 in the Italian city. Although not an EU initiative in the same way that Erasmus is, its goals are similar: promoting ease of movement between European countries; promoting the European education system more widely; broadening the European knowledge-base.

The principal way in which this aim is being worked towards is the European Credit Transfer and Accumulation System (ECTS). Because different countries have different educational traditions concerning length of degree course, what qualifications are required, course content and how students' knowledge is tested, a mechanism for recognising equivalences was needed. In the system that was chosen, ECTS credits are based on the workload students will undertake to fulfil course requirements. Each year of higher education study amounts to 60 ECTS credits (with 1 credit amounting to 25-30 hours' work).

Since this system is linked to time taken to complete studies, it has also been necessary to draw degree levels closer together. The typical pattern adopted is a 3-cycle system with a 3-year (180 ECTS) 1st cycle equivalent to a bachelors degree; 2-year (120 ECTS) 2nd cycle masters equivalent; 3-year (180 ECTS) doctorate. (Some Bologna-compliant institutions prefer a 4-year bachelors plus 1-year masters.)

That is not to say that the system has been adopted without difficulties. An obvious problem is the insistence that credits in one programme are transferable to another. As your proficiency in literature does not make you a concert-standard pianist, for example, so institutions are necessarily able to use discretion in who they accept. Some countries will be Bologna-compliant in certain areas but not in others; others adopted the proposals quickly, others are still in the process of taking them on board (the aim is for all to conform by 2010).

That said, the process was intended as a framework rather than an absolute rigid structure, and for most students, certainly music students looking to advance their training towards professional levels, much of this is immaterial. Conservatoires in particular are keen to promote themselves internationally, and the more cross-border movement there is, the more they will be helped in achieving this aim.

BOLOGNA PROCESS SIGNATORIES – THE EUROPEAN HIGHER EDUCATION AREA

Albania, Andorra, Armenia, Austria, Azerbaijan, Belgium, Bosnia & Herzegovina, Bulgaria, Croatia, Cyprus, Czech Republic, Denmark, Estonia, Finland, France, Georgia, Germany, Greece, Hungary, Iceland, Ireland, Italy, Latvia, Liechtenstein, Lithuania, Luxembourg, Malta, Moldova, Montenegro, the Netherlands, Norway, Poland, Portugal, Republic of Macedonia, Romania, Russia, Serbian, Slovakia, Slovenia, Spain, Sweden, Switzerland, Turkey, UK, Ukraine

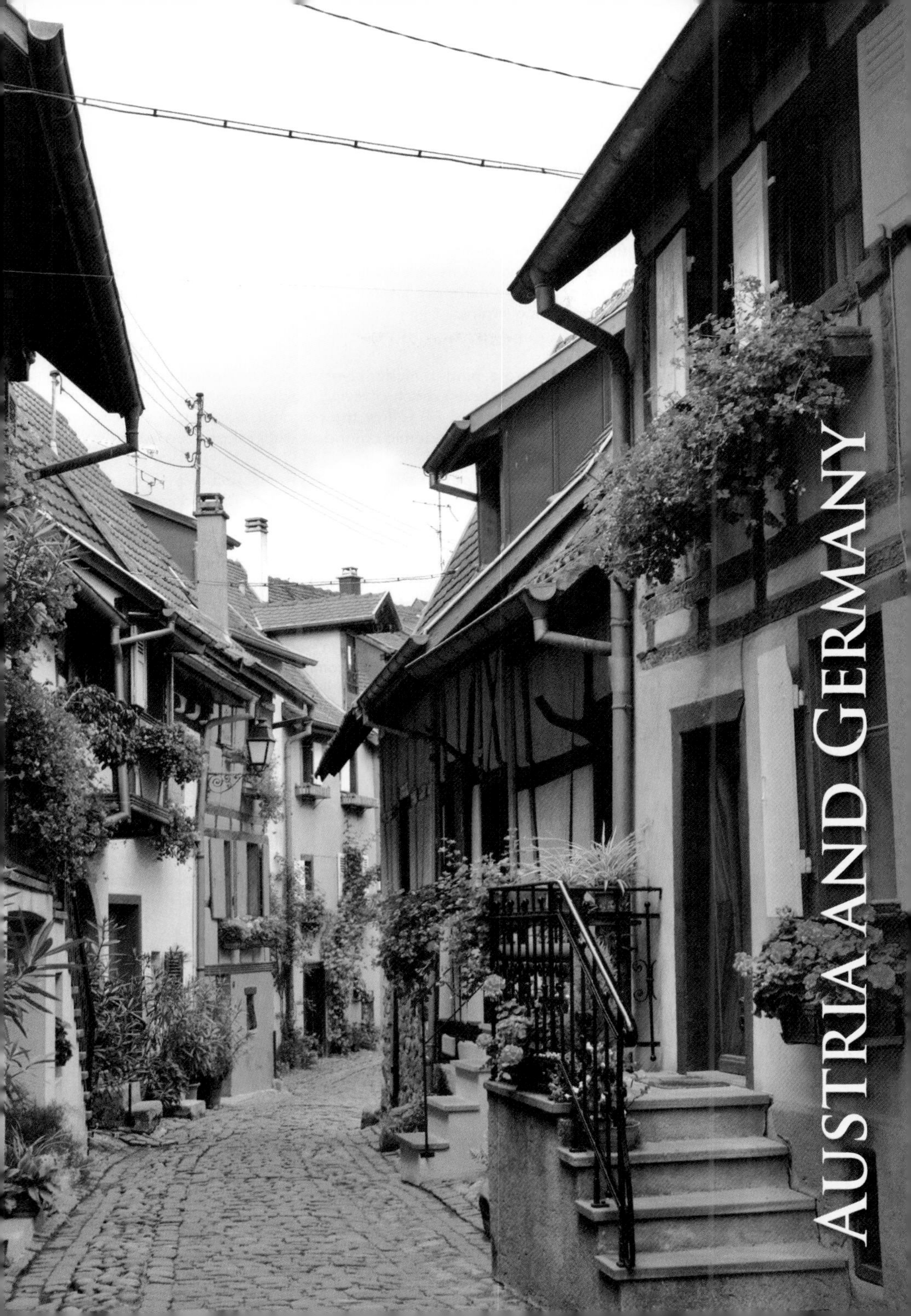

Austria and Germany

AUSTRIA AND GERMANY

Austria and Germany are surely the two countries most closely associated with the classical music tradition over the longest time. This is reflected in the sheer number of institutions dedicated to professional music training there, not to mention the number of professional opportunities open to qualified music graduates compared with many other countries.

Many German and Austrian cities have particular associations with composers or musical movements: Salzburg and Mozart, Brahms and Vienna, Beethoven and Bonn and so on. These connections undoubtedly enhance the musical experience of those studying, living and working there. However, thanks to the number of institutions waiting to welcome students from around the world, there are opportunities to discover many less well-known locations offering a different quality of life, or specific leisure activities – there are institutions in the big cities, but also in smaller locations near the countryside or the mountains.

EUROPE

AUSTRIA PAGE 73

Two types of institution are listed here: state-funded music university and 'Privatuniversität' (private university; actually funded at a municipal level), each offering bachelors and masters degrees following the Bologna system of equivalences. All follow the national 2-semester system, with institutions responsible for setting their own academic calendar within that. Curriculum is also determined by each institution.

In common with many countries, Austria operates a 3-cycle system: bachelor (3 or 4 years depending on the institution), magister (masters) and doktor (doctorate). ECTS credits are awarded at 60 per year of study in the first 2 cycles.

In summer semester 2009, a federal law came into force meaning students from Austria and the EU are be exempt from paying tuition fees, provided they complete each component of their degree course within the timeframe specified. For other students, fees will be capped at EUR 363.36 per semester. This only applies to recognised degree courses; fees for adult and continuing education are set by the colleges. The individual institutions will be able to advise further.

International students can get help finding accommodation in halls of residence across Austria via ÖAD Housing (www.housing.oead.at), with a range of accommodation available. This service is not open to Austrian students. You will, have to pay rent and living expenses, but conservatoires may offer grants and scholarships to help, and there are also various foundations and grant-awarding organisations which may be able to help. These will vary from place to place however; contact the international office at the institution you are interested in to find out more, or check websites.

GERMANY PAGE 79

Primarily, professional music training in Germany is through one of its 24 'Staatlichen Musikhochschule' (literally, state music high schools). Each of Germany's states administers one or more such institution; thanks to the government structure of the country, in which each state is an autonomous administrative area linked to the others through a federal apparatus, education systems (and hence the way conservatoires are run) differ from state to state.

Although the Hochschule are equivalent in status to universities, performance students, unlike their counterparts in Austria, do not have the opportunity for doctoral study (although this is under review) – studies at postgrad level conclude with the Konzertexamen. However, and this is where Hochschule differ from universities, undergraduate studies have traditionally lasted 5 years (10 semesters); this situation is changing only gradually. And music graduates usually receive a 'Diplom' rather than a bachelors degree (German law requires that bachelors degrees are completed early enough to allow a masters to be finished in 5 years).

Deutscher Acakadmischer Austausch Dienst (German Academic Exchange Service; www.daad.de) website has comprehensive information for overseas students wishing to study in Germany.

EISENSTADT

Small city in eastern Austria most noted for being the home for the Esterházy family, Haydn's principal employers – he was the Kapellmeister – for much of his working life; it is in the city that the composer is buried. The Schloss Esterházy is one of the city's key sights. The city is close to the countryside, with numerous vineyards and fruit orchards surrounding it

CLIMATE

Hottest months July and August (15-26°C), coldest month January (-3-3°C). Rainfall is modest throughout the year, reaching a peak in June (70mm), driest in January and February (around 30mm), although snow does occur during this time.

MUSICAL LIFE

Haydn Orchester is based in the city along with other ensembles blending the composer with city: the Haydn Trio Eisenstadt and Haydnbrass Eisenstadt.

OTHER CULTURAL INFORMATION

Haydn Haus is a display at the composer's residence. Leinnerhaus gallery hosts changing art exhibitions, plus other events including concerts.

FESTIVALS AND EVENTS

Main event is the Haydn Festival (September).

TOURIST INFORMATION

www.eisenstadt-tourism.at, tourismus@eisenstadt.at, +43 2682 705 0

JOSEPH HAYDN KONSERVATORIOM

Glorietteallee 2, 7000 Eisenstadt, Austria
t: +43 2682 63734 *f:* +43 2682 637344 *e:* erasmus@haydnkons.at *w:* www.haydnkons.at; erasmus.haydnkons.at; www.haydntheprogressive.at
Contact Regina Himmelbauer
Course information BA, MA (in conjunction with university), diploma, instrumental teaching qualifications. See http://erasmus.haydnkons.at and follow links to downloadcenter to find full course details online.
Admissions information *Term dates* Autumn term: Sep 6 2010-Feb 7 2011; spring term: Feb 14-July 1 2011 *Application requirements* Vary according to course. See website. *Application deadline* Jun 1 2010 (for autumn term), Jan 7 2011 (spring term) *Fees* EUR 240 per term. *Scholarships* None. *No of students* 200 *Language requirements* German language required.
Facilities *Music facilities* Electronic key system enables students to practise at any time of day, seven days a week. *Performance opportunities* At least one concert per term for each instrumental group. *Accommodation* Links with local halls of residence.

GRAZ

City in the south east of the country with a distinctively Austrian architectural style blending gothic and baroque with Balkan and Italian-influenced buildings, particularly evident in the city's old town area. Overlooking the city is the Schlossberg which includes a garden and open air performance space as well as the city's most recognisable landmark, the clock tower; the castle can be reached by funicular railway or picturesque wooded pathways. Graz is the second largest city in Austria and has a significant student population (6 universities attracting over 40,000 from around the world).

CLIMATE

Has a slightly Mediterranean feel. Hottest month August (13-26°C), coldest month January (-4-2°C). Wettest period is summer, but autumn-early spring is relatively dry.

MUSICAL LIFE

Home to Grazer Oper opera company, performing a season of opera at its own baroque opera house; also home to Grazer Philharmonische, which doubles as the opera orchestra. Visiting orchestras can be heard at the late 19th century Stefaniensaal.

OTHER CULTURAL INFORMATION

Modern Helmut-List-Halle stages a broad range of popular and contemporary performances from modern dance to rock. There is a large number of museums and galleries, including modern art gallery, natural history museum, city museum, gallery of old art, as well as more unusual exhibitions such as the Hans Gross Criminological Museum and the Hanns Schell Collection of locks and keys.

FESTIVALS AND EVENTS

Annual Styriarte music festival (named after Styria, the region of which Graz is the capital) in June and July. Summer is also when the American Institute of Music Studies sets up for its annual festival/summer school, providing a varied programme of vocal, orchestral, stage works and chamber music.

TOURIST INFORMATION

www.graztourism.at, info@graztourismus.at, +43 316 8075 0

KUNSTUNIVERSITÄT GRAZ (KUG) (UNIVERSITY OF MUSIC AND PERFORMING ARTS GRAZ)

Palais Meran, Leonhardstr 15, A-8010 Graz, Austria
t: +43 316 389 1100; +43 316 389 1160 (international relations) *f:* +43 316 389 1101
e: info@kug.ac.at *w:* www.kug.ac.at
Contact Irene Hofmann-Wellenhof, head of dept of international relations.
Course information Bachelors, masters and doctoral study programmes in instrumental or vocal performance, composition and theory, conducting, jazz, music education and musicology. Non-degree students also admitted at discretion of intended professor. Also, study programmes in stage design and performing arts/drama. *Instrumental* Accordion, bass tuba, clarinet, double bass, bassoon, flute, french horn, guitar, harp, oboe, organ, percussion instruments, piano, piano accompaniment, saxophone, trombone, trumpet, viola, violin, violoncello *Vocal* Vocal studies *Historical performance* Recorder, harpsichord, viola da gamba *Chamber music* Chamber music for strings and piano, piano/vocal accompaniment. *Other* Audio engineering, catholic and protestant church music, musicology.
Admissions information *Term dates* Early Oct-late Jan (winter semester); early Mar-late Jun (summer semester). *Application requirements* Min age 17 (15 for instrumentalists). Entrance exam (audition, theory & aural test); certain courses require university entrance qualifications equivalent to Austrian 'Matura'. Details of requirements for Erasmus students available on website. *Application deadline* Full schedule of application dates and deadlines on website. *Fees* None, or EUR 363.63 per semester (EU citizens), depending on course. For further information on fees, see education ministry website: www.bmwf.gv.at/submenue/studienbeitraege *Scholarships* See website for details. *No of students* 2287 students in total, 982 from overseas. *Language requirements* German.
Facilities *Music facilities* Library facilities: 190,000 volumes incl books, journals, sheet music, records, tapes and other media. *Accommodation* International students eligible for housing in halls of residence (dependent on space) via ÖAD organisation: www.housing.oead.at

LINZ

A city with a largely industrial background and generally lacking the characteristic 'fairytale' architectural style associated , but it has taken advantage of its location on the Danube to become a thriving, culturally active place. One the European Cities of Culture in 2009.

CLIMATE

Hottest month August (13-25°C), coldest months December-January (-3-1°C).

MUSICAL LIFE

Anton Bruckner born just outside the city, hence the riverside Brucknerhaus concert hall (actually 3 separate concert spaces), home to the Bruckner Orchester. As well as its own concerts, the orchestra provides accompaniment for the town's opera company.

OTHER CULTURAL INFORMATION

Very active cultural life, with its own modern art gallery (the Lentos, also near the Danube), and the Kulturmeile ('culture mile') riverside park with various culture venues and occasional open-air events. Theatre spaces at regional Landestheater Linz and the drama company based there.

FESTIVALS AND EVENTS

Annual Brucknerfest in September and October, a fairly traditional music festival complemented by the international Ars Electronica fair. Brucknerfest is preceded by the 3-day Pflasterspektakel, a festival of street art.

TOURIST INFORMATION

www.linz.at, tourist.info@linz.at, tel +43 732 7070

ANTON BRUCKNER PRIVATUNIVERSITAT FÜR MUSIK, SCHAUSPIEL UND TANZ

Wildbergstr 18, A-4040 Linz, Austria
t: +43 732 70 1000 0 *f:* +43 732 70 1000 30
e: information@bruckneruni.at *w:* www.bruckneruni.at
Course information 300 courses offered in music, dance and drama.
Admissions information *Term dates* 1 Oct-28 Feb

EUROPE

(winter term); 1 Mar-3 Jul (summer term). *Application requirements* Entrance exam. *Application deadline* End Jun. *Fees* EUR 100 per term. *No of students* 840 students, inc 280 from overseas.

SALZBURG

A Unesco world heritage site, place of pilgrimage for Mozart-lovers, and one of Europe's premier cultural tourist destinations, famed for its baroque architecture and overlooked by its dramatic hilltop fortress complex (the Festung Hohensalzburg). Its population of over 200,000 more than doubles during holiday times as visitors arrive from around the world, some of whom at least come to visit locations from the film The Sound of Music, such as the Mirabell Gardens.

CLIMATE

Typical continental climate with warm, if somewhat rainy, summers (typical temperatures in July and August range from 12°C to 23°C) and cold winters (temperatures around freezing from December to February) with snow.

MUSICAL LIFE

Camerata Salzburg is the city's high-quality chamber orchestra, and Mozarteum Orchester its busy regional symphony orchestra. Salzburg's profile makes it an attractive destination for touring performers, especially student choirs and orchestras; added to the numerous recitals and concerts which take place in the city's churches, museums and so on, it means there are ample opportunities to hear music. Opera comes via the Salzburger Landestheater.

OTHER CULTURAL INFORMATION

Landestheater is the biggest theatre venue in the city, and home also to a theatre company. History of the city told in the Carolino Augusteum museum and its five branches across the city; Mozarts Geburtshaus (birthplace) and Mozarts Wohnhaus (residence, actually a reconstruction) both contain museums. These are run by the Internationale Stiftung Mozarteum (International Mozart Foundation), an organisation promoting knowledge of Mozart and his work based in Salzburg. Among the city's galleries there are modern art museums and a gallery of baroque art; the Salzburg Museum covers a number of specialist exhibitions in different locations from the main display at the Residenz palace to smaller displays including a museum of musical instruments.

FESTIVALS AND EVENTS

Salzburger Festspiele festival during the summer is one of the world's foremost classical music events. Its sister festival, Salzburger Osterfestspiele takes place during the spring, with an annual opera performance by Berliner Philharmoniker. There is also a jazz festival in autumn.

TOURIST INFORMATION

www2.salzburg.info; tourist@salzburg.info; +43 662 88 98 7 0

UNIVERSITÄT MOZARTEUM SALZBURG

Mirabellplatz 1, A-5020 Salzburg, Austria
t: +43 662 6198; +43 662 6198 2230 (foreign relations) *f:* +43 662 6198 3033 *e:* ausland@moz.ac.at *w:* www.moz.ac.at
Contact Ilse Tiebert, foreign relations manager
Course information Over 40 artistic and education courses in music, performing and visual arts. International exchange of lecturers and students. *Instrumental* Keyboard, string, brass, wind percussion studies. *Vocal* Vocal studies and musical theatre. *Conducting* Conducting course *Composition* Offered in conjunction with music theory. *Opera* Research institute for Mozart opera interpretation *Other* Musicology, music education courses; also drama, stage design, music and dance; fine arts, arts and crafts. Several research institutes for different areas including new and old music, history of interpretation and reception, and LIA (Lab Inter Arts).
Admissions information *Term dates* 1 Oct-1 Mar (winter semester); 2 March-30 September (summer semester). *Application requirements* See website for details of entrance requirements. *Application deadline* 30 April. *Scholarships* Various scholarships available. *No of students* 1600 students, inc 60 from overseas.

VIENNA (WIEN)

A city with a particularly strong musical (perhaps the strongest of any) and intellectual influence, associated in particular with the music of Haydn, Mozart and Beethoven, but also including the likes of the Second Viennese School in music and the Third Viennese School in psychology. Viennese literature closely identified with the coffee-house culture of the late 19th and early 20th centuries, a culture which still survives today both in the many ornate or idiomatically designed rooms and in the continued tradition of cake-making and eating.

EUROPE

AUSTRIA

Today's combination of more modern attractions, including a diverse and vibrant nightlife, with its historical setting is gives the place an atmosphere of its own. A particular feature of the city is the Ringstrasse, a boulevard encircling the central city district and lined with interesting buildings (the late 19th century, gothic-style Rathaus is one example; another is the parliament building, completed around the same time but in a Greek revival style) and parks.

CLIMATE

Hottest month July (15-25°, though often hotter), coldest months December-February when temperatures struggle to reach above freezing. Rainfall is moderate throughout the year, although the summer months are typically wetter than the winter.

MUSICAL LIFE

The Wiener Philharmoniker play at the Musikverein whose main hall (nicknamed the Goldener Saal), as famed for its acoustics as the orchestra is for its quality. Alternatively there is the Konzerthaus, with its 4 halls of varying sizes and various resident performing groups (the Wiener Symphoniker, Wiener Kammerochester, Wiener Singakademie and one of the world's most renowned contemporary music groups, Klangforum Wien). Plenty of opera, with the Wiener Staatsoper, Volksoper Wien, Theater an der Wien (which leans towards musicals), and Wiener Kammeroper all promoting full seasons. Operetta and concerts of Viennese music typified by the Strauss family abound; Viennese balls are a firm feature of city life, not restricted to tourists.

OTHER CULTURAL INFORMATION

A relatively new addition to the city is the Haus der Musik, an innovative exploration of music using a battery of interactive features. Otherwise, the city's tradition of intellectual enquiry has left a legacy of theatre, both traditional and contemporary, the best known being the Burgtheater and the Volkstheater Wien, both housed in ornate buildings, and the somewhat more understated Theater in der Josefstadt. Several museums and galleries can be found at the Museumsquartier (museum quarter), including the Ludwig Foundation museum of modern art and the Leopold Museum. Elsewhere in the city are MAK, an exhibition and research centre devoted to applied and contemporary arts. A unique feature is the famous Spanish riding school and its Lipizzaner horses.

FESTIVALS AND EVENTS

Wiener Festwochen is the main annual arts festival; it has a classical music component based at the Wiener Konzerthaus. This is also the venue for the autumn Wien Modern festival of modern music and the early music festival Resonanzen.

TOURIST INFORMATION

www.vienna.info; info@wien.info

KONSERVATORIUM WIEN PRIVATUNIVERSITÄT
Johannesgasse 4a, A-1010 Wien, Austria
t: +43 1 512 77 47 89364 (international study programme) *e:* office@konswien.at; studieninfo@konswien.at (international study programme)
w: www.konservatorium-wien.ac.at
Contact Peter Königseder, international study programme manager
Course information Bachelors and masters programmes in music and dramatic arts. General training plus majors in jazz, early music, music theatre, drama and dance, and music education.
Admissions information *Fees* EUR 220 (Austrian and EU nationals) *No of students* Approx 850 students, 40% from overseas.

MUSIC FESTIVALS

Allegro Vivo International Chamber Music Festival Austria and Summer Academy, Wiener Str 2, A-3580 Horn, Austria *t:* +43 2982 4319 *f:* +43 2982 4314 *e:* office@allegro-vivo.at *w:* www.allegro-vivo.at Early, baroque, classic Viennese, romantic, contemporary music. Concerts, summer academy.

Bad Aussee Music Festival *e:* info@conductingmasterclasses.com *w:* www.conductingmasterclasses.com Orchestral and chamber music concerts, conducting masterclass.

Bregenz Festival Platz der Wiener Symphoniker 1, A-6900 Bregenz, Austria *t:* +43 5574 407 6 *f:* +43 5574 407 400 *e:* info@bregenzerfestspiele.com *w:* www.bregenzerfestspiele.com Aida on floating stage plus concerts and opera in theatre.

Bruckner Festival Linz Linzer Veranstaltungsgesellschaft mbH, Brucknerhaus Linz, Untere Donaulaende 7, A-4010 Linz, Austria *t:* +43 7327 76120 *f:* +43 7327 7612 2069 *e:* marketing@liva.co.at *w:* www.brucknerhaus.at Music festival with classical and modern music and a wide range of different musical events including orchestral concerts, opera, chamber music and dance.

Carinthischer Sommer Gumpendorfer Str 76, A-1060 Wien, Austria *t:* +43 1 596 81 98 *f:* +43 1 597 12 36 *e:* office@carinthischersommer.at *w:* www.carinthischersommer.at Festival in Ossiach and Villach featuring international musicians in a range of music performances.

Chopin Festival of the International Chopin Society in Vienna at Chartehouse Gaming Biberstr 4, A-1010 Wien, Austria *t:* +43 1 512 23 74 *f:* +43 1 512 23 74 75 *e:* office@chopin.at *w:* www.chopin.at Orchestral, choral, chamber and symphonic music, recitals.

Danube Music Festival Martin Randall Music Management, Voysey House, Barley Mow Passage, London, W4 4GF, United Kingdom *t:* +44 20 8742 3355 *f:* +44 20 8742 7766 *e:* info@martinrandall.co.uk *w:* www.martinrandall.com Annual. Concerts in abbeys, palaces and country homes beside or within easy reach of the Danube, with leading local ensembles and soloists.

Franz Liszt Festival Raiding Festival Office, Schloss Esterhazy, A-7000 Eisenstadt, Austria *t:* +43 2682 61866 *f:* +43 2682 61805 *e:* raiding@lisztzentrum.at *w:* www.lisztfestival.at Annual festival in the new concert hall at Liszt's birthplace in Raiding.

Haydn Festival - Eisenstadt Festival Office, Schloss Esterhazy, A-7000 Eisenstadt, Austria *t:* +43 2682 61866 *f:* +43 2682 61805 *e:* office@haydnfestival.at *w:* www.haydnfestival.at Annual festival at the Esterhazy Palace. Orchestras, chamber ensembles, vocal recitals, masses and oratorio. Focusing on Joseph Haydn, with references to other composers.

Innsbruck Festival of Early Music Herzog-Friedrich-Str 21/1, A-6020 Innsbruck, Austria *t:* +43 512 571032 *f:* +43 512 563142 *e:* festwochen@altemusik.at *w:* www.altemusik.at Annual event featuring baroque music (2 operas, 25 concerts) played on period instruments at historic sites.

International Music Festival Lothringerstr 20, A-1030 Wien, Austria *t:* +43 1 242 00 100 *w:* www.konzerthaus.at Part of Wiener Festwochen.

Kammermusikfest Lockenhaus Hauptplatz 5, A-7442 Lockenhaus, Austria *t:* +43 2616 2100 *f:* +43 2616 2023 *e:* info@kammermusikfest.at *w:* www.kammermusikfest.at Festival directed by Gidon Kremer.

Lehar Festival Bad Ischl Kurhausstr 8, A-4820 Bad Ischl, Austria *t:* +43 6132 23839 *f:* +43 6132 23839-39 *e:* info@leharfestival.at *w:* www.leharfestival.at

Mozart Week International Mozarteum Foundation, Schwarzstr 26, A-5020 Salzburg, Austria *t:* +43 662 87 31 54 *f:* +43 662 87 44 54 *e:* tickets@mozarteum.at *w:* www.mozarteum.at Internationally renowned soloists, orchs and conds.

Musik-Festival Grafenegg Grafenegg Kulturbetriebsgesellschaft.mbh, Kulturbezirk 2, A-3109 St Poelten, Austria *t:* +43 2742 908070 *f:* +44 2742 908071 *e:* office@tonkuenstler.at *w:* www.grafenegg.at International artists in both orchestral concerts and recitals; annual composer-in-residence. Concerts take place in newly built open air auditorium and concert hall.

Musikprotokoll ORF-Steiemark, Marburger Str 20, A-8042 Graz, Austria *t:* +43 316 47 028227 *f:* +43 316 47 028253 *e:* musikprotokoll@orf.at *w:* http://oe1.orf.at/musikprotokoll Contemporary music.

Musiktage Mondsee Postfach 3, A-5310 Mondsee, Austria *t:* +43 6232 2544, also fax *e:* info@musiktage-mondsee.at *w:* www.musiktage-mondsee.at Chamber music with international artists.

Opern Air Gars am Kamp Postfach 66, A-1091 Wien, Austria *t:* +43 1 319 39 39 *f:* +43 1 319 37 37 *e:* opernair@aon.at *w:* www.opernair.at Open air opera.

Opernfestspiele St Margarethen Kirchengasse 20, A-7062 Sankt Margarethen in Burgenland, Austria *t:* +43 2622 82605 *f:* +43 2622 82613 *e:* info@ofs.at *w:* www.ofs.at Mozart, Die Zauberflöte.

Osterfestspiele Salzburg Herbert-von-Karajan-Platz 9, A-5020 Salzburg, Austria *t:* +43 662 8045 361 *f:* +43 662 8045 790 *e:* karten@osterfestspiele-salzburg.at *w:* www.osterfestspiele-salzburg.at Annual festival of opera and classical music held in Salzburg during Easter week.

Richard Wagner Festival Wels *e:* info@wagner-festival-wels.com *w:* www.wagner-festival-wels.com

Salzburger Festspiele Hofstallgasse 1, A-5020 Salzburg, Austria *t:* +43 662 8045 500 *f:* +43 662 8045 555 *e:* presse@salzburgfestival.at *w:* www.salzburgfestival.at Opera, plays and concerts of the highest artistic standards. Over 200 performances, 12 venues; eminent opera performers, the best singers, performers and actors worldwide.

Schubertiade Hohenems Villa Rosenthal, Schweizer Str 1, A-6845 Hohenems, Postfach 100, Austria *t:* +43 5576 72091 *f:* +43 5576 75450 *e:* info@schubertiade.at *w:* www.schubertiade.at

AUSTRIA

Schubertiade Schwarzenberg Villa Rosenthal, Schweizer Str 1, A-6845 Hohenems, Postfach 100, Austria *t:* +43 5576 72091 *f:* +43 5576 75450 *e:* info@schubertiade.at *w:* www.schubertiade.at

Seefestspiele Moerbisch Joseph Haydngasse 40/1, A-7000 Eisenstadt, Austria *t:* +43 2682 66210 0 *f:* +43 2682 66210 14 *w:* www.seefestspiele-moerbisch.at Operetta festival

styriarte/Summer Music Festival in Styria Palais Attems, Sackstr 17, A-8010 Graz, Austria *t:* +43 316 8 12941 *f:* +43 316 825 00015 *e:* tickets@styriarte.com *w:* www.styriarte.com Theme for 2010: 'Heimat, bist du'. Classical and baroque music, chamber and orchestral music, operas, children's orchestra.

Tyrolean Festival Erl Adamgasse 1, A-6020 Innsbruck, Austria *t:* +43 512 57 88 88 *f:* +43 512 56 09 98 *e:* info@tiroler-festspiele.at *w:* www.tiroler-festspiele.at Classical music, opera, concerts, chamber music.

Wien Modern PO Box 140, Lothringerstr 20, A-1037 Wien, Austria *t:* +43 12 4200 *f:* +43 12 4200 111 *e:* kontakt@wienmodern.at *w:* www.wienmodern.at 20th C music. Interdisciplinary festival.

EUROPE

BERLIN

City in north eastern Germany on the river Spree and German capital since reunification in 1990, and a major international centre (a new airport is currently under construction and is due to open in 2011). As a point where eastern and western Europe met (West Berlin being from 1949 a western enclave made up of British, American and French sectors adjacent to the Soviet East Berlin and surrounded by the the communist GDR – and from 1961 until 1989 by the infamous Berlin Wall) it has a unique history, one leaving a city whose architecture, outlook and cultural activities are a diverse blend of old and new. Bombing during World War II necessitated thorough plans for rebuilding, the nature of which depended on which side of the city divide the buildings fell; today the city's various districts each have their own distinctive atmosphere. More recent developments include the Potsdamer Platz, one of the most modern, commercial sections of the city (designs for the renovations were passed after the fall of the Berlin Wall). Conversely, there is plenty of green space both in and surrounding Berlin. The city is home to some 3 and a half million people and the 130,000+ students help ensure there is a lively feel to it.

CLIMATE

Hottest months July and August (14-24°C), coldest month January (-2-3°C) with temperatures only picking up in later spring. Rainfall relatively light and steady throughout the year, monthly averages in the range 33-69mm.

MUSICAL LIFE

Berliner Philharmoniker is one of world's most prestigious orchestras and although concerts are well subscribed, it is usually possible to get tickets for concerts. Many others besides: Konzerthausorchester Berlin (formerly the Berliner Sinfonieorchester), Deutsches Symphonie-Orchester, Rundfunk Sinfonieorchester Berlin. Many international orchestras tour here. Similarly well provided with opera, with 3 main companies falling under the umbrella of the Stiftung Oper Berlin: Deutsche Oper Berlin, Staatsopera Unter den Linden, and Komische Oper. Modern music – techno, dance, jazz, experimental etc – is also a strong feature of Berlin nightlife and art music scene.

OTHER CULTURAL INFORMATION

As with music, various traditional activities (museums, theatres nd such like) abound in the city. Several traditional institutions are gathered on the Museum Island (an actual island in the Spree) – the Altegalerie has a wide-ranging collection; there are more modern exhibitions at the Neue Nationalgalerie, in the collection of buildings known as the Kulturforum (it includes a museum of musical instruments to go along with the Philharmonie building). The DDR Museum ensures that curious visitors can find out about life the city's unusual postwar period. Berlin is noted for adventurous activities in art and performance art. It hosts numerous street carnivals and festivals such as the annual Carnival of Cultures, although the famed Loveparade has had to move elsewhere. As for theatre, the famous Berliner Ensemble founded by playwright Bertolt Brecht still operates in the city, and there are numerous venues throughout the city from the classical Deutsches Theatre to modern drama at the Volksbühne and Schaubühne.

FESTIVALS AND EVENTS

Berliner Festspiele organisation runs several annual music events: MaerzMusik (March) concentrates on contemporary music; musikfest berlin (September) is major international music festival, featuring Berliner Philharmoniker; Jazz Fest Berlin runs in November, as does the young musicians' festival Treffen Junge Musik-Szene. Other events also: Inventionen is another modern music event; Berliner Tage für Alte Music is an autumn early music festival. Berlin hosts one of the world's major film festivals (known as the Berlinale) in February.

LOCAL PUBLICATIONS

One of the country's major international newspapers, Die Welt (www.welt.de), is published in Berlin. An English-language guide to events and cultural activity is Exberliner (www.exberliner.com); German-language guides include Zitty (www.zitty.de) and Tip (www.tip-berlin.de).

TOURIST INFORMATION

www.berlin-tourist-information.de; tel: +49 30 26 47 48 0; information@btm.de.

HOCHSCHULE FÜR MUSIK 'HANNS EISLER' BERLIN

Charlottenstr 55, D-10117 Berlin, Germany
t: +49 30 688305 700; +49 30 688305 831 (international relations) *f:* +49 30 688305 701; +49 30 688305 730 (international relations)
e: schmidt_ute@hfm.in-berlin.de *w:* www.hfm-berlin.de
Contact Ute Schmidt, international relations.
Course information Bachelor's and master's,

postgraduate courses: wind and string instruments, voice, piano, composition, coaching, music theory (harmony), percussion, conducting (orchestral, choral), music theatre direction, harp, guitar; jazz (instrumental and vocal).
Admissions information *Term dates* Oct- Feb (winter semester); Apr-mid Jul (summer semester). *Application requirements* Secondary school qualifications (Abitur) or outstanding musical talent; audition for main study; language test. *Application deadline* 15 Apr; 15 Dec. *Fees* No tuition fees; small admin fees (approx EUR 250 per semester). *No of students* 242 national, 329 international students. *Language requirements* German language test certificate (C1 level of the Goethe Institute)
Facilities *Music facilities* Various ensembles including symphony and chamber orchestras, contemporary music ensemble, chorus, symphonic wind orchestra.

UNIVERSITÄT DER KÜNSTE BERLIN
Fakultät Musik, Einsteinufer 43-53, D-10587 Berlin, Germany
t: +49 30 3185 2320; +49 30 3185 2196 (foreign student office) *f:* +49 30 3185 2687; +49 30 3185 2727 (foreign student office)
e: aaa@udk-berlin.de (foreign student office)
w: www.udk-berlin.de
Contact Ursula Stephan-Rechenmacher, foreign student office.
Course information Diplom study courses: artistic training (instrumental or conducting), composition, church music, sound engineering, jazz; pedagogical education (including jazz); musicology and music education (doctoral), and artistic training (choral conducting) available at further level.
Admissions information *No of students* Approx 130 students from partner institutions around the world.
Facilities *Music facilities* University theatre, 2 big concert halls; also studios, rehearsal rooms, library.

BREMEN

Town of about half a million people in northern Germany, linked by the river Weser to its port of Bremerhaven. It is based round a medieval old town and market square with its 13th century cathedral and Dutch Renaissance influenced town hall with its dramatic façade (there are numerous other similarly characteristic buildings in this area). The square is also the location of the twin-towered cathedral (St Peter's) and its 5 organs. The Schnoor quarter, based around the street of the same name, has a cultural feel thanks to a combination of its old buildings (it is part of the old quarter); galleries and workshops; bars, cafes and restaurants. The city is the location of a statue of the Musicians of Bremen, a tale by the Brothers Grimm, in which Bremen is the intended destination of three mistreated animals in search of a better life.

CLIMATE

Hottest months July and August (12-22°C), coldest month January (-2-3°C). Rainfall fairly constant throughout the year, though not excessive; driest months February-March (approx 45mm), wettest July (84mm).

MUSICAL LIFE

Main orchestra is Bremer Philharmoniker, which gives monthly concerts plus chamber music performances from smaller ensembles drawn from its ranks. There is also a chamber orchestra, the Deutsche Kammerphilharmonie Bremen.

OTHER CULTURAL INFORMATION

There is a particular maritime theme to town due to its nautical links – there is a maritime museum and even a theatre ship. The city is home to the Bremer Shakespeare Company. For art lovers, the New Weserburg Museum is a contemporary art gallery; the Kunsthalle includes Impressionist works in its collection

FESTIVALS AND EVENTS

Annual music festival in the autumn, plus triennial international contemporary dance festival, Tanz Bremen. Free Samba carnival in February. The Freimarkt is an annual civic fair, claimed to be the oldest in Germany.

TOURIST INFORMATION

www.bremen-tourism.de, btz@bremen-tourism.de, +49 1805 10 10 30

HOCHSCHULE FÜR KÜNSTE BREMEN
Am Speicher XI 8, D-28217 Bremen, Germany
t: +49 4 21 95 95 10 00 *f:* +49 4 21 95 9520 00 *w:* www.hfk-bremen.de
Contact Birgit Harte, international contact.
Course information Instrumental and vocal courses, plus church music, jazz, music education. 4-semester postgrad concert performance degree. Current diploma courses to be replaced by modular bachelors and masters courses, beginning 2010/11 year.
Facilities *Music facilities* Range of performance

opportunities offered; projects with local orchestras such as Bremer Philharmoniker.

COLOGNE (KÖLN)

City on the river Rhine, home to one of the world's oldest universities (and now the country's largest), with links back to ancient Rome; and now the fourth largest in the country. Apart from giving its name to the scent Eau de Cologne which was first produced in the city in the early 1700s, the city is probably most famous for its cathedral which survived the wartime bombing that destroyed the historic centre; architectural reconstruction is in a contrasting postwar style. Echoes of its history do remain, however, and some of the newer constructions such as the Hohenzollern railway bridge across the river are distinctive in their own way; recent architectural work has seen some more interesting developments. The city is home to the Köln International School of Design and Kölner Design Akademie, highlighting is credentials in this area.

CLIMATE

Hottest months July and August (13-22°C), coldest month January (0°-4°C). Rainfall is steady throughout the year at between 47mm and 90mm annually (summer is wettest).

MUSICAL LIFE

Oper Köln (which runs its own international opera studio) has a relatively varied repertoire. Kölner Philharmonie is the city's major concert hall, with two resident orchestras: WDR Sinfonieorchester Köln and Gürzenich-Orchester Köln, but a varied programme of events including jazz and contemporary music. City has a tradition in baroque music, even if the group that carried its name, Musica Antiqua Köln has now disbanded.

OTHER CULTURAL INFORMATION

Important centre for the art trade, with several trade fairs each year, including Cologne Fine Art, Art.Fair and Art Cologne; art galleries and dealers are plentiful. Among a variety of exhibitions on offer, the most important museum is surely the Imhoff-Stollwerck Museum of Chocolate! Theatre to suit different tastes, both at the Schauspielhaus (where opera also performed) and in more informal cabaret and comedy theatres. City the birthplace of Nobel winner Heinrich Böll.

FESTIVALS AND EVENTS

Triennial classical music festival (MusikTriennale Köln) features international performers. Best known city event is Carnival, beginning on the same day every year, 11 November (the event even has its own museum). Annual international literary festival and annual design festival.

LOCAL PUBLICATIONS

Stadt Revue Köln magazine (www.stadtrevue.de) has listings and reviews as well as local news.

TOURIST INFORMATION

www.koelntourismus.de, +49 221 221 304 00

HOCHSCHULE FÜR MUSIK KÖLN

Dagobertstr, 38, D-50668 Köln, Germany
t: +49 221 912818 0 *f:* +49 221 131204
e: kirstein@mhs-koeln.de *w:* www.mhs-koeln.de
Contact Birgit Kirstein, international affairs.
Course information Bachelors and masters courses introduced in 2008. Courses in 1st cycle for strings, winds, sax, harp, percussion, accordion, harpsichord, piano, organ, recorder, guitar, mandolin, lute, viola da gamba, opera/concert singing, choral/orchestral conducting, composition (electronic, instrumental), church music, jazz. Masters level for solo instruments, period instruments, new music interpretation, opera singing, lied/recital singing, piano accompaniment, chamber music, electronic composition.

DETMOLD

Small city in northern Germany with a tranquil and relatively rural setting in the Teutoberg forest (famous as a battlefield in which German tribes resisted Roman advances, establishing the northernmost limit of the Roman empire) and an attractive, largely intact old town with its own castle.

MUSICAL LIFE

Largely based round the music academy; there is a chamber orchestra in the town, the Detmolder Kammerorchester.

OTHER CULTURAL INFORMATION

Theatres, museums, cabaret and so on; its location and surroundings mean there are various other sport and leisure activities on offer. A large outdoor historical museum gives visitors an insight into the working life of previous eras in the region.

FESTIVALS AND EVENTS

Biggest events are biennial Strassentheater Festival

EUROPE

Detmold (even numbered years), and a summer theatre festival; also a festival of short films in Jun.

TOURIST INFORMATION
www.stadtdetmold.de, tourist.info@detmold.de, +49 5231 977 328

HOCHSCHULE FÜR MUSIK DETMOLD
Neustadt 22, D-32756 Detmold, Germany
t: +49 5231 975 773 *f:* +49 5231 975 754
e: info@hfm-detmold.de *w:* www.hfm-detmold.de
Course information Courses for training as composer, orchestral musician, pianist, singer (opera, recital or oratorio), conductor, church musician, music teacher. Additional orchestral training available at Orchesterzentrum in Dortmund.
Admissions information *Fees* EUR 500 per semester, plus EUR 115.07 registration fee.
Facilities *Music facilities* 10 specially equipped buildings in campus, including concert hall.

EUROPE

DRESDEN
Main city in Saxony, eastern Germany, lying on the river Elbe. Much of its historic built environment, a legacy of the city's role as a royal residence, was destroyed during a controversial World War II aerial bombing project. Since then, and particularly since German reunification, various restoration projects have got under way, most notably the spectacular Frauenkirche (the catholic Hofkirche is another church with an ornate exterior), and this has helped keep something of the city's baroque character to the fore, particularly in the Altstadt (old town) area.

CLIMATE
Hottest month July (13-23°C), coldest month January (-3-2°C). Rainfall peaks in summer (81mm in August) and is lowest in late winter/early spring (42mm in March) and autumn (46mm in October).

MUSICAL LIFE
The city has a strong musical heritage. Opera at the magnificent Semperoper, whose orchestra, the Sächsische Staatskapelle also presents a full season of symphony concerts at the house with various international conductors and soloists. Staatsoperette Dresden is one of those rare theatres devoted to light music, particularly known for performances of music by Johann Strauss. The city is also home to the Dresdner Philharmoniker and its associated choirs such as the Philharmonische Chor. Its reputation for choral singing added to by Dresdner Kreuzchor, the boys' choir which sings services at the church of the same name.

OTHER CULTURAL INFORMATION
Several theatres operate under the aegis of the Staatschauspiel Dresden. Several important art collections, with, among others, a gallery dedicated to old masters; a museum (the Grünes Gewölbe) of artefacts, statues, jewellery etc; and the Mathematisch-Physikalischer Salon, a collection of scientific instruments.

FESTIVALS AND EVENTS
Mainly classical music at the Dresdner Musikfestspiele in May-June. Trad jazz at the Dixieland Festival just beforehand; contemporary music at the Dresdner Tage der Zeitgenössischen Musik in October, mostly at the Festspielhaus Hellerau.

LOCAL PUBLICATIONS
Home to the main Saxon regional paper, the Sächsische Zeitung (www.sz-online.de).

TOURIST INFORMATION
www.dresden.de, info@dresden-tourist.de, +49 351 49192 100

HOCHSCHULE FÜR MUSIK CARL MARIA VON WEBER DRESDEN
Box 120039, D-01001 Dresden, Germany
t: +49 351 4923 641; +49 351 4923 638 (international relations); +49 351 4923 634 (registrar) *f:* +49 351 4923 604 *e:* rektorat@hfmdd.de; ausland@hfmdd.de (international relations); studsek@hfmdd.de (registrar) *w:* www.hfmdd.de
Contact Gerda Werner, international relations; Sebastian Bauer, head of admission/registrar's office
Course information Artistic studies in orchestral instruments, voice, piano, conducting, composition, music theory and accompaniment. Also wide range of studies in jazz/rock/pop, music education and musicology. Studies usually 5 years, leading to equivalent of masters degree; students with bachelor degrees are usually put into 4th year. See website for full breakdown of courses.
Admissions information *Term dates* Sep-Feb (winter semester); Mar-Aug (summer semester). *Application requirements* Audition in person, entrance exam, suitable proficiency in German. *Application deadline* 31 Mar. *Fees* EUR 160 admin fee per semester; tuition fees for postgrad students only (EUR 300 per semester standard rate). *No of students* 600

students. *Language requirements* German; no classes offered in foreign languages. Website gives details of institutions in Dresden offering language tuition.
Facilities *Accommodation* Independent organisation, Studentenwerk Dresden, manages halls of residence. See www.studentenwerk-dresden.de for more information.

DÜSSELDORF

Busy commercial city in Germany's western region, the Rhine-Ruhr area; the city is particularly well-known for its fashion industry. Large overseas population thanks to the presence of several educational institutions there. Among well-known musical figures from the city is the band Kraftwerk, pioneers in electronic music; Düsseldorf was home to Robert and Clara Schumann towards the end of his life, the Rhine there being the river into which he made his infamous leap under the influence of impending insanity.

CLIMATE

Hottest months July and August (13-22°C), coldest January (1-4°C). Rainfall averages fairly constant throughout the year, with the driest month in Feburary (56mm), the wettest in June (89mm).

MUSICAL LIFE

Two main concert venues: Palais Wittgenstein for smaller concerts and recitals; Tonhalle Düsseldorf for orchestral and larger scale performances – resident orchestra is the Düsseldorfer Symphoniker. This group provides orchestral players for certain performances of the Deutscher Oper am Rhine, based partly in the city, partly in nearby Duisburg. The organisation also runs a ballet company and a youth opera arm.

OTHER CULTURAL INFORMATION

Large number of theatres, including town's Schausspielhaus for traditional style theatre, Kom(m)-ödchen for political satire, Komödie for cabaret and comedy, a puppet theatre, children's theatre and venues devoted to more experimental and avant-garde performance. Several contemporary art galleries – these include the Kunsthalle Düsseldorf, with its uncomprompising 1960s architectural style, which hosts temporary exhibitions; and the Kunstsammlung whose collections, focus on 20th and 21st C art (it holds a substantial number of Paul Klee works, for instance) are held in 2 separate buildings in the city. City subsidises 'Art:card' promotions, giving free entry and discounts at various venues.

FESTIVALS AND EVENTS

Altstadtherbst Kulturfestival is an annual performing arts event not restricted to music; biennial Robert Schumann festival. Two connected street carnival events in February and November

TOURIST INFORMATION

www.duesseldorf-tourismus.de, info@duesseldorf-tourismus.de, +49 211 17 20 20.

ROBERT SCHUMANN HOCHSCHULE DÜSSELDORF

Fischerstr 110, D-40476 Düsseldorf, Germany
t: +49 211 49 18 0 *f:* +49 211 49 11 618
e: rsh@rsh-duesseldorf.de *w:* www.rsh-duesseldorf.de
Course information Programmes in conducting, church music (evangelical and catholic), composition, orchestrals instrumental music performance, organ, guitar, recorder, music education; musicology (available as accompanying subject, subject on Master's course, or subject of doctorate); also audio and video engineering (in association with University of Applied Sciences, Dusseldorf). Also postgrad courses, doctoral studies.
Admissions information *Term dates* Early Oct-mid Feb (winter term lecture period); early Apr-mid Jul (summer term lecture period). *Application requirements* General higher education entrance diploma; aptitude test for relevant subject. *Application deadline* 31 Mar. *Fees* EUR 500. *Scholarships* None. *No of students* 949. *Language requirements* Goethe-Institute certificate B2 in German.
Facilities *Accommodation* Accommodation available through www.studentenwerk-duesseldorf.de.

ESSEN

Ruhr valley city, named European City of Culture on behalf of the Ruhr area for 2010. Traditionally an industrial city not especially thought of as a tourist destination, nonetheless its history goes back beyond medieval times, and it boasts an impressive 14th century cathedral. Recent building includes imaginative recycling of industrial buildings for artistic commercial use, such as the converted Zollverein colliery (now a Unesco World Heritage Site).

CLIMATE

Rainfall levels relatively similar from month to

EUROPE

month, with summer totals ranging from 75mm to 90mm and March being typically driest (47mm). Summer temperatures range from 11°C to 21°C, winter temperatures -1-5°C.

MUSICAL LIFE
The modern design Aalto Theater opera house for opera and orchestral concerts (Philharmonie Essen and visiting orchestras).

OTHER CULTURAL INFORMATION
Grillo-Theater staging conventional drama productions; Grugahalle is for larger scale popular entertainment. Museums and galleries include a design museum and poster museum among its handful of the more conventional kind.

FESTIVALS AND EVENTS
Ruhr Triennale multi-disciplined arts festival in venues in Essen and neighbouring towns and cities during late summer/early autumn.

TOURIST INFORMATION
www.essen.de, touristikzentrale@essen.de, +49 201 8872041

FOLKWANG UNIVERSITY
Klemensborn 39, D-45239 Essen, Germany
t: +49 201 4903 0 *f:* +49 201 4903 288
e: info@folkwang-uni.de *w:* www.folkwang-uni.de

Course information 38 courses and programs, most of which lead to internationally recognised degrees (bachelors, masters, artist diploma). Doctoral studies, postdoctoral qualification and other higher degree study programmes are also available. *Instrumental* Accordion, bassoon, cello, clarinet, double bass, flute, guitar, harp, harpsichord, horn, oboe, organ, percussion, piano, recorder, saxophone, trombone, trumpet, tuba, viola, violin. *Vocal* Concert performance, lieder, oratorio and musical theatre. *Conducting* Vocal ensemble direction *Composition* Instrumental composition, electronic composition, jazz composition, pop composition, composition and visualisation. *Orchestral* orchestral performance *Jazz/world* Jazz & performing arts *Other* Church music; school music; music teaching and pedagogy; musicology in combination with an artistic subject.
Admissions information *Term dates* 1 Apr-30 Sep (summer term); 1 Oct - 31 Mar (winter term). *Application requirements* Entrance exam; sample theory test and application form available from website. *Application deadline* 15 Mar for winter term. Further details on website *Fees* EUR 30 application fee; study fees EUR 500 per term *Scholarships* Scholarships available. *No of students* 69% national, 31% international students. *Language requirements* Certificate A1 for instrument training, jazz/performing artist, composition, voice; Certificate B2 for musicals, school music, music pedagogy, musicology in combination with an artistic subject. Language courses offered by international office; must be completed before semester begins.
Facilities *Music facilities* Practice rooms equipped with piano, grand piano, harpsichord; concert hall, with concert and practice organ. Six in-house stages *Performance opportunities* 300+ public events held every year at the university and in local churches, museums, galleries and industrial sites. Regular collaborative projects with the regions theatres and concert halls. *Accommodation* Various options inc furnished apartment, flat let, flat share; information about accommodation available from www.studentenwerk.essen-duisburg.de

FRANKFURT AM MAIN
Transport hub on the river Main with Germany's main airport and the country's largest railway station in the city; it is also one of the largest in the country. Germany's financial centre, reflected in the preponderance of modern buildings and its high-rise skyline. Ironically, it is also home of Institute of Social Research with its history of Marxist enquiry in the so-called Frankfurt School. Also the location for many trade fairs such as Frankfurt Book Fair and Musikmesse, one of world's major music trade shows.

CLIMATE
Hottest month July (15-25°C), coldest month January (-2-3°C). Precipitation relatively low with spring monthly totals around 40-45mm per month; wettest months are June-August (at around 70-76mm).

MUSICAL LIFE
Alte Oper, former opera house reconstructed as a concert hall, with 2 halls (2500 and 700 seats) hosting touring orchestras plus popular shows. One of city's own orchestras, hr sinfonie orchester (actually run by regional radio company Hessische Rundfunk), plays there and elsewhere; Neue Philharmonie Frankfurt, whose repertoire encompasses much crossover work, based at Capitol Theater in nearby Offenbach. Modern design Opern-und Schauspielhaus Frankfurt is base for Oper Frankfurt, a major company with many premieres and new productions.

OTHER CULTURAL INFORMATION
City is birthplace of Goethe, and home of the Goethe-Haus. Riverside location is well exploited, with various museums along the banks of the Main – Städel Museum is an art gallery there. The city has its own modern art gallery, the Frankfurter Kunstverein, which puts on various exhibitions and other activities relating to modern art, as does the Schirn Kunsthalle.

FESTIVALS AND EVENTS
Auftakt Festival of contemporary music in autumn; Summer in the City open air festival. Other civic events not specific to classical music, like the summer Museumsuferfest by the river or Opernplatz Festival outside the Alte Oper. Festival of gay cinema, Verzaubert Internationales Queer Filmfestival, every spring.

LOCAL PUBLICATIONS
The Frankfurter Allgemeine Zeitung (www.faz.net) is one of the country's major daily papers.

TOURIST INFORMATION
www.frankfurt-tourismus.de, info@infofrankfurt.de, +49 69 212 38800

HOCHSCHULE FÜR MUSIK UND DARSTELLENDE KUNST FRANKFURT AM MAIN
Eschersheimer Landstr 29-39, D-60322 Frankfurt am Main, Germany
t: +49 69 154007 0; +49 69 154 007 256 (international office) *f:* +49 69 154007 108; +49 69 154 007 125 (international office)
e: albrecht.eitz@hfmdk-frankfurt.de *w:* www.hfmdk-frankfurt.de
Admissions information *Term dates* Early Oct-mid Feb (winter semester); early Apr-mid Jul (summer semester). *Application deadline* 1 Mar *Fees* None, except EUR 280 social welfare contribution per semester. *No of students* 850. *Language requirements* German language must be proven by one of the following language certificates: TestDaF level 3, Goethe-Zertifikat B2, DSH 1, or KMK 1. Other certificates not accepted.

FREIBURG-IM-BREISGAU
Black Forest city in south-westernmost tip of Germany, with the warmest climate in the country. At its heart is an agreeable old city area with many buildings of architectural interest like the Gothic minster with its vertiginous spire or the 16th century Kaufhaus across the market square (still actually used as a marketplace today) from it. One of the city's unique features is a network of gullies running throughout the streets used, once upon a time, to protect it from fire; another is the longest cable car in Germany (3600m) runs from the edge of the city into the hills which surround the city; also tram system throughout. Traditionally an academic city with several highly regarded institutions.

CLIMATE
Warmest months July and August (13-24°C, although hotter and more humid summer weather is not uncommon), coldest month January (-2-4°C). Summer rainfall tops 100mm per month in June to August.

MUSICAL LIFE
Most prestigious group is Freiburger Barockorchester, an internationally renowned period instrument group with a repertoire ranging to early romantics. More general orchestral music from SWR Baden-Baden und Freiburg Sinfonieorchester; its concerts in the city are in the Konzerthaus, a hall with a mixed programming of classical and popular music, and other entertainment. Also Philharmonische Orchester Freiburg at the Theater Freiburg (primarily for opera).

OTHER CULTURAL INFORMATION
Theater Freiburg also has programme of drama and other performing arts. Usual range of museums and galleries, many reflecting local history and activity.

FESTIVALS AND EVENTS
Main music event is Zelt-Musik-Festival, annual gathering of musicians of various kinds in a nature-inspired 'tent city' .

LOCAL PUBLICATIONS
The local newspaper is the Badische Zeitung (www.badische-zeitung.de).

TOURIST INFORMATION
www.freiburg.de, touristik@fwtm.freiburg.de, +49 761 3881 880

HOCHSCHULE FÜR MUSIK FREIBURG
Schwarzwaldstr 141, D-79102 Freiburg im Breisgau, Germany
t: +49 761 3 19 15 0 *f:* +49 761 3 19 15 42
e: info@mh-freiburg.de *w:* www.mh-freiburg.de
Course information Bachelors and masters courses,

specialist performer courses, contemporary music, early music, jazz.
Admissions information *Term dates* Winter and summer semesters. *Application requirements* Entrance exam; requirements vary depending on course level (see website for full details) *Application deadline* 1 May (winter semester); 1 Dec (summer semester) *Scholarships* 5 annual prizes for instrumentalists and vocalists, composers, chamber music ensembles and musicologists.
Facilities *Music facilities* 40 practice rooms open 24 hours a day; 4 concert halls. Performance opportunities at over 400 public concerts each year.

HAMBURG

Germany's second-largest city with a population of just under 2 million, and it principal port, on the North Sea; particularly well served with transport links including international rail. Criss-crossed by many canals (popular among tourists who can take tours of the city by boat) and the 2000+ bridges across them creating an interesting built environment (such as the city's warehouse district), the city is architecturally diverse with many modern building projects under way. The city's red light district, the Reeperbahn, is somewhat notorious, but more relaxed areas can be found too – the Schanzenviertel has a vibrant, student feel. At the heart of the city is a market square, flanked by a distinctive but characteristic Rathaus (town hall), where numerous events and public gatherings occur.

CLIMATE

Relatively moderate climate, though somewhat windy. Hottest month July (12-21°C), coldest month January (-2-4°C). Rainfall highest in summer with 80mm in July; lowest in late winter and spring (40mm in February).

MUSICAL LIFE

Two principal orchestras: Sinfonieorchester des Norddeutschen Rundfunks is based there but as the orchestra of the regional radio station also covers nearby towns of Lübeck, Kiel and Bremen; Philharmoniker Hamburg has its own concert season, and also provides orchestra for Staatsoper Hamburg (opera and ballet). The opera house has a reputation for new works. City has a established tradition as destination for pop and rock bands (the Beatles, for instance, are especially associated with venues there), particularly heavy metal in recent years. A brand new concert hall currently being built, the Elbphilharmonie, a spectacular ship-like construction situated in one of Hamburg's docks scheduled for completion at the end of 2010; when open it will work in tandem with the city's current concert hall, the Laeiszhalle.

OTHER CULTURAL INFORMATION

A place of pilgrimage for bikers, but it has, of course, more traditional entertainments including a state-owned theatre and independent theatres; the English Theatre stages English-language performances. City's maritime history contained in Internationales Maritimes Museum Hamburg. There are several art galleries, among them the Kunsthalle with a collection covering several centuries and a dedicated contemporary exhibition space with works from the 20th century; and the photo gallery the Deichtorhallen which puts on a diverse range of temporary exhibitions.

FESTIVALS AND EVENTS

Various street parties, parades and carnivals, and a busy annual port festival.

TOURIST INFORMATION

www.hamburg-tourism.de, info@hamburg-tourism.de, +49 40 300 51 300.

HOCHSCHULE FÜR MUSIK UND THEATER HAMBURG

Harvestehuder Weg 12, D-20148 Hamburg, Germany
t: +49 40 428482 415 (international relations
f: +49 40 428482 666 (international relations)
e: international@hfmt.hamburg.de *w:* www.hfmt-hamburg.de
Contact Svenja Tiedt, international co-ord.
Course information Various courses in solo instrumental, composition/theory, multimedia, orchestral conducting, choral conducting, protestant church music, jazz and jazz pedagogy, opera, oratorio; musicology, music education, culture and media management, music therapy. Bachelors and masters courses available as well as Diplom; see website for levels and degrees available, as well as course duration.
Admissions information *Term dates* Oct -Mar (winter); Apr-Sep (summer). *Application requirements* See website for details. *Application deadline* Differs depending on course. *Fees* EUR 375 per term. *Scholarships* Details available from international office *No of students* Approx 850 students. *Language requirements* German; some study programmes available in English.

Facilities *Accommodation* Help available through international office.

HANOVER (HANNOVER)

Smart central/northern German city with good transport links. Old town ruined during World War II bombing, subsequently reconstructed as a 'new old town'; the well-appointed new Rathaus is a good example. Particularly well-served with places of nature including landscaped gardens (the Herrenhäuser Gärten), a botanical garden, an award-winning zoo, deerpark and a lake (the Maschsee).

CLIMATE

Hottest month August (12-23°C), coldest month January (-3-3°C). Precipitation: driest month February (36mm), wettest month July (79mm).

MUSICAL LIFE

The Staatsoper Hannover for opera and ballet has its own orchestra. The city has a thriving amateur music scene.

OTHER CULTURAL INFORMATION

Wealth of museums on a range of topics from contemporary art, caricature and satire and textiles to the history of the city and its relationship with the British royal family, numismatics and the history of the police. Many theatres catering for a range of tastes from serious to cabaret and musicals. European Cheese Centre on the outskirts of the city.

FESTIVALS AND EVENTS

Fête de la Musique in July (an event celebrated in cities across the world). Lakeside Maschsee Festival with a range of entertainment in the summer.

TOURIST INFORMATION

www.hannover-tourismus.de, info@hannover-tourismus.de, +49 511 12345 111.

HOCHSCHULE FÜR MUSIK UND THEATER HANNOVER

Emmichplatz 1, D-30175 Hannover, Germany
t: +49 511 3100 1; +49 511 3100 369 (International office) *f:* +49 511 3100 368
e: hmt@hmt-hannover.de; international-office@hmt-hannover.de *w:* www.hmt-hannover.de
Contact Meike Martin, international office

Course information BMus in conducting (orch or choral), voice, jazz/rock/pop, church music, piano, composition, performance, performance and education (instrument teaching, elementary music education, rhythmics), popular music; BA in media management, education for sepcial needs or music (joint study); MMus in chamber music (piano, lied interpretation or ensemble), church music, conducting (orchestral, choral, operatic), composition, conducting child and youth choirs, jazz/rock/pop, keyboard instruments, performance, performance and education, music theory, voice (freelance), vocal/opera studies; MA in media management or media and production; MEd in higher education teaching; also diploma in acting.

Admissions information *Term dates* Oct-Feb (winter semester); Apr-Oct (summer semester). *Application requirements* Admission exam (Jun 2010 tbc) *Application deadline* 15 April. *Fees* EUR 500 *Scholarships* See website for details.

Facilities *Music facilities* Library with over 200,000 items.

KARLSRUHE

Small west German city, close to the border with France, based round early 18th century palace, with an unusual fan-shaped layout of streets radiating from the palace. Home to several science research institutions.

CLIMATE

Hottest month August (14-26°C), coldest month January (-2-3°C). Rainiest time of year is late spring/early summer (up to 87mm in June) with totals fairly similar throughout the remainder of the year.

MUSICAL LIFE

Badisches Staatstheater is main music venue for opera (and theatre), with an orchestra (the Badische Staatskapelle) attached to it. Zentrum für Kunst und Medientechnologie Karlsruhe incorporates the Institut für Musik und Akustik, a public-funded organisation combining research and academic activity with an artistic programme; grants made to individuals for residencies.

OTHER CULTURAL INFORMATION

Other cultural organisations at the ZKM include museum of modern art, media museum and library, institute for visual media and a film institute.

FESTIVALS AND EVENTS

Annual Handel festival and free open-air festival in July.

EUROPE

TOURIST INFORMATION
www.karlsruhe-tourism.de, +49 721 37 20 53 83.

HOCHSCHULE FÜR MUSIK KARLSRUHE
Postfach 6040, D-76040 Karlsruhe, Germany
t: +49 721 66 29 0; +49 721 66 29 285 (international relations) *f:* +49 721 66 29 266
e: isabel.eisenmann@hfm-karlsruhe.de *w:* www.hfm-karlsruhe.de
Contact Isabel Eisenmann, international relations co-ordinator
Admissions information *Term dates* Oct-Feb (winter semester); Apr-Jul 2010 (summer semester).
Facilities *Accommodation* Some accommodation available through Studentenwerk Karlsruhe. www.studentenwerk-karlsruhe.de

EUROPE

LEIPZIG
City in Saxony (eastern Germany) with a long musical history, it is particularly associated with Bach; Mendelssohn and Schumann also have strong connections, and it was the birthplace of Wagner; Mahler was conductor at the opera house for two years in the 1880s. Also has a strong educational tradition, its university being one of the world's oldest, and it is where Goethe studied. It is supposedly he who gave the city its nickname 'little Paris'.

MUSICAL LIFE
Thomaskirche, Bach's church, still has an active and celebrated boys' choir. Gewandhausorchester Leipzig dates back over 200 years with a long line of celebrated principal conductors, and is one of world's most highly regarded. The Gewandhaus is the official orchestra of Oper Leipzig, itself an organisation with long history; the current imposing opera house replaced its neo-classical predecessor destroyed during World War II. Bach-Archiv Leipzig is centre for Bach scholarship; also organises concerts and events, and houses a museum dedicated to the composer. Many concert venues around the town.

OTHER CULTURAL INFORMATION
Mendelssohn-Haus museum, based in a house he lived in, is devoted to the composer. City zoo specialises in primates. Among various civic museums are a coffee museum; Goethe's literary counterpart Schiller has a museum there. Various cabaret and variety theatres, hence the city's nickname. The city's art collection is housed in the Museum of Fine Arts; other exhibitions include the Grassi Museum of Musical Instruments, an arts and crafts museum and a museum of ethnography, all grouped together in a complex on Johannisplatz. The city was HQ to the East German secret police, today revealed in a museum dedicated to it.

FESTIVALS AND EVENTS
Bachfest Leipzig is a major annual event in June, also a biennial Bach Competition, both organised by the Bach Archive; Mendelssohn is also honoured with an annual event at the Gewandhaus in September. International choral and piano festivals during the summer. The city hosts an annual book fair in March, second only in Germany to the one in Frankfurt.

TOURIST INFORMATION
www.leipzig.de, info@ltm-leipzig.de, +49 341 7104 265

HOCHSCHULE FÜR MUSIK UND THEATER 'FELIX MENDELSSOHN BARTHOLDY'
Postfach 10 08 09, D-04008 Leipzig, Germany
t: +49 3 41 21 44 645 *f:* +49 3 41 21 44 521
e: presse@hmt-leipzig.de *w:* www.hmt-leipzig.de
Contact Dr Katrin Schmidinger
Course information Instrumental, voice, piano, conducting, composition, jazz and pop music, early music. For full course details, see www.hmt-leipzig.de/index.php?prospective_stud *Instrumental* Artistic and teacher training in all orchestral instruments; special courses for instruments taken as minors (eg piccolo, sax, contrabassoon); répétiteur training. *Vocal* Lieder, musicals. *Conducting* Orchestral or choral *Jazz/world* Jazz and pop. *Other* Church music, organ.
Admissions information *Term dates* 1 Sep-28 Feb (winter semester); 1 Mar-31 Aug (summer semester). *Application requirements* Auditions for performance courses, details of repertoire and other requirements available on website; conductors must take piano and piano accompaniment audition; composers submit scores, sit composition and piano exams. *Application deadline* 31 Mar (for winter semester); 30 Nov (for summer semester) *Fees* Vary, depending on course, from free to EUR 253. *Scholarships* Yes. *No of students* 613 national students, 297 from overseas. German *language requirements* Language required; see website for details of proof of ability accepted.
Facilities *Music facilities* Advanced students can take audition as stand-in for Gewandhaus or MDR orchestras. *Accommodation* All students entitled to

apply for accommodation; information available via www.studentenwerk-leipzig.de

LÜBECK

A Baltic port city (it connects, via the ferry terminal at Travemünde, to Norway, Sweden, Finland and Poland) and a Unesco world heritage site since 1987 thanks to its exceptionally attractive and characteristic gothic brick architecture typified by the almost fairy-tale Holstentor gate with its twin conical turrets. The city's old town has 1800 listed buildings and is also surrounded by the rivers and canals which are, together with the sea itself, an integral part of life there. Noted as a producer of quality marzipan and as home of writer Thomas Mann, one of 3 Nobel prize-winners to have lived in the city. Famously, Bach walked from Arnstadt, over 400km away, to Lübeck to meet Buxtehude.

CLIMATE

Warmest months July/August (12-21°C), coldest month January (-2-1°C). Rainfall levels quite high throughout the year, peaking in August at some 28mm.

MUSICAL LIFE

Theater Lübeck holds concerts and music theatre (opera and musicals) performances; city is home to Lübecker Philharmoniker. Visiting performances at Lübeckongress (Musik- und Kongresshalle).

OTHER CULTURAL INFORMATION

Each of the 3 Nobel winners is recognised with a museum: Günter Grass-Haus, Willy-Brandt-Haus; Buddenbrookhaus, named after the novel by Thomas Mann celebrates his work and that of his brother Heinrich. Kunsthalle St Annen is an art gallery (and occasional concert venue).

FESTIVALS AND EVENTS

Schleswig-Holstein Musik Festival during July and August for classical music; Duckstein Festival, also in summer, for all-round arts and entertainment. In November, the Nordic Film Days festival specialises in cinema from the north of Europe. July sees a major sailing event, Travemünde Week (named after the main coastal district of the city – its name means 'mouth of the (river) Trave').

TOURIST INFORMATION

www.luebeck-tourism.de

MUSIKHOCHSCHULE LÜBECK
Grosse Petersgrube 21, D-23552 Lübeck, Germany
t: +49 451 1505 0; +49 451 1505 323 (international office) *f:* +49 451 1505 300; +49 451 150 303 (international office)
e: international@mh-luebeck.de *w:* www.mh-luebeck.de
Contact Iwona Alexandra Kwiatkowski, international contact.

Course information Runs Bologna Process compliant bachelor of music (instrumental, vocal, church music, composition, theory); bachelor of arts; advanced courses (instrumental music, composition, opera/concert singing, soloist class, church music); extension courses in chamber music, piano accompaniment, vocal pedagogy.

Admissions information *Term dates* Oct-Feb (winter term); Apr-Jul (summer term). *Application requirements* Entrance audition; for details see website. *Application deadline* 1 Apr (for winter term); 1 Dec (for summer term). *Fees* None; EUR 83.50 student welfare contributions. *No of students* 240 national and 226 international students. *Language requirements* German language courses available.

Facilities *Music facilities* Concert halls and practice rooms, sound and media studios, large library; instruments available for loan. Wide number of performance opportunities; several ensembles inlcuding orchestras, choirs, samba project, gamelan, pop groups. *Accommodation* No campus accommodation service; limited number of rooms available through independent student services such as Studentenwerk Schleswig-Holstein (www.studentenwerk-s-h.de)

MANNHEIM

City in south west Germany. Home of 18th century Mannheim 'school' of composers such as Johann and Carl Stamitz, and the various techniques of orchestration they developed. Streets are laid out in grid pattern, unusual in Germany, leading up to a grand baroque palace, now home to the Universität Mannheim (although parts are still open to the public). In common with a number of German cities, its historical built environment was destroyed during the war today it does not have the volume and concentration of characteristic architecture that can be found in other cities.

CLIMATE

Boasts some of the hottest summer temperatures in

EUROPE

the country, although this is matched by higher humidity and rainfall. Hottest months July-August (13-25°C, but often higher), coldest January (-2-3°C). Wettest month June (86mm), driest months January-March (around 55mm).

MUSICAL LIFE

Nationaltheater Mannheim houses opera and ballet companies, as well as theatre. Rosengarten congress centre also serves as concert hall for rock and classical concerts. Stamitz-Orchester Mannheim is one of Europe's oldest amateur/semi-professional orchestras. Alte Feuerwache is a venue for jazz as well as poetry readings.

OTHER CULTURAL INFORMATION

Kulturmeile Mannheim links the main cultural institutions: the national theatre, Reiss-Engelhorn-Museums (city's history, theatre museum), plantetarium, municipal art gallery.

FESTIVALS AND EVENTS

Major film event, the Internationales Filmfestival Mannheim-Heidelberg. Jazz festival.

TOURIST INFORMATION

www.tourist-mannheim.de, info@tourist-mannheim.de, +49 621 293 8700

STAATLICHEN HOCHSCHULE FÜR MUSIK UND DARSTELLENDE KUNST MANNHEIM

N7, 18, D-68161 Mannheim, Germany
t: +49 6212923511 *f:* +49 621292 2072
e: studienbuero@muho-mannheim.de
w: www.muho-mannheim.de

Course information Main subjects include orchestral instruments, keyboard instruments, voice (concert and opera), conducting (orchestra and choir); taught in artistic training, music teacher studies, soloist training (postgrad) degree courses. Doctoral studies available in musicology and music pedagogy. Also jazz/popular music studies at degree level.

Admissions information *Term dates* 1 Oct-31 Mar (winter semester); 1 Apr-30 Sep (summer semester). *Application requirements* Full details of requirements for entrance exams available on website; generally, for performers exam will include solo and chamber music, plus sight reading. *Application deadline* 30 Apr (for winter semester); 1 Dec (for summer semester). *Fees* EUR 500 tuition fee, plus EUR 158 admin costs. *Scholarships* Some scholarships and grants available, as well as student loans.

MUNICH (MÜNCHEN)

Bavarian capital near the Alps, and Germany's third largest city with approaching 1.5 million residents. Characterised by dramatic modern buildings (BMW headquarters, Allianz Arena football stadium, the Olympiapark) but also older architecture on a grand scale such as the Frauenkirche and Theatinerkirche or the Maximilianeum. It is also a city of bold streets, notably its four royal avenues such as the Maximilianstrasse. Major centre for the brewing industry, as well as, coincidentally, higher education institutions.

CLIMATE

Hottest month July (12-23°C), coldest month January (-5-2°C). Wettest month June (115mm), driest January/February (around 45mm).

MUSICAL LIFE

Home of Bayerische Staatsoper which, with its orchestra the Bayerisches Staatsorchester), performs at the Nationaltheater (as does its associated ballet company); some performances at the Prinzregentheater. Two other orchestras of international importance: Münchner Philharmoniker, based at the Gasteig cultural centre; and, of even greater renown, the Symphonieorchester des Bayerischen Rundfunks, which also appears at the Gasteig centre as well as the former royal palace, the Residenz. 'Munich's smallest opera house', the Pasinger Fabrik, puts on quirky opera and music theatre performances, alongside other performing arts.

OTHER CULTURAL INFORMATION

Huge number of museums; the Jüdisches Museum München is a new addition. Galleries also abound, although a scheme open to Munich citizens also allows them to rent art for domestic display. Theatre for all, including for children at the Schauburg; Volkstheater focuses on Bavarian writers; contemporary theatre at the art nouveau Kammerspiele; the Deutsches Theater is angled towards the more popular end.

FESTIVALS AND EVENTS

Münchener Biennale (founded by Hans Werner Henze) is a festival of new music theatre, held every 2 years. A city-wide opera festival in June and July offers a varied programme including contemporary events and chamber music. Olympic park area stages the free Tollwood Festival in the summer, with rock, pop, world music and jazz concerts, plus theatre and other entertainment. Oktoberfest in early autumn is hugely popular.

LOCAL PUBLICATIONS
The daily Suddeutsche Zeitung (www.sueddeutsche.de) features national and international news, with a supplement covering news and events in Munich; Münchner Merkur (www.merkur-online.de) is a more locally focused daily with events and entertainment information, community news and lifestyle features.

TOURIST INFORMATION
www.muenchen.de, tourismus@muenchen.de, +49 89 233 96 555

HOCHSCHULE FÜR MUSIK UND THEATRE MÜNCHEN
Arcisstr 12, D-80333 München, Germany
t: +49 89 289 27 450; +49 89 289 27459 (exchange contact) *f:* +49 89 289 27 419
e: verwaltung@musikhochschule-muenchen.de; karin.betz@musikhochschule-muenchen.de *w:* www.musikhochschule-muenchen.de
Contact Karin Betz, Socrates/Erasmus co-ordinator.
Admissions information *Application requirements* Evidence of sufficient knowledge of German to follow course of study (not essential, though desirable, for postgrad), see website for details of accepted qualifications. Min age 16, max age depends on year of study. *Fees* EUR 500. *Scholarships* None available.
Facilities *Accommodation* Approx 181 rooms looked after by the Hochschule.

MÜNSTER
City in north west Germany, population of 280,000. Smart in appearance, it has a particular reputation for education, with around 50,000 students enrolled in institutions there, and for its quality of life – its environment encompasses elements of rural and town living, and includes Lake Aa. It was the location for the signing of the Treaty of Münster which helped end the catastrophically destructive Thirty Years' War in 1648. Sometimes referred to as the bicycle capital of Germany, with a wide network of cycle paths, a secure bike parking space and rental schemes.

CLIMATE
Warmest months are July and August (14-23°C), coldest month December (1-4°C). Wettest month July (87mm), driest month March (42mm).

MUSICAL LIFE
Informal events such as jazz nights predominate. Halle Münsterland is a congress hall promoting some larger scale events, mostly pop and lighter entertainment.

OTHER CULTURAL INFORMATION
Museums such as the Graphikmuseum Pablo Picasso in the old town area; the regional (Westphalian) art and culture museum has a range of interesting exhibitions and events. 2 particular areas of the city are worth mentioning: Kreativkai for nightlife, theatre, jazz; Kuhviertel is a favourite student hangout.

FESTIVALS AND EVENTS
Schauraum culture festival in Sep; Hafenfest Münster in Jun for all-round entertainment and sporting events.

TOURIST INFORMATION
www.muenster.de, info@stadt-muenster.de, +49 2 51 4 92 27 10

MUSIKHOCHSCHULE MÜNSTER
Ludgeriplatz 1, D-48151 Münster, Germany
t: +49 251 83 27410 *f:* +49 251 83 27430
e: info.mhs@uni-muenster.de
w: www.uni-muenster.de
Course information Bachelor of music and bachelor of arts qualifications.

ROSTOCK
Northern German city, situated on the Warnow river with a link to the nearby Baltic coast in the district of Warnemünde (literally 'mouth of the Warnow'), a picturesque area with 100m of sandy beach. Its university, Universität Rostock, is one of the oldest in Germany, dating back to 1419. Its port location means the city has ferry links to countries around the Baltic.

CLIMATE
Warmest month July (13-22°C), coldest month January (-2-2°C). Wettest month July (79mm), driest month March (30mm).

MUSICAL LIFE
Norddeutscher Philharmonie performs at the Volkstheater Rostock, also a venue for opera, music theatre, ballet and drama. Concerts also take place

at the medieval town hall's baroque banqueting hall. Music academy's concerts add to city's cultural calendar.

OTHER CULTURAL INFORMATION
A maritime museum reflects the city's background.

FESTIVALS AND EVENTS
Main music event is the annual jazz festival, OstseeJazz, in July. The Rostocker Sommer festival covers various artforms.

TOURIST INFORMATION
www.rostock.de touristinfo@rostock.de

HOCHSCHULE FÜR MUSIK UND THEATER ROSTOCK
Beim St-Katharinenstift 8, D-18055 Rostock, Germany
t: +49 381 5108 0 *f:* +49 381 5108 101
e: hmt@hmt-rostock.de *w:* www.hmt-rostock.de
Course information Courses for all orchestral instruments, piano, piano chamber music, guitar, orchestral conducting, coaching, composition, music theory, singing, popular music. Also music education and acting.
Admissions information *Term dates* 1 Oct-31 Mar (winter semester); 1 Apr-30 Sep (summer semester) *Application requirements* Entrance exam. *Application deadline* 1 Jan-1 Feb (for summer semester). *Scholarships* Available for highly talented students. *No of students* 350 national, 160 overseas students.
Facilities *Music facilities* Institution is housed in converted monastery. Includes large opera and concert hall and 2 fully equipped theatre stages. Library with facilities for listening to CDs, records, cassettes. Multimedia studio and recording studios. *Performance opportunities* 300 concerts and performances per year.

SAARBRÜCKEN
City on the river Saar near the border with France with a history that has seen it occasionally become French, just as certain nearby French towns and provinces have been German. Now maintains close cultural and economic links with neighbours in the so-called SarLorLux (Saarland, Lorraine, Luxembourg) region.

CLIMATE
Warmest months July and August (13-23°C), coldest month January (-1-3°C). Rainfall is modest throughout the year, slightly, although not hugely, wetter during the winter.

MUSICAL LIFE
Two main venues: Saarländisches Staatstheater for opera, concerts and ballet; Sparte4 for more informal, unconventional or experimental performances. City shares one of Germany's newest orchestras, the Deutsche Radio Philharmonie Saarbrücken Kaiserslauten.

OTHER CULTURAL INFORMATION
Riverside modern art gallery has permanent display of German art and puts on special exhibitions; also museum devoted to region's history, a prehistory museum and museum for ecclesiastical art. Theatres of various sizes from the state theatre down to studios such as the Theater im Viertel; also a puppet theatre and a theatre for children.

FESTIVALS AND EVENTS
Home to a well-established film festival named after Max Ophüls (born in Saarbrücken); festival of French theatre.

TOURIST INFORMATION
www.saarbruecken.de, info@kontour.de, +49 681 93809 0

HOCHSCHULE FÜR MUSIK SAAR - UNIVERSITY OF MUSIC
Bismarckstr 1, D-66111 Saarbrücken, Germany
t: +49 681 96731 0 *f:* +49 681 96731 30
e: i.kessler@hfm.saarland.de
w: www.hfm.saarland.de
Course information Basic courses in voice (opera/recital), orchestral instruments, church music, composition, jazz and popular music; postgrad studies in voice (opera/recital), orchestral instruments, orchestral conducting, choral directing, composition, contemporary music, lied duo, chamber music, jazz and popular music, ear training. Bachelors (8 semesters, except for vocal courses where duration is 10) and masters courses (4 additional semesters).
Admissions information *Scholarships* Various subsidiary and stipend programmes, plus competitions for students. *No of students* Over 400 students.
Facilities *Music facilities* Concert hall with pipe organ. New media rooms for digital sound and music processing; jazz studio. The Hochschule makes use of other facilities in the city for teaching and performing.

STUTTGART

City in south western Germany on the river Neckar, came into importance during 18th and 19th centuries, and its architecture reflects this period. It has a significant amount of green space in the centre of the city, including a botanic gardens. The main castle square is another dominant space in the city centre, the castle in question being the Neues Schloss, a substantial late baroque building, bombed during World War II but rebuilt afterwards. This is one of several buildings in the city with an aristocratic history, a legacy of its status as a home to counts, princes, kings and emperors. The city's location and climate make it one of Germany's main wine-making areas, although the city probably best known for its engineering and technology (particularly relating to cars – it is home to a number of automobile manufacturers).

CLIMATE

Hottest months July and August (15-25°C), coldest months December and January (-1-5°C). Wettest months over the summer (up to 85mm May-June); driest over winter (max 20mm December-March).

MUSICAL LIFE

Strong musical presence in city. Radio-Sinfonieorchester Stuttgart des SWR, with a programme of about 90 concerts per year, based in the city (and is also known for touring abroad). As well as promoting concerts and chamber music events in its own right, the 400 year old Staatsorchester Stuttgart is orchestra for the Staatsoper Stuttgart, and both have their home in the rotunda-shaped Staatstheater; the company also runs a music theatre group performing contemporary works in non-theatrical locations, and a youth opera group. Stuttgarter Philharmoniker is another symphony orchestra; Stuttgarter Kammerorchester a smaller but internationally renowned group with many concerts in the city.

OTHER CULTURAL INFORMATION

The regional museum (Landesmuseum Württemberg) is housed in the old castle building. The Staatsgalerie Stuttgart has a collection ranging over several centuries, with older work in the Alte Staatsgalerie building and 20th century work in the suitably more modern Neue Staatsgalerie structure; there is more modern art at the glass cube Kunstmuseum Stuttgart which has its own collection and puts on temporary exhibitions also. For motor enthusiasts there is the Mercedes Benz museum.

FESTIVALS AND EVENTS

Musikfest Stuttgart in September; ECLAT festival of contemporary music is in February, as is the Stuttgarter Bachwoche.

LOCAL PUBLICATIONS

The Stuttgarter Zeitung (www.stuttgarter-zeitung.de) is the main regional daily newspaper

TOURIST INFORMATION

www.stuttgart-tourist.de, info@stuttgart-tourist.de, +49 711 22 28 240

STAATLICHE HOCHSCHULE FÜR MUSIK UND DARSTELLENDE KUNST STUTTGART

Urbanstr 25, D-70182 Stuttgart, Germany
t: +49 711 212 4631 *f:* +49 711 212 4632
e: rektor@mh-stuttgart.de
w: www.mh-stuttgart.de

Course information Artist's diploma (10 semesters) in various areas: strings and plucked instruments, wind instruments, percussion, voice, piano, organ, historical keyboard instruments, composition and music theory, conducting, opera studies, jazz and popular music. Advanced students can follow soloist class courses (4 semesters). Also 8-semester music education courses and church music courses.
Admissions information *Term dates* Early Oct-mid Feb (winter semester); mid Apr-mid Jul (summer semester). *No of students* 770 studients from over 40 countries.
Facilities *Music facilities* 500-seat concert hall with Rieger organ; chamber music hall (180 seats). Professionally managed theatre, studio for spoken word, electronic music studio, early music studio, recording studio; library with over 100,000 items. More than 200 teaching rooms and 40 oractice rooms (some available 24 hours a day). Average of 450 concerts per year.

TROSSINGEN

Small town in south west corner of Germany, but well known for its musical contribution (it is home to Hohner, probably the world's best known harmonica and accordion company); refers to itself as 'Die Stadt der Musik'.

MUSICAL LIFE

Dominated by harmonicas, accordions and associated instruments, the town hosts harmonica workshops, there is a harmonica museum, and it is home to the Hohner-Konservatorium dedicated to the instrument and its uses. As a result, there are

EUROPE

many blues, jazz and folk performances around the town. Visits from regional orchestras for mainstream classical.

TOURIST INFORMATION

www.trossingen.de, stadt@trossingen.de, +49 7425 25 0

STAATLICHE HOCHSCHULE FÜR MUSIK TROSSINGEN

Schultheiss-Koch-Platz 3, D-78647 Trossingen, Germany
t: +49 7425 94910; +49 7425 9491 17 (international office); +49 7425 949115 (admission/exams) *f:* +49 7425 949148
e: lenke@mh-trossingen.de
w: www.mhs-trossingen.de
Contact Martina Lenke, admissions & exams office
Course information Bachelor and masters study, Solistische Ausbildung (soloist training), doctorate.
Admissions information *Term dates* 1 Oct-end Feb (winter semester); 1 Apr-end Jul (summer semester). *Application requirements* Audition. *Application deadline* 15 Apr (winter semester); 15 Nov (summer semester). *Fees* EUR 500 per semester. *Scholarships* DAAD scholarship. *No of students* 400 students, inc 190 international students. *Language requirements* Basic German.
Facilities *Music facilities* Concert halls, rehearsal rooms, sound studio; also instrument loans. *Accommodation* Student hostel available: hohnerstiftung@gmx.de

EUROPE

WEIMAR

City in central Germany (in what was the GDR) with a strong artistic and intellectual, not to mention political, history. Original home to the Bauhaus design school (a new institution in the city has taken its name); associated with Bach and Liszt, Goethe and Schiller and numerous figures from world of art and design. A number of ornate palaces are dotted about the city, along with numerous parks and gardens, some large and others more intimate.

CLIMATE

Warmest month August (14-25°C), coldest months December and January (0-3°C).

MUSICAL LIFE

Staatskapelle Weimar linked with the city for over 400 years, counting Bach, Hummel and Liszt among its Kapellmeisters. Now performs, along with theatre, ballet and opera counterparts, at the national theatre building. Liszt museum, run by the music school bearing his name, with exhibition about him.

OTHER CULTURAL INFORMATION

Bauhaus museum houses one of biggest collections of Bauhaus artefacts. A museum devoted to Goethe is housed in the baroque building where the writer used to live, likewise the Schiller House; both feature exhibitions about the writers and their life and times; there is also a purpose-built archive containing research materials relating to the two writers, including manuscripts. The Palace Museum has its own art collection spanning several centuries. There is a grisly aspect to the city's history due to its proximity to the infamous Buchenwald World War II death camp.

FESTIVALS AND EVENTS

Principal festival is Pèlerinages Kunstfest in late summer, primarily art festival but including music, dance and literature. City contributes to the Thuringia Bach Festival taking place all over the region in April. Yiddish Summer Weimar, July, is Germany's main festival of Yiddish music.

TOURIST INFORMATION

www.weimar.de, tourist-info@weimar.de

HOCHSCHULE FÜR MUSIK FRANZ LISZT WEIMAR

Postfach 2552, D-99406 Weimar, Germany
t: +49 3643 555 184; +49 3643 555 148 (applications) *f:* +49 3643 555 147 *e:* study@hfm-weimar.de *w:* www.hfm-weimar.de
Contact Signe Pribbernow, Hans-Peter Hoffmann.
Course information Undergraduate and postgraduate courses in music performance; all instruments, singing/opera, church music, conducting, composition, jazz, early music. Also musicology, arts management and school music. Various orchestras and smaller ensembles, choirs and music theatre group.
Admissions information *Term dates* Early Oct-mid Feb (winter semester); early Apr-mid Jul (summer semester). *Application requirements* Entrance exam or audition. *Application deadline* Mid Mar (winter semester); mid Nov 2009 (summer semester). *Scholarships* Not usually available. *No of students* c 600 national students, c 300 international students. *Language requirements* German language certificate B2 or test during audition; for musicology test Daf 4
Facilities *Music facilities* Main building houses

concert hall, recording studio, studio for electroacoustic music, book and media library. Individual faculties located in several buildings around the city. *Accommodation* International students guaranteed place in student accommodation; single rooms available from EUR 88-287 per month.

WÜRZBURG

Northern Bavarian city just over 100 km upstream from Frankfurt on the river Main. Apart from its many churches in various styles, the city's main architectural feature is the Residenz, a spectacularly ornate baroque palace (it is on Unesco's list of world heritage sites) containing halls, chapel, gardens, frescoes and grand staircases. The city is overlooked by a hilltop castle, the Marienberg Fortress, and an impressive medieval stone bridge crosses the river.

CLIMATE

Typical climate of the region with warm summers (14-25°C in August) and relatively mild winters (0-4°C in January), and peak rainfall in the summer (50mm and above in June to August).

MUSICAL LIFE

Numerous churches hold concerts (including the Festungskirche at the castle), but main concert venues are Congress Centrum Würzburg and s. Oliver Arena for a variety of events; Philharmonisches Orchester Würzburg performs at the Mainfranken Theater, home also to music theatre, ballet and theatre companies.

OTHER CULTURAL INFORMATION

Visitors can discover more about the city's history at the Fürstenbau Museum; there is a range of art exhibited at the Museum am Dom, including contemporary works; the Siebold-Museum focuses on the scientist's work in Japan and houses a German-Japanese forum aimed at promoting understanding between the countries.

FESTIVALS AND EVENTS

Mozartfest in May-July; Africa Festival Würzburg is one of Europe's longest-standing and largest festivals of African music and culture. Many other smaller festivals throughout the year.

TOURIST INFORMATION

www.wuerzburg.de, tourismus@wuerzburg.de, +49 9 31 37 23 35

HOCHSCHULE FÜR MUSIK WÜRZBURG
Hofstallstr 6-8, D-97070 Würzburg, Germany
t: +49 931 32187 0 *f:* +49 931 32187 2800
e: dirk.braeuer@hfm-wuerzburg.de *w:* www.hfm-wuerzburg.de
Course information Diplommusikers/Diplommusikerin qualification available in accordion, early/period music, conducting (choir and orchestra), voice, music theatre, guitar, jazz, church music, piano, orchestral instruments, organ, composition.
Admissions information *Term dates* Begins in Oct. *Application deadline* 31 March. *Fees* EUR 386.60. *No of students* 565 students, of whom 145 are from overseas.
Facilities *Music facilities* 5 concert halls of various sizes (largest seats 799), computer studio with 12 workstations, small studio, recording studio, experimental music studio. Also extensive library.

MUSIC FESTIVALS

Altstadtherbst Kulturfestival Düsseldorf Bolkerstr 57, D-40213 Düsseldorf, Germany *t:* +49 211 322332 *f:* +49 211 322203 *e:* info@altstadtherbst.de *w:* www.altstadtherbst.de Aims to make a new experience out of classical music, bring old and new together, concerts in unfamiliar venues, etc.

Art Point Trombacher Hof, D-55583 Bad Münster, Germany *t:* +494 670 83616 *f:* +49 670 83653 *e:* info@artpoint-th.com *w:* www.artpoint-th.com Contemporary and traditional music, multicultural, crossover; audiovisual; soundsculptures, light art; poetry and literature.

Bach Festival Leipzig c/o Bach-Archiv Leipzig, Thomaskirchhof 15-16, D-04109 Leipzig, Germany *t:* +49 341 913 7333 *f:* +49 341 913 7335 *e:* bachfest@bach-leipzig.de *w:* www.bachfestleipzig.de Annual. 2010 theme Bach-Schumann-Brahms.

Bachwoche Stuttgart Johann-Sebastian-Bach-Platz, D-70178 Stuttgart, Germany *t:* +49 711 61921 0 *f:* +49 711 61921 23 *e:* office@bachakademie.de *w:* www.bachakademie.de Concerts, symposium, masterclasses.

Bayreuther Barock Stadt Bayreuth / Kulturamt, Wahnfriedstr 1, D-95444 Bayreuth, Germany *t:* +49 921 50 72 01 60 *f:* +49 921 50 72 01 70 *e:* kulturamt@stadt.bayreuth.de *w:* www.bayreuther-barock.bayreuth.de

Beethoven Festival Bonn Kurt-Schumacher-Str 3, D-53113 Bonn, Germany *t:* +49 228 20 10 345 *f:* +49 228 20 10 333 *e:* info@beethovenfest.de *w:* www.beethovenfest.de Annual festival bringing together world-famous artists and young, highly talented musicians to the Rhineland region.

Berliner Tage für Alte Musik Postfach 580411, D-10414 Berlin, Germany *t:* +49 30 447 6082, also fax *e:* BerlinAlteMusik@t-online.de; ars.musica@knoware.nl *w:* www.berlinaltemusik.com Concerts, instrument market, workshops.

Berlin Jazz Festival Schapenstr 24, D-10719 Berlin, Germany *t:* +49 30 254 89 0 *f:* +49 30 254 89 111 *e:* info@berlinerfestspiele.de *w:* www.berlinerfestspiele.de Established stars of jazz in the same programme as musicians who have led jazz in the direction of electronics, pop, ethnic and new music.

Donaueschinger Musiktage Karlstr 58, D-78166 Donaueschingen, Germany *t:* +49 771 857266 *f:* +49 771 857263 *w:* www.swr.de/donaueschingen New music festival.

Dresden Days of Contemporary Music Europaeisches Zentrum der Künste Hellerau, Karl-Liebknecht-Str 56, D-01109 Dresden, Germany *t:* +49 351 26462 0 *f:* +49 351 26462 23 *w:* www.zeitmusik.de

Dresden Music Festival PO Box 10 04 53, D-01074 Dresden *t:* +49 351 478 56 0 *f:* +49 351 478 56 23 *w:* www.musikfestspiele.com 2010 festival presents retrospective of Russian music.

ECLAT - Festival for New Music Stuttgart Musik der Jahrhunderte, Siemenstr 13, D-70469 Stuttgart, Germany *t:* +49 711 629 0510 *f:* +49 711 629 0516 *e:* mdj@mdjstuttgart.de *w:* www.eclat.org Annual. Contemporary music.

European Youth Music Festival Young Classic Nibelungenstr 8, D-94032 Passau, Germany *t:* +49 851 52575 *f:* +49 851 71551 *e:* info@young-classic.eu *w:* www.young-classic.eu Annual. Classical music, etc. Artists aged 10-26, singers up to 30 from all European countries.

Festival Alte Musik Knechtsteden Ostpreussenallee 5, D-41539 Dormagen, Germany *t:* +49 2133 210992 *f:* +49 2133 214097 *e:* altemusik@t-online.de *w:* www.knechtsteden-altemusik.de Concerts with music in authentic interpretation (early, baroque, classical and romantic music); vocal and instrumental.

Festival Orff in Andechs Kloster Andechs, Bergstr 2, D-82346 Andechs, Germany *t:* +49 8152 376271 *f:* +49 8152 376239 *e:* orff@andechs.de *w:* www.orff-in-andechs.de

Halle Handel Festival Grosse Nikolaistr 5, D-06108 Halle, Germany *t:* +49 345 5009 0222 *f:* +49 345 5009 0416 *e:* festspiele@haendelhaus.de *w:* www.haendelfestspiele.halle.de Opera, concerts, oratorio, open-air performances, scientifc conference.

Händel-Festspiele des Bad Staatstheaters *w:* www.staatstheater.karlsruhe.de

Heidelberg Castle Festival Friedrichstr 5, D-69117 Heidelberg, Germany *t:* +49 622 158 35020 *f:* +49 622 158 35990 *e:* scholssfestspiele@heidelberg.de *w:* www.schlossfestspiele-heidelberg.de Opera, musicals, plays, concerts.

International Festival of Young Opera Singers Kammeroper Schloss Rheinsberg GmbH, Kavalierhaus, D-16831 Rheinsberg, Germany *t:* +49 33931 725 0 *f:* +49 33931 725 15 *e:* info@kammeroper-schloss-rheinsberg.de *w:* www.kammeroper-rheinsberg.de

International Handel Festival Göttingen Hainholzweg 3-5, D-37085 Goettingen, Germany *t:* +49 551 384813 0 *f:* +49 551 384813 10 *e:* info@haendel-festspiele.de *w:* www.haendel-festspiele.de Annual. Baroque music festival. Fringe programme, open air concerts.

International May Festival c/o Hessisches Staatstheater Wiesbaden, PO Box 3247, D-65022 Wiesbaden, Germany *t:* +49 611 132264 *f:* +49 611 132244 *e:* intendanz@staatstheater-wiesbaden.de *w:* www.maifestspiele.de International performances of opera, drama, ballet, musicals, gala performances, recitals, children's and youth theatre.

Inventionen - Berliner Festival Neuer Musik c/o DAAD, Berliner Kuenstlerprogramm, Markgrafenstr 37, D-10117 Berlin, Germany *t:* +49 302 022080 *f:* +49 302 041267 *e:* musik.berlin@daad.de *w:* www.inventionen.de Sound installations, international electroacoustic music, lectures, concerts.

Kammeroper Schloss Rheinsberg Kavalierhaus, D-16831 Rheinsberg, Germany *t:* +49 33 931 725 0 *e:* info@kammeroper-schloss-rheinsberg.de *w:* http://kammeroper-rheinsberg.de

Kissinger Sommer Festival Stadtverwaltung, Rathausplatz 4, D-97688 Bad Kissingen, Germany *t:* +49 971 807 1110 *f:* +49 971 807 1109 *e:* kissingersommer@stadt.badkissingen.de *w:* www.kissingersommer.de Annual. Symphony concerts, chamber music, Lieder, jazz.

Klosterkonzerte Maulbronn Postfach 47, D-75433 Maulbronn, Germany *t:* +49 7043 7734 *f:* +49 7043 10345 *e:* info@klosterkonzerte.de *w:* www.klosterkonzerte.de Sacred music concerts, chamber music, all kinds of secular music. Held in different rooms of the monastery of Maulbronn as well as open air.

Kronberg Academy Cello Festival Friedrich Ebert

Str 6, D-61476 Kronberg, Germany *t:* +49 6173 783378 *f:* +49 6173 783379 *e:* info@kronbergacademy.de *w:* www.kronbergacademy.de

Kronberg Academy Viola Festival Friedrich Ebert Str 6, D-61476 Kronberg, Germany *t:* +49 3176 783378 *f:* +49 6173 783379 *e:* o.laue@kronbergacademy.de *w:* www.kronbergacademy.de Approx every 6 years.

Kurt Weill Festival Ebertallee 63, D-06846 Dessau, Germany *t:* +49 340 619595 *f:* +49 340 611907 *e:* intendant@kurt-weill.de *w:* www.kurt-weill-fest.de

Leipzig International Choral Festival Festival UK Office, Salcombe House, Long St, Sherborne, DT9 3BU, United Kingdom *t:* +44 1935 810810 *f:* +44 1935 815815 *e:* info@leipzigchoralfestival.com *w:* www.leipzigchoralfestival.com Annual 4-day festival in Leipzig. Cultural exchange of choral music with choirs from around the world gathering in one of the most musically dedicated cities in Europe.

Ludwigsburg International Festival Festspiele Baden-Württemburg, Marstallstr 5, D-71634 Ludwigsburg, Germany *t:* +49 7141 939636 *f:* +49 7141 939697 *e:* info@schlossfestspiele.de *w:* www.schlossfestspiele.de Annual. Classical music, opera, modern dance, theatre, jazz, world music, literature.

MaerzMusik Berlin - International Festival of Contemporary Music Berliner Festspiele, Schaperstr 24, D-10719 Berlin, Germany *t:* +49 302 54890 *f:* +49 302 5489114 *e:* maerzmusik@berlinerfestspiele.de *w:* www.maerzmusik.de; www.berlinerfestspiele.de Festival of contemporary music. Established artists and emerging talents present programme of premieres, new and commissioned works. Range from orchestral and chamber music to innovative music theatre, experimental and new media.

Mendelssohn-Festtage Gewandhaus zu Leipzig, Augustusplatz 8, D-04109 Leipzig, Germany *t:* +49 341 127 0316 *f:* +49 341 127 0408 *e:* presse@gewandhaus.de *w:* www.gewandhaus.de 2010 theme: Mendelssohn and Schumann.

Moritzburg Festival Maxstr 8, D-01067 Dresden, Germany *t:* +49 351 810 5495 *f:* +49 351 810 5496 *e:* buero@moritzburgfestival.de *w:* www.moritzburgfestival.de Chamber music in royal settings with internationally renowned artists.15 performances.

Mozartfest Würzburg Oeggstr 2, D-97070 Würzburg, Germany *t:* +49 931 37 23 36 *f:* +49 931 37 39 39 *e:* info@mozartfest-wuerzburg.de *w:* www.mozartfest.de

Münchener Biennale - Internationales Festival für neues Musiktheater Ludwigstr 8, D-80539 München, Germany *t:* +49 89 280 5607 *f:* +49 89 280 5679 *e:* biennale@spielmotor.de *w:* www.muenchenerbiennale.de New music theatre, world premieres; associated orchestral concerts.

Münchener Opernfestspiele Max-Joseph-Platz 2, D-80539 München, Germany *w:* www.bayerische-staatsoper.de

Musica Bayreuth Ludwigstr 26, D-95444 Bayreuth, Germany *t:* +49 921 67367, also fax *e:* info@musica-bayreuth.de *w:* www.musica-bayreuth.de Annual. Classical orchestral, choral and chamber music.

Musica Sacra International Arnauer Str 14, D-87616 Marktoberdorf, Germany *t:* +49 83 42 8964033 *f:* +49 83 4240 370 *e:* office@modfestivals.org *w:* www.modfestivals.org Biennial. Music from the 5 major world religions' choirs, instrumentalists, singers, dancers, combinations of music and other artforms.

Musikfest Berlin Schaperstr 24, D-10719 Berlin, Germany *t:* +49 30 254 89 0 *f:* +49 30 254 89 111 *e:* info@berlinerfestspiele.de *w:* www.berlinerfestspiele.de Presents new and unknown pieces alongside significant works of traditional symphonic repertoire. Provides forum for artistic innovation by orchestras, ensembles, composers, conductors and soloists of international standing.

Musikfest Bremen Postfach 10 30 63, D-28030 Bremen, Germany *t:* +49 421 33 66 77 *f:* +49 421 33 66 880 *e:* preisler@musikfest-bremen.de *w:* www.musikfest-bremen.de Opera, orchestral, oratorio, chamber music of various eras; jazz.

Musikfestspiele Potsdam Sanssouci Wilhelm-Staab-Str 10/11, D-14467 Potsdam, Germany *t:* +49 331 28 888 0 *f:* +49 331 28 888 29 *e:* info@musikfestspiele-potsdam.de *w:* www.musikfestspiele-potsdam.de

Musikfest Stuttgart Johann-Sebastian-Bach-Platz, D-70178 Stuttgart, Germany *t:* +49 711 619210 *f:* +49 711 6192123 *e:* musikfest@bachakademie.de *w:* www.musikfest.de Annual. Features Festivalensemble Stuttgart.

MusikTriennale Köln Bischofsgartenstr 1, D-50667 Koln, Germany *e:* kontakt@musiktriennale.de *w:* www.musiktriennale.de International music festival.

Oleg Kagan Music Festival - Tegernseer Tal Musikfest Kreuth eV Geschäftsstelle, Nördliche Hauptstr 3, D-83708 Kreuth, Germany *t:* +49 8029 1820 *f:* +49 8029 1828 *e:* musikfest@kreuth.de *w:* www.oleg-kagan-musikfest.de Classical and modern chamber music represented by internationally acclaimed artists.

Open Air Klassik Postfach 30, D-52153 Monschau, Germany *t:* +49 24 72 80 48 0 *f:* +49 24 72 4534 *w:* www.monschau-klassik.de

Opernfestival Gut Immling Unsere Oper e V, Gut Immling, D-83128 Halfing, Germany *t:* +49 8055 90 34 0 *f:* +49 8055 90 34 28 *e:* sekretariat@gut-immling.de *w:* www.gut-immling.de Opera productions.

Opernfestspiele Heidenheim Grabenstr 15, D-89522 Heidenheim, Germany *t:* +49 7 321 327 46 10 *f:* +49 7 321 327 46 11 *e:* opernfestspiele@heidenheim.de *w:* www.opernfestspiele.de Open-air opera festival.

Pèlerinages Kunstfest Weimar Am Palais 13, D-99423 Weimar, Germany *t:* +49 3643 81 14 0 *f:* +49 3643 81 14 44 *e:* pelerinages@kunstfest-weimar.de *w:* www.kunstfest-weimar.de

Rheingau Musik Festival Konzertgesellschaft Rheinallee 1, D-65375 Oestrich-Winkel, Germany *t:* +49 6723 91770 *f:* +49 6723 917719 *e:* info@rheingau-musik-festival.de *w:* www.rheingau-musik-festival.de Classical, jazz and cabaret music.

Richard Strauss Festival Kulturbuero im Richard-Strauss-Institut, Schnitzschulstr 19, D-82467 Garmisch-Partenkirchen, Germany *t:* +49 8821 910 9511 *f:* +49 8821 910 960 *e:* rsi@gapa.de *w:* www.richard-strauss-institut.de; www.richard-strauss-festival.de Opera, orch concerts, lieder recitals etc presenting music by Richard Strauss and others.

Rossini in Wildbad Touristik Bad Wildbad GmbH, Postfach 100326, D-75314 Bad Wildbad, Germany *t:* +49 7081 10284 *f:* +49 7081 10290 *e:* touristik@bad-wildbad.de *w:* www.rossini-in-wildbad.de Belcanto opera festival.

Ruhrtriennale Kultur Ruhr GmbH, Leithestr 35, D-45886 Gelsenkirchen, Germany *t:* +49 209 167 1702 *f:* +49 209 167 1710 *e:* am.boegel@kulturruhr.com *w:* www.ruhrtriennale.de International mixed discipline festival of arts with venues throughout the Ruhr district.

Schleswig Holstein Music Festival Palais Rantzau, Parade 1, D-23552 Luebeck, Germany *t:* +49 451 38957 0 *f:* +49 451 38957 57 *e:* info@shmf.de *w:* www.shmf.de More than 130 classical music events in the countryside; concerts in churches, barns, mansions, traditional concert halls.

Schumannfest Düsseldorf Bolkerstr 57, D-40213 Düsseldorf, Germany *t:* +49 211 133222 *f:* +49 211 322203 *e:* info@schumannfest-duesseldorf.de *w:* www.schumannfest-duesseldorf.de Biennial festival.

Schwetzinger SWR Festspiele Hans-Bredow-Str, D-76530 Baden-Baden, Germany *t:* +49 7221 929 4990 *f:* +49 7221 929 4995 *e:* schwetzinger-festspiele@swr.de *w:* www.schwetzinger-festspiele.de Annual. Opera and concerts.

Sommerkonzerte Audi AG, D-85045 Ingolstadt, Germany *t:* +49 841 8931515 *f:* +49 841 8936195 *e:* sommerkonzerte@audi.de *w:* www.sommerkonzerte.de Classical, pop, jazz.

Stockstädter Musiktage Berlinerstr 65, D-64589 Stockstaedt-am-Rhein, Germany *t:* +49 615 884818, also fax *w:* www.stockstaedter-musiktage.de Recorder music festival on period instruments, recorder masterclasses, concerts, exhibitions.

Tage Alter Musik Regensburg Postfach 100903, D-93009 Regensburg, Germany *t:* +49 941 8979786 *f:* +49 941 8979836 *e:* TageAlterMusik@t-online.de *w:* www.tagealtermusik-regensburg.de Early music from Middle Ages to romantic era on period instruments. Also large exhibition of period instruments.

Thüringer Bachwochen Schwanseestr 33, D-66423 Weimar, Germany *t:* +49 3643 77 69 41 *f:* +49 3643 77 69 48 *e:* info@thueringer-bachwochen.de *w:* www.thueringer-bachwochen.de Baroque music festival focusing on Bach.

Yiddish Summer Weimar Other Music Academy eV, Ernst-Kohl-Str 23, Goetheplatz 3, D-99423 Weimar, Germany *t:* +49 3643 858310 *f:* +49 3643 804836 *e:* yiddish-summer@other-music.net *w:* www.yiddish-summer-weimar.de Festival of Yiddish music, culture and identity.

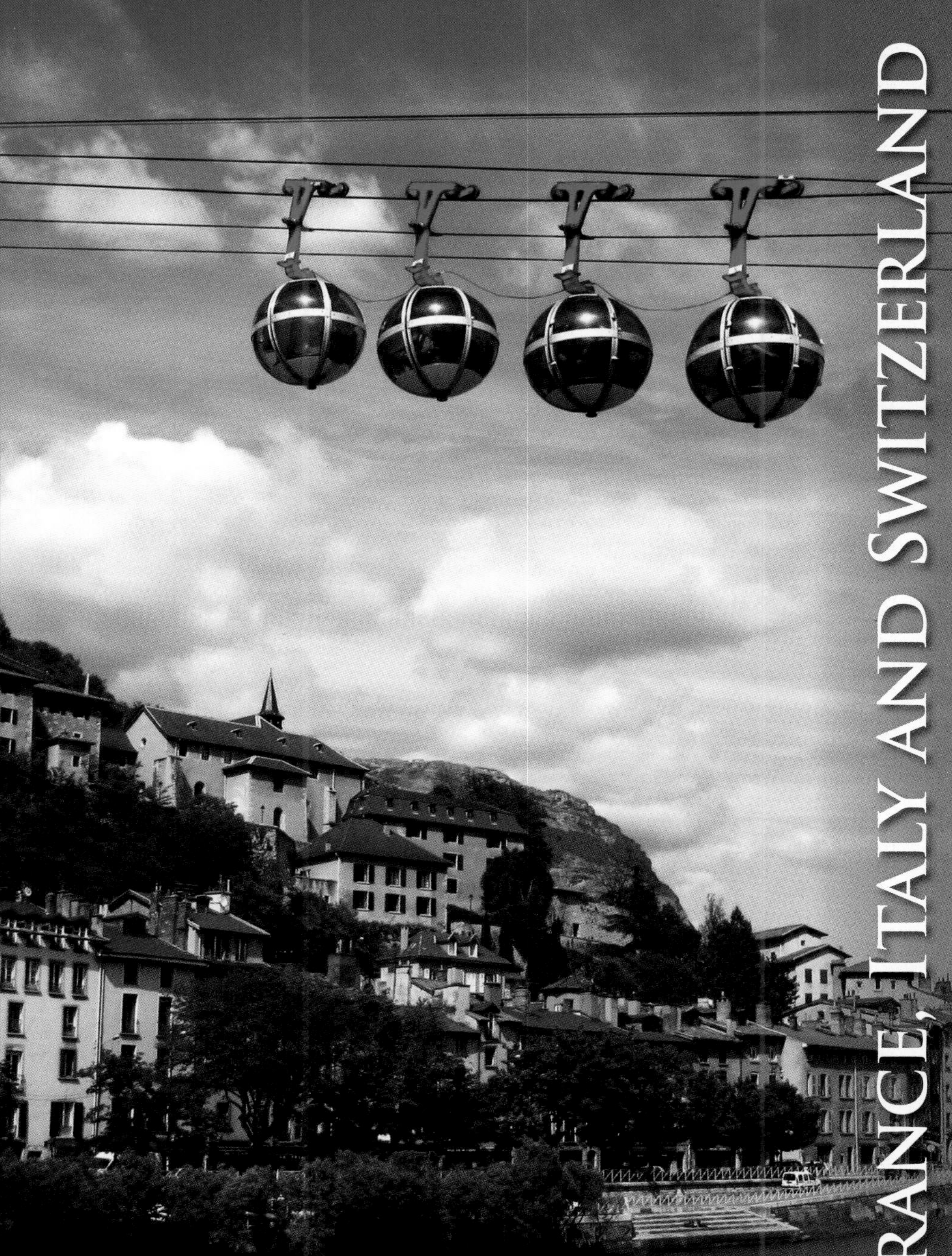

France, Italy and Switzerland

FRANCE, ITALY AND SWITZERLAND

Three countries especially popular with visitors, whether due to their reputations for quality of life or their traditions, whether artistic, historic, architectural or gastronomic. All three benefit from their national languages, French, Italian and German (all three in the case of Switzerland, a country divided into regions in each of which one language dominates), being among the more widely taught (along with Spanish).

Although linked geographically, however, their musical cultures are distinctive. Thanks to its international artistic and cultural importance in a 50-year period spanning the late 19th and early 20th centuries, and significant postwar investment in the arts and its infrastructure, France has a strong reputation in both modern and period music (a 'movement' which only took hold in the latter half of the century). Across Italy, opera and vocal music predominate, with local and/or municipal companies deeply embedded in the cultural life of their regions. Switzerland has an impressive all-round musical culture, testament to the resources allocated to performing arts and, no doubt, the relative wealth of the country.

FRANCE PAGE 101

Music education in France is highly structured. As far as training for performers goes, this is restricted to the two state-run Conservatoires Nationaux Supérieurs de Musique (managed by the culture ministry) and the independent, but state-recognised, Ecole Normale Supérieure de Musique. Although all three offer practical training at various levels of ability, the ENSM has its a course structure and hierarchy different from the CNSMs, and makes its own decisions about the acceptability of external qualifications. Training at the CNSMs falls into a 2-cycle structure, although it is not exactly equivalent to the model prescribed by the Bologna Process.

Music teacher training is, in the main, handled elsewhere at dedicated training schools (Centres de Formation des Enseignants de la Danse et de la Musique) at a few locations across the country. Music education for children and young people does not take place in schools but in the 30-odd Conservatoires Nationaux de Région.

ITALY PAGE 105

In contrast with France, Italy has numerous professional music training colleges spread across the country – indeed, there is a national network of pre-college music schools as well whose aim is not specifically to train musicians but to provide a more general music education. And alongside the numerous government-funded conservatoires, there are around 20 Istituti Musicali Pareggiati, funded with a mixture of local and state money. These are usually located in smaller towns, allowing more students access to some form of advanced tuition, with the conservatoires based in the bigger regional cities. In terms of educational structure, conservatoires have in practice adopted the pan-European model of 1st and 2nd cycle ('livello') higher education (Triennio followed by Biennio), although many offer it alongside the more traditional system in which attendance at conservatoires begins around age 10, continuing until a set number of years (depending on the instrument/discipline) have been completed.

SWITZERLAND PAGE 121

Switzerland is one of the European countries keenest to adopt the Bologna ideals, both by adopting the 3 years bachelors plus 2 years masters course structure, and by centralising responsibility for the administration of institutions – what was a locally run conservatoire becomes a university equivalent Hochschule, Haute Ecole de Musique or Scuola Universitaria di Musica. To gain this level, institutions must meet certain educational standards stipulated by the government, and in general, authorities are conscientious about the issue of quality assurance.

Many students (some 90%) at Swiss institutions go on to masters level, a strong indication that the most advanced professional performance training is concentrated here and that bachelors level education does no more, in career terms, than equip students with skills appropriate for the wider workplace.

PARIS

As one of the world's most visited capitals – and a favourite of film-makers, not least because of the French passion for cinema – it virtually needs no introduction; it has long been a popular destination for visiting students. Being relatively small, it is surprisingly easy to get around on foot, although the Cité de la Musique area where the conservatoire is based is not centrally located but in the north east corner. Different districts have their own distinct feels, from the vibrant and iconic area around Montmartre, the busy Latin Quarter in the centre of the city, the cluster of academic institutions south of that, and the relaxed Marais area to the more residential areas towards the west. In general, the urban environment, particularly in domestic architecture and street layout, deeply reflects its 19th century make-over. As capital of the country with an international reputation for cooking, Paris is home to countless restaurants; these have recently begun broadened in scope to include global food traditions.

CLIMATE

Hottest month August (17-25°C), coldest month January (3-7°C). Monthly rainfall consistent throughout the year at around 45-65mm.

MUSICAL LIFE

As a musical city, punches a little below its weight in terms of international profile – outside a well-supported mainstream classical music is harder to come by. Opéra National de Paris is one exception, with main house the newer building at Bastille with old Opéra Garnier staging most of the ballet and some other opera. Outstanding reputation for contemporary music at IRCAM research facility and via the Ensemble Intercontemporain. Main orchestras are Orchestre de Paris; the two radio orchestras l'Orchestre Philharmonique de Radio-France and l'Orchestre National de France; the regional Orchestre National d'Ile de France is based nearby but performs in town. Salle Pleyel, Théâtre des Champs-Elysées and Salle Gaveau are the main concert halls, with Théâtre du Châtelet venue for opera and music theatre as well as recitals. Orchestre des Champs-Elysées for period music (classical/romantic), an area where Paris (and France) do have excellent reputation – Les Arts Florissants are based there, for instance.

OTHER CULTURAL INFORMATION

Large range of all-round cultural activity, particularly art, theatre, cinema and literature. The distinctive, centrally located, Centre Georges Pompidou is home to the Musée National d'Art Moderne, with its enormous collection (it is the venue for many temporary exhibitions too), but also a free public library. Becoming increasingly diverse with more cultures from France's colonial past gaining some representation (Paris has become a centre for world music recording). A number of popular museums and galleries plus many more of a more specialist nature.

FESTIVALS AND EVENTS

Fête de la Musique street festival in June is most popular music event across the city, with many different styles featuring. Festival d'Automne covers all performing art forms. Various film festivals (Festival du Film and Festival de Films des Femmes in March). Otherwise cultural events tend to be more local – many arrondissements (districts) have their own local festivals – or run by particular institutions.

LOCAL PUBLICATIONS

L'officiel des spectacles and Pariscope the main listings/entertainment guides. The city is home to the country's main newspapers, Le Monde, Le Figaro and the left-leaning Libération.

TOURIST INFORMATION

www.parisinfo.com, agenda@parisinfo.com, +33 8 92 68 30 00

LE CONSERVATOIRE DE PARIS

209 av Jean-Jaurès, F-75019 Paris, France
t: +33 1 40 40 45 45; +33 1 40 40 45 79 (international exchanges). *e:* scolarite@cnsmdp.fr; gamussen@cnsmdp.fr *w:* www.cnsmdp.fr
Contact Gretchen Amussen, Ania Sergueeva, international exchanges.

Course information Classes in 7 departments: classical and contemporary instruments; early music; musicology & analysis; vocal disciplines; writing, composition and orchestral conducting; jazz and improvised music; pedagogy and teacher training.

Admissions information *Term dates* Mid Sep-end Jun; various holiday breaks. *Application requirements* Entry by audition; request for application form via website. *Fees* EUR 400 plus EUR 189 social security payment. *Scholarships* Scholarships available to French and EU students from Ministry of Culture and Communication; also some private grants (see website for conditions).

Facilities *Accommodation* Various housing

possibilities available through affaires scolaires dept, including halls of residence, studios, university residences. Students seeking accommodation must have guarantor undertaking to pay rent if student tenant is unable.

ECOLE NORMALE DE MUSIQUE DE PARIS

114bis blvd Malesherbes, F-75017 Paris, France
t: +33 1 47 63 85 72 *f:* +33 1 47 63 50 42
e: info@ecolenormalecortot.com; admission@ecolenormalecortot.com; administration@ecolenormalecortot.com *w:* www.ecolenormalecortot.com

Course information Instrument and voice classes, complementary classes, ensemble classes, theory and composition classes, orchestral conducting classes.

Admissions information *Term dates* 1 Oct-30 Jun. *Application requirements* Application to include letter of motivation, music CV, full personal details, tape/CD/MD recording, EUR 340 admin fee, 2 photos. If accepted, an audition will determine your level of entry, teachers and obligatory classes. All complementary subjects required for the instrumental or vocal degree must have been passed, or equivalent foreign certificates granted. *Application deadline* 15 Dec. *Fees* Vary depending on level and class; see website for details. *Scholarships* Part and full scholarships available; can be applied for when students receive certificate of pre-registration. *No of students* 1100 students, of whom 750 international. *Language requirements* Intermediate French or English

Facilities *Performance opportunities* At the Cortot concert hall in Paris and at other venues in Paris and France. *Accommodation* Accommodation available through student services CROUS or Les Foyers: Union Nationale des Maisons d'Etudiants. Website gives details of other student accommodation in Paris.

EUROPE

LYON

City in the southern French Rhône area at the confluence of Rhône and Saône rivers and dominated by its twin hills: Fourvière with its dramatic basilica, Croix-Rousse with its characteristic narrow streets and passageways. Its historical importance goes back to Roman times (name Lugdunum), and architectural styles of the city reflect development in various eras. Particular reputation for its food and wine culture. Educational centre with large number of institutions based there.

CLIMATE

Hottest month July (15-27°C), coldest month January (0-6°C). Wettest month October (95mm), driest month February (50mm).

MUSICAL LIFE

Outside the conservatoire, Lyon's 2 main musical performing organisations are Orchestre National de Lyon and Opéra National de Lyon. Opera (which has been led by a number of important music directors recently) performs full programme based at the Nouvel Opéra house, a modernised version of an early 19th century building. Ballet and occasional concerts also put on there; main concert hall the Auditorium de Lyon, home to Orchestre National de Lyon. City is also home to Grame: Centre National de Création Musicale, a facility for contemporary composers either resident there or associated with it.

OTHER CULTURAL INFORMATION

Museums reflecting Lyon's history include Musée Gallo-Romain archeological museum and a Centre d'Histoire de la Résistance et de la Déportation. Newest museum is Musée des Confluences, situated where the two rivers meet and devoted to connections between science and society. Several theatres in and around city; some city-centre companies are Théâtre des Celestins covers plays from various different eras; Théâtre des Marronniers for interdisciplinary forms; Théâtre les Ateliers also more contemporary, with international visiting companies.

FESTIVALS AND EVENTS

Musiques en Scène biennial festival based at Grame (even numbered years). City celebrates Fête de la Musique along with the rest of the country. Non-musical events include a festival of lights (dating back over 150 years); biennial contemporary art festival (odd-numbered years); more unusually, a festival of detective fiction.

TOURIST INFORMATION

www.lyon.fr, +33 4 72 10 30 30

CONSERVATOIRE NATIONAL SUPÉRIEUR MUSIQUE ET DANSE DE LYON

3 quai Chauveau, CP 120, F-69266 Lyon Cedex 09, France
t: +33 4 72 19 26 26 *f:* +33 4 72 19 26 00
w: www.cnsmd-lyon.fr
Contact Isabelle Replumaz, head of international relations

Course information Bachelors and masters courses in 2 cycles, 3 years + 2 years. Courses based around 4 core areas: main study (instrument, voice, composition etc), complementary study (chamber music, orchestra etc), cultural studies (eg history of music), associated study (foreign language, practical aspects of being a musician).
Admissions information *Term dates* Beginning Sep-end Jun, in 2 semesters. *Application requirements* Application via website. Students in music dept must be aged 16-30. *Fees* EUR 628 (includes fees, access to mediatheque and student social security contribution). Bursaries available for EU students in case of need, as well as French students. *No of students* 500 students, 15% of whom come from overseas.
Facilities *Music facilities* 110 teaching rooms, 300-seat concert hall with audio-visual recording facilities, orchestral rehearsal room, 120-seat recital room (with organ), choir room, 2 other performance rooms. Annual programme of over 200 concerts. *Accommodation* 73-bed hall of residence.

MUSIC FESTIVALS

Besançon International Music Festival 3 bis rue Léonel de Moustier, F-25000 Besancon, France *t:* +33 3 81 25 05 85 *f:* +33 3 81 81 52 15 *e:* contact@festival-besancon.com *w:* www.festival-besancon.com
Biennale Musiques en Scene BP 1185, 9 rue du Garet, F-69202 Lyon Cedex 01, France *t:* +33 4 72 07 37 00 *f:* +33 4 72 7 37 01 *w:* www.grame.fr Biennial. Interdisciplinary showcase for musical creation.
Chorégies d'Orange *t:* +33 4 90 51 83 83 *e:* administration@choregies.com *w:* www.choregies.asso.fr Opera and concert performances in ancient Roman theatre
Colmar International Festival 8 rue Kleber, F-68000 Colmar, France *t:* +33 89 20 68 97 *f:* +33 89 41 34 13 *e:* infofestival@ot-colmar.fr *w:* www.festival-colmar.com
Coups de Vents: Festival International de Musique à Vent c/o Domaine Musiques, 2 rue des Buisses, 59000 Lille, France *t:* +33 3 20 63 65 98 *f:* +33 3 20 63 65 90 *e:* coupsdevents@domaine-musiques.com *w:* www.coupsdevents.com
Festival d'Ambronay *e:* contact@ambronay.org *w:* www.ambronay.org
Festival de l'Epau Centre Culturel de la Sarthe, Hotel du Departement, 40 rue Joinville, F-72072 Le Mans Cedex 9, France *t:* +33 2 43 54 73 45 *f:* +33 2 43 54 71 02 *e:* culture@sarthe.com *w:* www.festivaldelepau.com Classical music, symphonic and chamber.
Festival de L'Opérette *w:* http://perso.wanadoo.fr/aix-operettes Operetta festival in Aix-les-Bains.
Festival de La Chaise-Dieu 10 rue Jules Vallès, BP 150, F-43004 Le Puy-en-Velay Cedex, France *t:* +33 4 71 09 48 28 *f:* +33 4 71 09 55 58 *e:* festival@chaise-dieu.com *w:* www.chaise-dieu.com Baroque, classical, romantic, contemporary, symphonic, sacred and spiritual music.
Festival de Musique du Haut-Jura 3 rue Reybert, F-39200 Saint-Claude, France *e:* contact@fmhj.com *w:* www.festivalmusiquehautjura.com Early music festival.
Le Festival de Radio France et Montpellier Languedoc-Roussillon Allée des Républicains Espagnols, F-34043 Montpellier Cedex 1, France *t:* +33 4 67 02 02 01 *f:* +33 4 67 61 6682 *e:* v.samuel@opus64.com *w:* www.festivalradiofrancemontpellier.com Orchestral concerts, chamber music, recitals, contemporary music, baroque music, opera.
Festival de Saintes Abbaye aux Dames, 11 place de l'Abbaye, BP 125, F-17104 Saintes Cedex, France *t:* +33 5 46 97 48 30 *f:* +33 5 46 97 48 40 *e:* info@abbayeauxdames.org; bernheim@abbayeauxdames.org *w:* www.abbayeauxdames.org
Festival International d'Art Lyrique d'Aix en Provence et Académie Européenne de Musique Palais de l'Ancien Archevêché, F-13100 Aix-en-Provence, France *t:* +33 4 42 17 34 00 *f:* +33 4 42 96 12 61 *e:* direction.artistique@festival-aix.com *w:* www.festival-aix.com Opera, chamber music concerts, recitals, public rehearsals, masterclasses.
Festival International d'Opéra Baroque de Beaune *e:* festival.beaune@orange.fr *w:* www.festivalbeaune.com
Festival International de Musique d'Uzerche c/o Erin Arts Centre, Victoria Square, Port Erin, Isle of Man *t:* +44 1624 835858 *f:* +44 1624 836658 *e:* information@erinartscentre.com *w:* www.erinartscentre.com Chamber, opera, choral and brass band music, held in the Abbatiale Saint Pierre.
Festival International de Musique de Chambre de Charente Le Pavillion, Le Rocher, F-16210 Yviers, France *t:* +33 5 45 98 67 83 *e:* chalaismusique@gmail.com International chamber music festival based in Chalais, SW France.

EUROPE

FRANCE

Festival International de Piano de La Roque d'Anthéron Parc du Chateau de Florans, F-13640 La Roque d'Antheron, France *t:* +33 4 42 50 51 15 *e:* isabel.roz@festival-piano.com *w:* www.festival-piano.com Features music of all styles, outdoor pno recitals and a mixture of young and established pno talent.

Festival Saint-Cére 18 ave du Docteur Roux, BP 59, F-46400 Saint-Cere, France *t:* +33 5 65 38 28 08 *f:* +33 5 65 38 35 94 *e:* public@opera-eclate.com *w:* www.festival-saint-cere.com

Heures Musicales de l'Abbaye de Lessay *t:* +33 2 33 45 14 34 *f:* +33 2 33 45 77 17 *e:* concertsheuresmusicales@canton-lessay.com *w:* www.francefestivals.com/lessay 14 concerts, with leading artists and music from the Renaissance to the 20th century.

Hummel & Friends Festival Le Faure, F-33890 Gensac, France *t:* +44 78 08 72 77 35 *f:* +49 30 2759 4174 *e:* ian@orpheusandbacchus.com *w:* www.orpheusandbacchus.com International festival with Howard Shelley.

International Celtic Harp Festival of Dinan La Galerie, F-22490 Plouer, France *t:* +33 2 96 86 84 94, also fax *e:* contact@maisondelaharpe.org *w:* www.harpe-celtique.com Concerts, workshops, harp exhibition.

Latour de France International Festival of Music and the Arts c/o Mananan Festival Office, Erin Arts Centre, Port Erin, Isle of Man, United Kingdom *t:* +44 1624 835858 *f:* +44 1624 836658 *e:* information@erinartscentre.com; latourfestival@orange.fr *w:* www.erinartscentre.com Festival near Perpignan/Estagel, S of France.

Les Azuriales Opera Festival Villa Serpolette, 46 blvd du Mont Boron, F-06300 Nice, France *t:* +33 4 9356 5141 *f:* +33 4 9326 5368 *e:* sarah.holford@thomasmiller.com *w:* www.azurialopera.com Intimate festival distinguished by the audience's proximity to the performance. Takes place in the Villa Ephrussi de Rothschild on Cap Ferrat, with post-performance dinner in the world-renowned gardens.

Musica International Festival of Contemporary Music 1 place Dauphine, F-67065 Strasbourg, France *t:* +33 3 88 23 46 46 *f:* +33 3 88 23 46 47 *e:* info@festival-musica.org *w:* www.festival-musica.org Annual. Contemporary music; concerts, operas, music theatre, dance, films, seminars.

Musique-Cordiale 39 Minster Rd, London *t:* +44 20 7794 0494 *e:* info@musique-cordiale.com *w:* www.musique-cordiale.com Annual festival of choral/opera and chamber music in the S of France, between Nice and Aix-en-Provence.

Orpheus and Bacchus Festival Le Faure, F-33890 Gensac, Frances *t:* +44 78 08 72 77 35 *f:* +49 30 2759 4174 *e:* ian@orpheusandbacchus.com *w:* www.orpheusandbacchus.com Residential chamber music festival linking to educational wine tours to top Bordeaux chateaux.

Piano aux Jacobins 9 rue Tripière, F-31000 Toulouse, France *t:* +33 5 61 22 40 05 *f:* +33 5 61 29 80 46 *e:* contact@pianojacobins.com *w:* www.pianojacobins.com Annual. Classical and contemporary music, piano festival.

Strasbourg Music Festival 9 avenue de la Liberté, F-67000 Strasbourg, France *t:* +33 3 88 15 29 29 *f:* +33 3 88 24 0316 *w:* www.festival-strasbourg.com Concerts, operas, recitals, jazz. Also international singing competition (president of the jury: Barbara Hendricks)

Synthèse - Festival International de Musiques et Creations Electroniques Institut International de Musique Electroacoustique de Bourges, F-18001 Bourges, France *t:* +33 2 48 20 41 87 *f:* +33 2 48 20 45 51 *e:* administration@ime-bourges.org *w:* www.imeb.net Annual. Electroacoustic music.

BOLOGNA

Northern Italian city founded around 2500 years ago but which gained importance during the 11th century in particular when its university – the first in the world – was established (the city still attracts numerous students today). Its architecture still has a strong medieval feel to it, but it also has a distinctive architectural feature not only in the terracotta colour of its rooftops but in its numerous covered walkways (the longest 'portico' comprises over 650 arches and stretches to 3500m). Along with other Italian cities, it has a lingering influence in the kitchen – 'Bolognaise' tomato sauce takes its name from the city.

CLIMATE

Hottest month July (18-30°C), coldest month January (-1-5°C). Wettest month November (80mm), driest months January and February (45mm) though with some snowfall.

MUSICAL LIFE

Teatro Comunale di Bologna is the main centre for classical music, housing the city's opera house and orchestra; the latter gives a varied concert season as well as accompanying the opera and ballet performances. Oratorio di San Rocco is a smaller venue with chamber music and recitals. Various music associations based in the city, such as Musicaper, organising concerts and events which promote musical activity.

OTHER CULTURAL INFORMATION

The city is home to a music museum and library. National picture galler has a variety of old paintings (up to the 18th century); also a modern art gallery. Numerous smaller museums and galleries, including some at the university. Various theatre venues such as Arena del Sole and Teatro delle Moline.

FESTIVALS AND EVENTS

Bologna Festival is more of a concert series (running March-October), but it does feature international soloists and conductors. Film festival in July.

TOURIST INFORMATION

www.comune.bologna.it

CONSERVATORIO DI MUSICA 'GB MARTINI'

piazza Rossini, 2, I-40126, Italy
t: +39 051 221483 *f:* +39 051 223168
e: segretaria@conservatorio-bologna.com
w: www.conservatorio-bologna.com
Course information 3-year 1st cycle and 2-year 2nd cycle courses in orchestral instruments, guitar, composition, conducting, harpsichord jazz, multimedia music, electronic music, piano, singing. ***Admissions information*** *Application requirements* Entrance exam. *Application deadline* 30 Apr.

CATANIA

Sicilian city on the coast at the foot of Mount Etna of nearly a third of a million people, part of which has been designated a Unesco world heritage site. Enormous number of churches and religious institutions, in baroque and earlier styles; numerous ruined buildings, a legacy of volcanic eruptions and seismic activity.

CLIMATE

Hottest month August (19-32°C), coolest month January (5-16°C). Rainiest during autumn and early winter (106mm in October).

MUSICAL LIFE

Birthplace of Bellini, hence his presence is relatively strong – the city's opera house is named after him, though repertoire by no means restricted to his music. The house also presents concerts by its resident orchestra and chorus as well as visiting artists. A second venue is the Teatro Sangiorgi, originally an opera house but now renovated and turned over to more general musical use.

OTHER CULTURAL INFORMATION

Numerous theatres presenting different styles of work. Sites relating to Greek and Roman history, including 2 amphitheatres, though series of eruptions of Mt Etna have buried much early sites. Hilltop Ursino Castle houses a museum. Street markets for food: fish market is well known.

FESTIVALS AND EVENTS

Festival celebrating patron saint Sant'Agata in February

TOURIST INFORMATION

www.apt.catania.it, apt@apt.catania.it, +39 095 7306211

ISTITUTO MUSICALE VINCENZO BELLINI CATANIA

Via Istituto Sacro Cuore, 3, I-95125 Catania, Italy
t: +39 095 7194400; +39 095 7194440 (Erasmus office) *f:* +39 095 502782
e: erasmus@istitutobellini.it
w: www.istitutobellini.it

EUROPE

COMO

City in the north of Italy on the shore of the lake of the same name, a location which makes it a popular visitor destination.

CLIMATE

Hottest month July (12-29°C), coldest month January (-4-3°C). Generally quite rainy, with up to 200mm in July and well over 100mm per month from March to November.

MUSICAL LIFE

Teatro Sociale has recitals, opera and dance as well as plays.

FESTIVALS AND EVENTS

Autumn music festival.

TOURIST INFORMATION

www.lakecomo.it, lakecomo@tin.it

CONSERVATORIO DI MUSICA G VERDI - COMO

Via Cadorna 4, I-22100 Como, Italy
t: +39 031 279827 *w:* www.conservatoriocomo.it
Course information Course outlines depend on which of 7 areas of study degree falls into: singing; 'maestro al cembalo'; choral music and choral direction; organ and organ composition; piano; strings, harp, guitar, wind and brass instruments; compostion, electronic music, jazz, percussion. Certain modules are obligatory and common to more than one study area. Biennio (2nd cycle) courses in: singing, guitar, harpsichord, composition, technology; choral music/direction; electronic music and sound technology; chamber music; piano; bowed instruments; wind and brass instruments; percussion. ***Admissions information*** *Application requirements* Applicants tested on ability on chosen instrument/ voice; good general musical knowledge, plus secondary school education. *Language requirements* Italian.

COSENZA

Small city located towards the south west tip of Italy in the Calabria region with old town rising from the Crati river.

MUSICAL LIFE

Teatro Rendano is only major performance venue in the town, but for theatre as well as opera. Otherwise most musical performance based at the consevatoire.

OTHER CULTURAL INFORMATION

Teatro Morelli for popular music and entertainment.

FESTIVALS AND EVENTS

Main arts event is Festival delle Invasioni (the name reflects the town's repeated occupation, by the Visigoths, the Spanish etc). Hosts an annual jazz festival, and a celebration of chocolate.

CONSERVATORIO DI MUSICA S GIACOMANTONIO

Via Portapiana, I-87100 Cosenza, Italy
t: +39 098476627 *f:* +39 098429224
e: longorf@gmail.com *w:* www.conservatoriodicosenza.it
Contact Raffaele Longo, international relations
Course information 1st and 2nd cycle studies at all levels. *Instrumental* Flute, recorder, oboe, clarinet, bassoon, saxophone, trumbet, trombone, french horn, tuba, violin, viola, cello, double bass, harp, piano, organ, guitar, percussion *Vocal* Vocal studies and chamber music. *Conducting* choral conducting and direction. *Historical performance* harpsichord, recorder. *Contemporary* Electronic music elective. *Jazz/world* Jazz course for all instruments
Admissions information *Application requirements* Admission exam *Application deadline* 30 Apr *Fees* EUR 450 (1st cycle); EUR 650 (2nd cycle) *Scholarships* International grants; regional scholarships. *No of students* 400 national, 10 international. *Language requirements* Italian, English
Facilities *Music facilities* Practice rooms. *Performance opportunities* Annual concert season, conservatory orchestra, early music ensemble, percussion ensemble, wind ensemble; opportunities to participate in Festivart - international festival organised by the University of Calabria *Accommodation* Flats on university campus or in the old town.

CUNEO

Small city in northern Italy's Alpine (Piedmont) region. Good rural links to mountains, vineyard areas, the Argentera national park and Valdieri hot springs.

CLIMATE

Summer temperatures reach average maximums of around 27°C in July; winters relatively mild, with temperatures generally remaining above freezing. Wettest in spring and autumn.

MUSICAL LIFE
Teatro Toselli holds a small series of concerts each year, alongside theatre and cinema.

OTHER CULTURAL INFORMATION
Gastronomy in the Piedmontese tradition, with various food and produce fairs in the region.

TOURIST INFORMATION
www.comune.cuneo.it, turismoacuneo@comune.cuneo.it, +39 0171 693258

CONSERVATORIO DI MUSICA 'GIORGIO GHEDINI'
via Roma 19, I-12100 Cuneo, Italy
t: +39 0171 693 148 *f:* +39 0171 699 181 *e:* cons.amministrativa@tiscali.it *w:* http://web.tiscali.it/conservatorioghedini
Course information Main courses for harp, singing, guitar, woodwind, strings, brass, music teaching, choral music and choral direction, electronic music, organ and organ composition, piano, percussion. Various complementary courses, including general music culture, musical aesthetics, poetic/dramatic literature, score-reading, chamber music, music history, theory/solfege.

FLORENCE (FIRENZE)
Main city in Tuscany famed for its architecture, legacy of its importance during the renaissance, and a Unesco world heritage site. Consequently, one of the most popular tourist destinations in Italy. Most distinctive landmark is the domed cathedral Santa Maria del Fiore, with its façade and bell tower; Ponte Vecchio over the city's river (the Arno) is noted for the shops on it, many of which are built out over the river. City's name also known in culinary circles, most notably as kind of steak (Bistecca alla Fiorentina). Significant in terms of music history, being the birthplace of opera in the form of early experiments in blending music and drama.

CLIMATE
Hottest months July and August (17-31°C), coolest month January (1-10°C). Rainfall relatively uniform throughout the year, dropping off in summer (40mm in July) and somewhat wetter in winter (111mm in November)

MUSICAL LIFE
Teatro del Maggio Musicale Fiorentino opera house and concert hall, home to opera company and orchestra named after it; together with a smaller 600-seat Piccolo Teatro it makes up the Teatro Comunale.
Orchestra della Toscana based in the city, but performs widely across region; Orchestra da Camera Fiorentina and Florence Symphonietta are 2 smaller orchestras. Amici della Musica arranges concerts featuring international performers in Teatro della Pergola; also other concert promoters and series, and various churches and other venues round the city put on one-off concerts.

OTHER CULTURAL INFORMATION
Uffizi gallery is one of world's important and most visited galleries thanks to its collection of renaissance masterpieces; other examples of art of the period can be found throughout city in churches and other galleries. Teatro Puccini, contrary to what its name suggests, is a venue for plays.

FESTIVALS AND EVENTS
Maggio Musicale festival, which gave its name to the main concert venue, one of the more prestigious European music festival events, running late April-June. Tango festival in early spring.

TOURIST INFORMATION
www.firenzeturismo.it,
+39 055 23320

CONSERVATORIO STATALE DI MUSICA 'L CHERUBINI'
Piazza Belle Arti, 2, I-50122 Firenze, Italy
w: www.conservatorio.firenze.it
Course information New 2-cycle system and traditional Licenze system run parallel. 1st cycle Triennio and 2nd cycle Biennio in singing, orchestral instruments, composition, harpsichord, recorder, music and new technology, chamber music, choral music/choral music direction, chamber music, jazz, organ, piano accompaniment, percussion, viola da gamba. 1st cycle students take options in several core areas: insturmental/vocal training; music theory, history and culture; music technology; ensembles; composition.

GENOA (GENOVA)
Port city in far north west of Italy, birthplace of Christopher Columbus and Nicolo Paganini. Old harbour area recently modernised and redeveloped by the Genoese architect Renzo Piano (designer of the Pompidou Centre) giving a new flavour to city; main centre is Piazza de Ferrari (location of opera house). Some major educational establishments

EUROPE

besides conservatoire, notably the university; also base for Istituto Italiano di Tecnologia research institute.

CLIMATE
Temperate throughout the year: hottest months July and August (20-24°C), coolest month January (5-8°C); relatively wet from August through to April (80-150mm), with July the driest month (27mm).

MUSICAL LIFE
Teatro Carlo Felice is the main opera house and concert hall, with full opera season plus many concerts; aso ballet. Teatro Gustavo Modena is another multi-purpose venue, presenting concerts and theatre.

OTHER CULTURAL INFORMATION
Numerous museums, galleries and exhibitions both in and around the city. Museo d'Arte Orientale Edoardo Chiossone is a major collection of Japanese arts and artefacts; a museum of world cultures reflects city's past as an international port, as does Galata maritime museum. Another important historical role was in Italy's path to reunification, documented in the Istituto Mazziniano. The city houses one of the largest aquariums in Eruope.

FESTIVALS AND EVENTS
Mediterranean Music Festival, every year in June and July, presents arange of world music not limited to the Mediterranean area. Also a popular Festival of Science during autumn.

TOURIST INFORMATION
www.turismo.comune.genova.it

CONSERVATORIO STATALE DI MUSICA 'NICCOLO PAGANINI' - GENOVA
via Albaro 38, I-16145 Genova, Italy
t: +34 010 3620747 *f:* +34 010 3620819
e: info@conservatoriopaganini.org; erasmus@conservatoriopaganini.org *w:* www.conservatoriopaganini.org
Contact Patrizia Conti, director; Maurizio Tarrini (international enquiries).
Course information 1st level 'undergraduate' (3 yrs), 2nd level 'postgraduate' (2 yrs): all musical instruments, singing, composition, jazz, electronic music, didactics.
Admissions information *Term dates* 1 Nov-mid Jun. *Application requirements* High level of ability on chosen instrument (or voice/composition), tested by admission recital; secondary school-leaving diploma. *Application deadline* 1-30 Apr (EU students); non-EU students, check: www.miur.it/0004Alta_F/0029Studen/0716Studen/index_cf4.htm *Fees* EUR 350-1200. *Scholarships* Scholarships available. *No of students* Approx 600, of whom 6% from overseas. *Language requirements* Basic knowledge of Italian (at least level A2 of Common European Framework for Languages).
Facilities *Accommodation* Information and advice on accommodation available on www.arssu.it.

L'AQUILA
Medieval central Italian town in the Apennine mountain area with a walled centre. Capital of remote Abruzzo region, a picturesque, largely mountainous area that stretches down to the east coast. City well placed for excursions into the area. Prone to earthquakes, most recently in 2009 – the conservatoire itself suffered, and launched a worldwide appeal for its rebuilding and restocking.

CLIMATE
Hottest month July (20-28°C), coldest month January (-2-7°C).

MUSICAL LIFE
Home to Istituzione Sinfonica Abruzzese, the region's state orchestra (about 4 concerts per month) and concert organisation, performing most of its concerts at the baroque Teatro San Filippo. Chamber ensemble I Solisti Aquilani takes its name from the town and performs widely around the world. Auditorium Nino Carloni another music venue. Soc Aquilana dei Concerti 'B Barattelli' promotes subscription concerts throughout the year; similar organisations in other towns in the Abruzzi region.

OTHER CULTURAL INFORMATION
As well as Teatro San Filippo, Teatro Comunale de L'Aquila has range of productions. Hilltop castle houses the museum of the region. As well as conservatoire, the town hosts a fine arts academy.

FESTIVALS AND EVENTS
Festival of Argentinian tango in July; also short film festival in October, attracts productions from over 30 countries each year.

TOURIST INFORMATION
www.comune.laquila.it

CONSERVATORIO DI MUSICA 'ALFREDO CASELLA' L'AQUILA
Via Francesco Savini, I-67100 L'Aquila, Italy

t: +39 086222122 *f:* +39 086262325
e: studenti@consaq.it; erasmus@consaq.it; l.prayer@consaq.it *w:* www.consaq.it
Contact Luisa Prayer, Erasmus co-ord.
Course information Principal study: orchestral instruments, harpsichord, composition, mandolin, choral conducting, jazz, organ, sax; complementary courses in various areas including general musical culture, literatur courses, theory and solfeggio, piano accompaniment, string quartet, music history and aesthetics. Triennio and biennio system currently being trialled.
Admissions information *Term dates* 1 Nov-31 Oct 2011. *Application requirements* Admission exam. *Application deadline* 31 Jul. *Fees* None. *No of students* 750. *Language requirements* Italian or English.

LIVORNO

West Italian coastal city, some of whose characteristic renaissance architecture (canals, bridges, narrow streets, squares and numerous churches and religious buildings) survived World War II damage. In previous centuries contained a noted Jewish settlement (a community into which the painter Modigliani was born).

CLIMATE

Mild climate all year due to maritime influence. Hottest month July (16-29°C), coolest month January (2-11°C); rainfall highest in autumn (around 120mm in October and November), relatively uniform winter-spring, and low in summer.

MUSICAL LIFE

Museo Mascagnano celebrates life and work of Mascagni who was born there; the composer is also the subject of the 'Progetto Mascagni' run via the Fondazione Teatro Goldoni. Restored in 2004, this serves as the main opera house of the city, with a short annual season, as well as concert hall, theatre and entertainment venue. Several choirs rehearse and perform in the city.

OTHER CULTURAL INFORMATION

Yeshiva Marini museum focuses on Jewish influence in city's past. Summer programme of performing arts events.

FESTIVALS AND EVENTS

Programme of arts events during summer, particularly at Fortezza Vecchia; there are also the Effetto Venezia festivities with numerous street events.

TOURIST INFORMATION

www.comune.livorno.it, turismo@comune.livorno.it, +39 0586 820454

ISTITUTO SUPERIORE DI STUDI MUSICALI 'PIETRO MASCAGNI'

Palazzo della Gherardesca, Via G Galilei 40, I-57122 Livorno, Italy
t: +39 0586 403724 *f:* +39 0586 426089
e: segreteria@istitutomascagni.it *w:* www.istitutomascagni.it
Contact Gabriele Micheli, Erasmus & international co-ord.
Course information Bachelor and doctorate in performance (also lower levels) in voice, guitar, cello, clarinet, composition, double bass, french horn, bassoon, flute, oboe, percussion, piano, sax, trumpet, viola, violin,
Admissions information *Term dates* 15 Oct-30 Sep. *Application requirements* High school degree and audition. *Application deadline* 1 Apr-30 Sep. *Fees* EUR 76, EUR 1200, EUR 1800, depending on levels. *Scholarships* Number of scholarships available for each study level. *No of students* 500 students. *Language requirements* Italian or English.
Facilities *Music facilities* Study rooms, recording studio, concert hall, library.

MILAN (MILANO)

Italy's second city, in the north of the country, famous for its fashion industry, as a global financial centre and for its 2 rival football clubs (who share the famous San Siro stadium). Also attracts students from around the world to higher education institutions covering a wide range of specialisms as well as the 2 more general universities. Well connected by road and rail (the city holds 5 railway stations) to other parts of Italy, and Europe to the north and west. Most famous architectural site the Duomo, the city's spectacular Gothic cathedral, dating back to the 14th century.

CLIMATE

Hottest months July and August (15-28°C), coldest month January (-4-6°C). Wettest months April and May (120mm), relatively uniform throughout the remainder of the year (60-80mm).

MUSICAL LIFE

Most celebrated for La Scala, its world-renowned opera house, where the most important conductors and singers brave a vocal audience of opera-lovers. Unlike many opera houses, its orchestra has a strong reputation in its own right, touring internationally as well as giving a year-long concert series at its home. City's other main orchestra is named laVerdi and gives concerts in the Auditorium de Milano; I Pomeriggi Musicali is a chamber orchestra performing at the Teatro dal Verme. Teatro degli Arcimboldi for musical theatre.

OTHER CULTURAL INFORMATION

Vast range of museums, including one at La Scala and a museum of musical instruments. 2 big modern art galleries, Padiglione Arte Contemporanea and Civico Museo Arte Contemporanea; other institutions (including art in churches) cover earlier eras. Despite its name, Piccolo Teatro di Milano is a major company producing work over a range of genres.

FESTIVALS AND EVENTS

MITO Settembre Musica festival in collaboration with the city of Turin and other smaller towns in the region. Also annual film and jazz festivals.

TOURIST INFORMATION

www.turismo.milano.it

CONSERVATORIO DI MUSICA 'G VERDI' DI MILANO

Via Conservatorio 12, I-20122 Milano, Italy
t: +39 027 62110216; +39 027 62110221 (international relations) *f:* +39 027 6020259
e: p.rimoldi@consmilano.it; erasmus@consmilano.it *w:* www.consmilano.it

Contact Paolo Rimoldi, head of international relations; Roberto de Thierry, assistant Erasmus/ international relations.

Course information Majors in harp, singing, guitar and lute, clarinet, harpsichord, composition, double bass, horn, teaching methods, conducting (choral, orchestral or band), bassoon, accordion, flute, recorder and transverse flute, vocal chamber music, musicology, oboe, organ, percussion, piano, saxophone, sound technology, trumpet, trombone, tuba, viola, viola da gamba, violin, cello. Complementary subjects: harmony, scenic art, 'letterature poetica e dramatica' (music lyrics), score-reading, chamber music, string quartet, theory and analysis, history of music, aesthetics.

Admissions information *Term dates* Nov-mid June (official academic year); tuition Oct-end Jun. *Application requirements* High school diploma, audition. *Application deadline* 1 Apr-31 Jul (regular students); Erasmus students, see website. *Fees* Bachelors: EUR 400-1000, plus registration and government tax; masters: EUR 600-1500, plus registration and government tax; registration tax in 1st year only. *Scholarships* For regular students only (ie not Erasmus): scholarships for opera singers, chamber music, composition, wind ensembles, piano and chamber music, chamber and vocal music, wind instruments, string instruments, piano, string quartet. *No of students* Approx 1500, of whom approx 300 from overseas. *Language requirements* Italian level B1 (test prior to admission).

NAPLES (NAPOLI)

Ancient city (it is close to Pompeii and Herculaneum, destroyed by the still active Mount Vesuvius) in the bay bearing its name on the Mediterranean coast, but characterised today by architecture from the medieval to baroque periods. Home to one of world's oldest universities, the Frederick II university, and one of Italy's most important (around 100,000 students). One of most famous products connected with the city is the original tomato pizza (the recipe for Neapolitan pizza is now protected by law).

CLIMATE

Warmest months July and August (18-24°C), coolest month January (3-8°C). Wettest month November (162mm), driest month July (24mm).

MUSICAL LIFE

By tradition, the city strongly associated with music, and not only opera. In singing, Neapolitan song is a characteristic form of popular music and singing itself has strong place in popular culture generally (Caruso was from the city). Strong association also with development of the guitar. Teatro San Carlo is main opera house, but also runs a concert programme with performances by house and visiting orchestras. Smaller scale concerts at Teatro delle Palme, plus occasional venues around city. Centro di Musica Antica dedicated to research into and presentation of Neapolitan baroque music.

OTHER CULTURAL INFORMATION

Teatro Bellini is mixture of more popular musicals and drama productions. Roman artefacts at the Museo Archeologico Nazionale di Napoli; 500 years' worth of Italian art at the distinctive Museo di Capodimonte.

FESTIVALS AND EVENTS

Theatre festival in June; film festival also.

TOURIST INFORMATION
www.inaples.it, +39 081 2457475

CONSERVATORIO DI MUSICA 'SAN PIETRO A MAJELLA' - NAPOLI
Via San Pietro a Majella, 35, I-80138 Napoli, Italy
t: +39 081 5644411 *f:* +39 081 5644415
e: conservatorio_di_napoli@sanpietromajella.it
w: www.sanpietromajella.it
Course information Principal and secondary/ complementary study courses (eg literature, ensemble playing, harmony, music history and aesthetics etc).
Admissions information *Application requirements* Admission exam. *Application deadline* 1-30 Apr.

PADUA (PADOVA)
Northern Italian city, not far from Venice, home to numerous medieval and renaissance palaces and churches, including the Cappella degla Scrovegni with its early 14th century Giotto frescoes. City characterised by mix of open spaces such as Prato della Valle near the Santa Giustina basilica and denser streets; historically surrounded by walls, still in evidence in certain areas. Home to one of the oldest universities and which founded the world's oldest botanical gardens, still extant today.

CLIMATE
Hottest month July (18-28°C), coldest month January (-1-6°C). Rainfall levels more or less uniform from month to month (roughly 55-90mm).

MUSICAL LIFE
Home to Orchestra di Padova e del Veneto, a well-regarded orchestra collaborating with international performers in concerts at the Teatro Verdi or at the conservatoire, as well as further afield in the region. Amici della Musica a concert promoting organisation inviting performers from locally and internationally.

OTHER CULTURAL INFORMATION
Several museums displaying archaeological material relating to the area art and artefacts; there is also a museum devoted to pre-cinematic optical shows.

FESTIVALS AND EVENTS
Annual Festival Internazionale 'G Tartini' in spring and early summer spreads beyond Padua to the region as a whole.

TOURIST INFORMATION
www.turismopadova.it, info@turismopadova.it, +39 049 8767927

CONSERVATORIO STATALE DI MUSICA 'CESARE POLLINI' - PADOVA
Via Eremitani 18, I-35121 Padova PD, Italy
e: resp.socrates-erasmus@conservatoriopollini.it
w: www.conservatoriopollini.it
Course information Most courses use traditional system of inferiore/medio/superiore studies; some experimental courses available in new form: music and disability, ethnomusicology, composition, recording studio technique. 2nd cycle courses available for bowed or string instruments, wind and brass, piano, vocal ensemble, organ/choirmaster.
Facilities *Music facilities* Conservatoire has its own concert halls.

PALERMO
Principal city on Sicily whose architecture and overall appearance attests to a history in which different cultural influences have taken hold. Numerous churches, cathedrals and palaces of various styles.

CLIMATE
Hottest month August (23-26°C), coolest month January (8-11°C). Wettest month October (100mm), driest month July when rainfall is negligible.

MUSICAL LIFE
Teatro Massimo lives up to its name, being built in a monumental neoclassical style and seating well over 3000 for opera and ballet performances and a small selection of concerts by resident orchestra. Late 19th century Teatro Politeama Garibaldi is home for Orchestra Sinfonica Siciliana.

OTHER CULTURAL INFORMATION
Various museums and galleries including, archeological and anthropological displays, observatory, botanic gardens, puppet museum, wine museum. Teatro Biondo is the city's main theatre, with several performance areas and with a varied repertoire of plays staged.

FESTIVALS AND EVENTS
Summer Palermo di Scena festival features music and theatrical performances; summer is also when the streets see numerous outdoor musical and theatrical shows, plus other entertainments. The annual Festival di Morgana celebrates a local art/

craft, the 'pupi', marionettes used in various shows based on medieval chivalric tales.

TOURIST INFORMATION
www.palermotourism.com, info@palermotourism.com

CONSERVATORIO DE MUSICA VINCENZO BELLINI
Via Squarcialupo 45, I-90133 Palermo, Italy
t: +39 091 580921 *e:* info@conservatoriobellini.it; erasmus@conservatoriobellini.it *w:* www.conservatoriobellini.it
Facilities *Music facilities* 2 concert halls: Sala Scarlatti and Sala Sollima. Various ensembles including symphony and chamber orchestras, new music ensemble. opera chorus. Conservatoire has collection of historic instruments.

EUROPE

PARMA
Northern Italian city, famous as the location of an 11th century university (one of the world's first) and as centre for a particular cured ham, but also with a strong cultural tradition. Several parks and gardens, including a botanic garden, add to the city's relaxed atmosphere.

CLIMATE
Hottest month July (19-30°C), coldest month January (2-4°C). Wettest months in autumn and spring (91mm in October, 73mm in April).

MUSICAL LIFE
Teatro Regio is a well known opera house, although produces only a few (3 or 4) operas per year; various orchestral concerts put on also. Auditorium Paganini in the Barilla Center for more concerts. Other concert events around the city, such as Sunday morning concerts at the Palazzo Marchi; Controtempi is a series of contemporary music events.

OTHER CULTURAL INFORMATION
Palazzo della Pilotta is a 16th century palace now used as a cultural centre housing museums, an art gallery, library and theatre (Teatro Farnese). Museums with musical theme include the Casa della Musica (exhibitions plus courses in music appreciation etc), a Toscanini museum and the Casa del Suono (historic recording equipment); the Mondo Piccolo museum, however, is not dedicated to flutes but the work of humourist Giovannni Guareschi.

FESTIVALS AND EVENTS
Festival Verdi at the Teatro Regio every October featuring productions of Verdi operas plus concerts. Teatro Festival Parma is a theatre festival with elements from other art forms.

TOURIST INFORMATION
http://turismo.comune.parma.it, turismo@comune.parma.it, +39 0521218707

CONSERVATORIO DI MUSICA ARRIGO BOITO DI PARMA
Via del Conservatorio 27/A, I-43100 Parma, Italy
t: +39 0521 381911 *f:* +39 0521 200398
e: direttore.amministrativo@conservatorio.pr.it
w: www.conservatorio.pr.it
Course information 1st and 2nd cycle studies; also diplomi di specializzazione and traditional style courses. Courses have both optional and obligatory elements.

PERUGIA
Central Italian city, whose built environment fully reflects its medieval history and the various changes in architectural style along the way. Enormous number of churches, palaces, fountains, squares, gates and other constructions associated with the 'typical' Italian town. University dates back to 13th century; city is still popular with students now, with a fine arts academy and a university specifically for overseas students to learn Italian language and culture as well as conservatoire.

CLIMATE
Hottest month July (15-30°C), coldest month January (0-9°C). Wettest month November (94mm), driest month July (45mm); rainfall fairly uniform the rest of the year at around 60-70mm.

MUSICAL LIFE
Fondazione Perugia Musica Classica promotes a concert series and other projects throughout the year. Teatro Morlacchi is main venue for concerts, but others held in various churches such as the San Pietro basilica. Unusually for an Italian city, there is no opera house.

OTHER CULTURAL INFORMATION
Teatro Stabile dell'Umbria theatre company performs at Teatro Morlacchi as well as in other towns in the region. Range of museums and galleries.

FESTIVALS AND EVENTS

For classical music, the Sagra Musicale Umbria takes place in September each year, spreading across the Umbria region. Also exhibition of musical instruments during same month. Umbria Jazz festival, in July, is one of world's biggest. In October, one of Perugia's main products celebrated during an international chocolate festival.

TOURIST INFORMATION

http://turismo.comune.perugia.it, info@comune.perugia.it, +39 075 5772805-2834

CONSERVATORIO DI MUSICA DI PERUGIA

Piazza Mariotti 2, I-06100 Perugia, Italy
t: +39 075 57 33 844 *f:* +39 075 57 36 943
e: direttore@conservatorioperugia.it *w:* www.conservatorioperugia.it
Contact Nancy Greene, international co-ord.
Admissions information *Term dates* Nov-Jun. *Application deadline* Jul.

PESARO

Town towards the north of Italy's Adriatic coast characterised by baroque and romanesque architecture. Birthplace of the composer Rossini.

CLIMATE

Hottest month July (17-28°C), coldest month January (-1-7°C). Rainfall highest in autumn (75mm in October and November), driest in early part of the year (under 50mm in January and February).

MUSICAL LIFE

Concerts (as well as theatre) at the Teatro Rossini

FESTIVALS AND EVENTS

Opera festival commemorating Rossini (August) with performances in various venues. Also film festival in summer.

TOURIST INFORMATION

www.comune.pesaro.pu.it

CONSERVATORIO STATALE DI MUSICA 'G ROSSINI' - PESARO

Piazza Olivieri 5, I-61100 Pesaro, Italy
t: +39 072133671 *f:* +39 072135295
e: segretaria@conservatoriorossini.it
w: www.conservatoriorossini.it
Course information Operates traditional system and experimental triennio/biennio system in parallel.
Admissions information *Application deadline* 14 Apr-24 May.
Facilities *Music facilities* Auditorium Pedrotti is conservatoire's own concert hall. Various performance opportunities, including ensembles (symphony orchestra, wind orchestra, jazz group, Gregorian choir, flute ensemble)

ROME

Italy's capital and a major European destination for tourists and other visitors. Vast number of major buildings and architectural features still survive from ancient Rome (the Colosseum, Circus Maximus, Pantheon etc), but also from medieval, renaissance and baroque eras. 'Home' to the pope's residence – and hence place of pilgrimage – the Vatican City, which is in fact a sovereign state in its own right. As well as the buildings and monuments (and fountains, as immortalised musically by composer Ottorino Respighi), which are so integral a part of its built environment, Rome has a large number of parks and gardens, such as the English-style landscape gardens at the Villa Borghese. This building is itself just one of very many villas – residences built as private houses for the nobility – dotted around the city.

CLIMATE

Hottest months July and August (18-29°C), coolest month January (3-13°C). Wettest during winter (110mm in November), drier during summer (less than 20mm in July/August).

MUSICAL LIFE

Parco della Musica is a Renzo Piano-designed complex dedicated to music, containing 3 concert halls and an open-air auditorium as well as the city's conservatoire. Substantial classical programme there, but not limited to classical, and other art forms are incorporated (drama, film, exhibitions etc). Main opera based at the Teatro dell'Opera di Roma; the Opera di Roma has its own orchestra, also plays for ballet. Large number of open-air concerts during summer months; the city's many churches hold concerts and opera performances.

OTHER CULTURAL INFORMATION

Home of Italian cinema, Cinecittà, is in Rome, the city being an iconic film landscape due to the number of well-known sights like the Trevi Fountain and Piazza San Pietro. Several museums devoted to Rome's history, and its importance in art history reflected in its galleries; there is also a national gallery of modern art with a large collection of

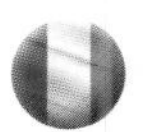

20th century Italian and international artists to go with its temporary exhibitions. There is English-language theatre at the English Theatre of Rome.

FESTIVALS AND EVENTS

Large number of festival events throughout the year, such as Romaeuropa. Summer opera and music events at the Caracalla thermal baths.

TOURIST INFORMATION

www.romaturismo.it, turismo@comune.roma.it

CONSERVATORIO DI MUSICA SANTA CECILIA

Via dei Greci, 18, I-00187 Roma, Italy
t: +39 06 36096721 *f:* +39 06 36001800
e: segretaria@conservatoriosantacecilia.it
w: www.conservatoriosantacecilia.it

Course information Courses in piano accompaniment, harp, opera singing, guitar, harpsichord, composition, double bass, clarinet, french horn, orchestral conducting, flute, bassoon, jazz accordion, lute, harpsichord direction, choral music and choral conducting, chamber music, electronic music, vocal chamber music, musicology, music education, organ and organ composition, oboe, piano, band orchestration, percussion, saxophone, trumpet, trombone, tuba, violin, viola, cello, viola da gamba.

Admissions information *Term dates* 1 Nov-31 Oct. *Application requirements* Admission exam; preliminary Italian exam for overseas students. High school diploma for 3-year degree course; for the 2nd level degree, high school diploma plus conservatory diploma/university degree. *Application deadline* Applications for admission 1-30 Apr; for university courses, 1 Jul-9 Aug. *Fees* EUR 175-950, depending on course, plus EUR 150 government tax; EUR 95 for entrance exam. *Scholarships* Details of scholarships, awarded based on musical merit, available on request. *No of students* Over 1500 students in total.

SALERNO

Southern Italian town on the Amalfi coast on the west of the country (it has a long seafront promenade that makes the most of its seaside location). Town with its historic centre based at the foot of hills which overlook it and there are spectacular views of it from them and surrounding areas – eg from the hilltop Castello d'Arechi. Numerous old churches, many decorated with typical artwork and ornamentation; Cattedrale di Salerno has a spectacular interior.

CLIMATE

Hottest months July and August (19-30°C), coolest month January (6-13°C). Winters are fairly wet, with over 100mm a month from October-February (over 150mm November-January).

MUSICAL LIFE

The Teatro Municipale Giuseppe Verdi hosts a relatively substantial season, also incorporating concerts by its orchestra the Orchestra Filarmonica Salernitana 'Giuseppe Verdi' (which tours and gives concerts elsewhere) and visiting artists.

FESTIVALS AND EVENTS

Festival di Musica Antica runs from November-December. Also an international film festival in November.

TOURIST INFORMATION

www.turismosalerno.it, info@turismosalerno.it

CONSERVATORIO DI MUSICA 'GIUSEPPE MARTUCCI' SALERNO

Via Salvatore De Renzi 62, I-84100 Salerno, Italy
t: +39 089241086; +39 089231977; +39 089237713 *f:* +39 0892582440 *e:* international@consalerno.com; protocollo@consalerno.com *w:* www.consalerno.com
Contact Fulvio Maffia, dir; Francesco Paolone, international relations co-ord.

Course information 3 year undergrad degrees with many courses in all orch instruments, plus conducting (inc choral), composition, early music, electronic music, guitar, band instrumentation, jazz and improvisation, multimedia music, musicology (inc pedagogy and management), piano, saxophone, sound technician. 2 year masters in interpretation/composition, technology, teaching.

Admissions information *Term dates* 15 Sep-15 Jun. *Application requirements* Entrance examination *Application deadline* 1-30 Apr; no fixed deadline for Erasmus international students. *Fees* Bachelor's and master's entrance exam: EUR 100; enrolment EUR 83.43; annual contribution of EUR 300-500 (bachelor's) or EUR 500-700 (master's) depending on income. *Scholarships* Ravello Prize annual grant for best student of the year. *No of students* 1500. *Language requirements* Italian or English. Special arrangement with Salerno University for Italian language, culture and other courses for international students.

Facilities *Music facilities* Town facilities used by students, inc Casino Sociale and Teatro delle Arte;

recording studio for sound technicians. Some students engaged by Teatro Municipale Giuseppe Verdi opera house in chorus and orch and as accompanists/repetiteurs. *Performance opportunities* International m/classes; possibility of performance at the Ravello Festival (www.ravellofestival.com) or the Giffoni Film Festival www.giffoniff.it *Accommodation* Special arrangements with Ave Gratia Plena hostel in Salerno; AEGEE Salerno helps students find accommodation.

TURIN (TORINO)

Busy city in the Piedmont region of northern Italy with a population of over 2 million and a strong industrial heritage that continues today (motor vehicles and aerospace industries in particular). As Italy's third city, it has added a contemporary feel alongside the baroque and other historical architecture – as well as dramatic buildings such at the Palazzo Reale with its wide open square, the Museo del Risorgimento or the city's cathedral, there are numerous open-air art installations, for instance.

CLIMATE

Hottest month July (17-27°C), coldest January (-2-6°C). Spring is wettest time, with 110mm in May; winter relatively dry (around 40mm).

MUSICAL LIFE

Comparatively well-served orchestrally: Orchestra Filarmonica di Torino is city orchestra, giving concerts in conservatoire concert hall; Orchestra Sinfonica Nazionale della RAI is national radio orchestra has its own concert hall, the Auditorium RAI. 2-theatre Teatro Regio Torino is home to eponymous opera company; performs full season on stage, plus a smaller 6-month evening concert season and other ancillary concert events. Other concerts in the city include those organised by Lingotto Musica and Unione Musicale, both concert promoting organisations. Teatro Alfa for operetta.

OTHER CULTURAL INFORMATION

Numerous theatres and museums. The latter include weapons museum, museum of typography, national gallery of cinema and new gallery of Asian art as well as more usual art galleries and local history museums. Major theatres include Teatro Stabile Torino (new work and adaptations); more specialist venues too, such as Teatro Gianduja (puppets). Contemporary arts well represented: there is a modern and contemporary art gallery; the Castello Rivoli is another institution dedicated to modern art with both collection and temporary exhibitions.

FESTIVALS AND EVENTS

Various festivals and events covering a range of art forms. In music, Festival Internazionale di Musica Antica e Contemporanea run by Ensemble Antidogme in June is series of varied concert programmes; city hosts a major music festival in September in association with city of Milan. Dance also well represented in festivals, such as Torinodanza. International book fair and film festival.

TOURIST INFORMATION

www.turismotorino.org, info.torino@turismotorino.org, +39 011 535181.

CONSERVATORIO STATALE DI MUSICA 'GIUSEPPE VERDI'

Via Mazzini 11, I-10123 Torino, Italy
t: +39 011888470; +39 0118178458 *f:* +39 011885165 *e:* segreteria.direzione@conservatoriotorino.eu; paolotarallo@tin.it; m.mclara@tin.it *w:* www.conservatoriotorino.eu
Contact Paolo Tarallo, Erasmus; Mariaclara Monetti, international co-ord.

Course information New degrees based on the European model: 3-yr "diploma accademico di primo livello" equivalent to a bachelor's degree; 2-yr "diploma accademico di secondo nivello" equivalent to a master's degree. *Instrumental* Piano, percussion, organ and organ improvisation, orchestral instruments, saxophone. *Vocal* Concert and opera singing *Conducting* Choral and orchestral *Historical performance* Study of pre-polyphony. Instrumental study offered: transverse flute, baroque oboe, harpsichord and historical keyboards, baroque violin, viola da gamba. *Composition* Classical and electronic *Opera* Stage direction for opera and theatre technique *Jazz/world* Jazz course offered *Other* Band orchestration.

Admissions information *Term dates* Nov -Jun. *Application requirements* Applicants assessed on musical ability, musical knowledge (theory and history), and knowledge of Italian language; selection exam during summer. *Application deadline* 10 Jun. *Fees* EUR 600-800 depending on level. *No of students* Approx 900. *Language requirements* Italian, French or English.

Facilities *Music facilities* 690-seat concert hall; recital hall; library with 100,000 titles; historical instrument collection (can sometimes used by students). *Accommodation* Accommodation in university college or private flats.

EUROPE

ITALY

TRENTO

City in the mountain region of the far north of Italy. Its particular history – for part of the 19th century the town was under Austrian ownership as part of the Hapsburg Empire – is reflected in the built environment which demonstrates both Italian and Austrian influences.

 CLIMATE

Hottest month July (14-29°C), coldest month January (-6-6°C). Snow is common in winter, with rainfall highest in July and August (around 91mm).

MUSICAL LIFE

Societa Filarmonica Trento organises events at the Sala dei Concerti. Centro Servizi Culturali Santa Chiara is a more general performing arts centre, including concerts in its programme. No major symphony orchestra, but, along with Bolzano, the town is home to the Orchestra Haydn chamber orchestra.

OTHER CULTURAL INFORMATION

Teatro San Marco and other venues at the Santa Chiara cultural centre stage theatre, dance and other performances.

FESTIVALS AND EVENTS

Annual jazz festival. Mountainfilm Festival a distinctive festival showing films about mountains, exploration and related subjects, plus other events. Autumn harvest festival shows off produce from the region.

 TOURIST INFORMATION

www.apt.trento.it, informazioni@apt.trento.it, +39 0461 216000

CONSERVATORIO DI MUSICA 'FA BONPORTI' TRENTO

Gallerie dei Legionari 5, I-38100 Trento, Italy
t: +39 0461 261673 *f:* +39 0461 263888
e: direttore@conservatorio.tn.it *w:* www.conservatorio.tn.it
Contact Antonella Costa

Course information 23 3-year courses (level 1), 28 2-year courses (level 2); also masters course and course for specialists.

Admissions information *Term dates* Early Nov-end Oct. *Application requirements* Entrance exam and appropriate prior qualifications. *Application deadline* 1 Jul-30 Aug. *Fees* EUR 400 (level 1), EUR 650 (level 2), EUR 1300 (masters), EUR 1500 (specialism) *Scholarships* Contact university. *No of students* 750 students in total. *Language requirements* Italian or English.

Facilities *Music facilities* Practice rooms can be booked in early morning or late afternoon (3 days a week until 10pm). *Accommodation* Accommodation available through Opera Universitaria (www.operauni.tn.it) which manages a network of accommodation, canteens, leisure services, sport and cultural activities. Accommodation prices from EUR 160 per month (depending on type).

TRIESTE

North eastern Italian port on the east side of the Adriatic whose location has given it a unique flavour. It was part of the Austrian empire until the 1920s; there is a strong influence from Slovenia, whose border surrounds the city on 2 sides, and whose language is spoken in some quarters; Churchill pinpointed the city as the southernmost end of the iron curtain – prior to that it attracted cultural tourists from all over Europe. City maintains a 'Mitteleuropa' feel in line with the likes of Austrian, Czech and Hungarian capitals. Traditionally, it is also a strong region for wine-making.

 CLIMATE

Hottest month July (20-28°C), coolest month January (3-7°C). Rainfall relatively high throughout the year, ranging from 70mm to 110mm.

MUSICAL LIFE

Teatro Lirico Giuseppe Verdi, with its opera company, orchestra, chorus and ballet company, is the main music venue; the Sala Tripcovich, part of the same theatre foundation but located elsewhere, provides another venue for the city.

OTHER CULTURAL INFORMATION

Teatre Stabile del Friuli-Venezia Giulia – Il Rossetti, with its distinctive ceiling decorated with twinkling stars, stages both drama and musical theatre. Reflecting its geography, there is a Slovenian-language theatre, with performances surtitled in Italian.

FESTIVALS AND EVENTS

2 music festivals in particular, at opposite ends of scale: operetta festival at the Teatro Verdi during the summer; in November, Trieste Prima is a contemporary music gathering.

 TOURIST INFORMATION

www.turismofvg.it, info@turismo.fvg.it, +39 432 815111

CONSERVATORIO DI MUSICA GIUSEPPE TARTINI TRIESTE
Via Ghega 12, I-34134 Trieste, Italy
t: +39 040 6724911 *f:* +39 040 370265
e: triennio@conservatorio.trieste.it; erasmus@conservatorio.trieste.it
w: www.conservatorio.trieste.it
Course information Courses in all classical instruments, electronic music, jazz.
Admissions information *Term dates* Nov -Jun. *Application requirements* Italian high school diploma (contact Italian embassy for equivalents). *Application deadline* 15 Jul & 15 Oct. *Fees* Approx EUR 500 pa. ***Scholarships*** ERDISU, Fondazione Ananian and private. *No of students* Approx 600 students.
Facilities *Performance opportunities* At I Mercoledi del Conservatorio and other possibilities. *Accommodation* Available through the Welcomeofficetrieste and the ERDISU.

UDINE

Small city in north east Italy. There are many characteristic buildings dating as far back as the 16th century, and the city is overlooked by a palace-like hilltop castle.

CLIMATE

Hottest months July and August (17-28°C), coldest month January (-1-7°C). Rainfall heaviest in spring and autumn, although even in summer totals are relatively high (eg 90mm in August).

MUSICAL LIFE

City has a modern theatre and concert hall presenting concerts from visiting artists as well as local Orchestra Sinfonica del Friuli Venezia Giulia based in the city (but performs across the region), opera (some from nearby Trieste company), musicals, dance and other kinds of entertainment.

OTHER CULTURAL INFORMATION

Art gallery housed in the castle.

FESTIVALS AND EVENTS

Mittelfest is an arts festival in July that which includes music. Far East Film Festival is a major event of its kind.

TOURIST INFORMATION

www.udine-turismo.it, info@udine-turismo.it, +39 0432 295972

CONSERVATORIO STATALE DI MUSICA JACOPO TOMADINI - UDINE
Piazza 1° Maggio 29, I-33100 Udine, Italy
t: +39 0432 502755 *f:* +39 0432 510740
e: erasmus@conservatorio.udine.it; coranglais58@hotmail.com
w: www.conservatorio.udine.it
Contact Sandro Caldini.
Course information Bachelor and masters courses for strings, woodwind, brass, piano, organ, harpsichord, percussion, harp, guitar, singing, chamber music for singers, composition, wind band composition, choral music. Special courses in baroque oboe and cor anglais.
Admissions information *Term dates* 1 Nov-31 Oct. *Application requirements* Admission exam. *Application deadline* 30 Apr. *Fees* EUR 400 (bachelor); EUR 600 (masters); EUR 400 (special courses). *Scholarships* Scholarships available. *No of students* 600 national students and 15 from overseas. *Language requirements* Italian, English or German.
Facilities *Music facilities* Vivaldi Hall, Monteverdi Hall, concert hall. *Accommodation* Contact Prof Sandro Caldini for details of accommodation available.

VERONA

Historical northern Italian city and Unesco world heritage site with a number of buildings and monuments surviving from ancient Roman times such as its amphitheatre, still in use today (though not for gladiatorial competitions). City's historic architectural character added to by large number of medieval Romanesque buildings such as the Basilica di San Zeno. Its attractiveness to visitors increased by proximity of Lake Garda.

CLIMATE

Hottest month July (17-24°C), coldest month January (-2-5°C). Rainfall varies between 50mm or so in winter to 80mm+ late spring and early summer.

MUSICAL LIFE

Teatro Filarmonico holds a series of concerts from Oct to May, similarly opera and ballet. Concert society Amici della Musica di Verona runs substantial concert season of mostly chamber music and recitals in churches; Accademia Filarmonica di Verona another musical organisation, promoting concerts at its premises like the Sala Maffeiana.

OTHER CULTURAL INFORMATION

Teatro Nuovo is the main theatre, focusing on classics

EUROPE

but with other spaces hosting comedy and other entertainment. Variety of museums and exhibitions.

FESTIVALS AND EVENTS

Major opera festival at the arena throughout the summer attracts many spectators from around the world. Also choral festival/competition. The Settembre dell'Accademia is a short season of concerts by prestigious visiting orchestras, arranged by the Accademia.

TOURIST INFORMATION

www.tourism.verona.it, iatverona@provincia.vr.it, +39 045 8068680

CONSERVATORIO STATALE DI MUSICA EVARISTO FELICE DALL'ABACO

Via Abramo Massalongo 2, I-37121 Verona, Italy
t: +34 045 8002814 045 *f:* +34 045 8009018
e: abaco@conservatorioverona.it; internazionale@conservatorioverona.it *w:* www.conservatorioverona.it
Contact Hugh Ward-Perkins, international relations & Erasmus co-ordinator.
Course information Traditional and experimental triennio/biennio systems run in parallel. Triennio available in orchestral instruments, composition, singing, viola da gamba, harpsichord, lute. Taught via 4 core modules: principal and complementary study; common subjects (harmony, analysis etc); other ancillary subjects (eg psychology of music); other options (eg languages). After biennio, also various specialist courses: music therapy; chamber music with piano; early music.
Admissions information *Application requirements* Admission exams in Jun; CD/DVD recordings accepted in some circumstances. *Application deadline* 30 April. Non-EU students must apply through Italian embassy in home country. *Fees* Approx EUR 540 (1st cycle); approx EUR 800 (2nd cycle and specialist courses). *No of students* Approx 150 higher education students
Facilities *Music facilities* 150-seat auditorium, chamber music rooms. Concerts also arranged in churches in and around Verona; there are several regular series.

VENICE

One of the world's foremost destinations for visitors (around 3 million tourists annually), with its unique lagoon location on the Adriatic coast providing its signature network of canals (the city is exclusively negotiated on foot or by some form of river transport – vaporetto, gondola or other kind of boat – or on foot). As a result, it is a favourite film location and literary setting. Famous for many other things besides, from its glass-making to its bridges, palaces and squares. The largest of these, the Piazza San Marco is one of the world's best known gathering places.

CLIMATE

Hottest month July (18-28°C), coldest month January (-1-6°C). Monthly rainfall ranges between 60mm and 85mm.

MUSICAL LIFE

La Fenice, an opera house of international repute with a habit of living up to its name, 'phoenix' – twice the current building has been damaged by fire and rebuilt, most recently in 1996 (it reopened in 2003). A second venue, run by Fenice foundation, is Teatro Malibran, another opera house. As well as opera, the theatres host chamber concerts, perhaps arranged by the Societa Veneziana di Concerti, and orchestral concerts by its own orchestra.

OTHER CULTURAL INFORMATION

No shortage of historical interest; beyond the architecture and location of the place, there are extensive museums and galleries. City gave its name to a school of painting from the mid-15th century on, Titian foremost among them but Tintoretto and Bellini are 2 others whose work is also very evident in Venice. Native to the city, the artist Canaletto (his name is a diminutive of his actual surname, Canal, rather than a nod to the city's most distinctive feature) is famous for his details landscape paintings of it.

FESTIVALS AND EVENTS

The Venice Biennale is one of the top art events in the world, and an international contemporary music festival, Biennale Musica (actually an annual event) runs alongside it. There are also events dedicated to theatre, cinema and architecture. A custom of the city is the wearing of masks during carnival time.

TOURIST INFORMATION

www.turismovenezia.it, info@turismovenezia.it, +39 0415298711

CONSERVATORIO DI MUSICA 'BENEDETTO MARCELLO' DI VENEZIA

Palazzo Pisani, San Marco 2810, I-30124 Venezia, Italy

t: +39 041 522 56 04 *f:* +39 041 523 92 68 *w:* www.conseve.it

VICENZA

City in northern Italy not far from Venice. Closely associated with the 16th century architect Palladio; the connection, and its generally elegant historic atmosphere with numerous churches and palaces, has led to the city being listetd as a Unesco world heritage site.

CLIMATE

Hottest month July (17-29°C), coldest month January (-2-6°C). Rainfall levels are fairly even throughout the year, with averages ranging between 75 and 110mm per month

TOURIST INFORMATION

www.comune.vicenza.it, assturismo@comune.vicenza.it, +39 444 222 169

CONSERVATORIO DI MUSICA DI VICENZA 'ARRIGO PEDROLLO'

Contra San Domenico 33, I-36100 Vicenza, Italy
t: +39 0444 507551 *f:* +39 0444 302 706
e: relazioniinternazionali@consvi.org
w: www.consvi.org
Contact Franca Moretto, Terrell Stone (international enquiries).
Course information 1st and 2nd level diploma courses following international credit system. Courses in orchestral instruments (baroque, classical and modern), harpsichord, lute, sax, viola da gamba; also courses in Indian instruments (sitar, tabla) at 1st level. At 2nd level can also take liturgical music, piano accompaniment
Admissions information *Term dates* Mid Oct -end Jun. *Application requirements* Admission exam, testing musical ability, language test, musical knowledge test. *Application deadline* 10 June. *Fees* EUR 600 pa (1st level); EUR 800 pa (2nd level). *Scholarships* Limited number of scholarships offered by local, regional and national entities for conservatory students. *No of students* 684 students, of which 31 from overseas. *Language requirements* Italian.

MUSIC FESTIVALS

The Anghiari Festival Southbank Sinfonia, St John's Waterloo, Waterloo Rd, London *t:* 020 7921 0370 *f:* 020 7921 0371 *w:* www.southbank-anghiari.co.uk Southbank Sinfonia's annual residency in Tuscan hill town; orch, choral, chmbr, children's concerts and, every other yr, a fully staged opera.

ANTIQUA 2010 *e:* mail@antiquabz.it *w:* www.antiquabz.it International early music festival in Bolzano.

Autunno Musicale Centro Attivita Musicali e Teatrali, Via Cantoni 1, I-22100 Como, Italy *t:* +39 031 570184 *f:* +39 031 570540 *w:* www.camtam.it

Cantiere Internazionale d'Arte di Montepulciano Via Fiorenzuola Vecchia n 5, I-53045 Montepulciano (Siena), Italy *t:* +39 0578 757089 *f:* +39 0578 758307 *e:* info@fondazionecantiere.it *w:* www.fondazionecantiere.it

Festival della Valle d'Itria Centro Artistico Musicale Paolo Grassi, Palazzo Ducale, I-74015 Martina Franca, Italy *t:* +39 080 4805100 *f:* +39 080 4805120 *e:* festivaldellavalleditria@tin.it *w:* www.festivaldellavalleditria.it

Festival di Musica Antica di Salerno c/o Associazione Koine, Via S Giovanni Bosco, 3, I-84100 Salerno, Italy *t:* +39 089 792163 *e:* info@salernofestival.it *w:* www.salernofestival.it

Festival Internazionale di Musica Antica e Contemporanea Antidogma Musica Via Cernaia 38, I-10122 Torino, Italy *e:* info@antidogmamusica.it *w:* www.antidogmamusica.it Varied concert programmes with a range of performers.

Festival Internazionale di Musica e Arte Sacra Via Paolo VI n 29 (Piazza S Pietro), I-00193 Roma, Italy *t:* +39 06 6869187 *f:* +39 06 6873300 *e:* dir@promusicaeartesacra.it *w:* www.festivalmusicaeartesacra.net Sacred music concerts in the Roman papal basilicas, fundraising concerts for the support of the conservation and restoration of sacred art treasures. Concerts are for supporters of the Foundation; see website for details.

Festival Musica Antica a Magnano Via Roma 43, I-13887 Magnano (BI), Italy *t:* +39 015 67 93 69; +39 015 67 91 76 *e:* info@MusicaAnticaMagnano.com *w:* www.MusicaAnticaMagnano.com

Festival Musicale del Mediterraneo *e:* info@echoart.org *w:* www.echoart.org Festival of traditional and contemporary world music.

Festival Organistico Internazionale Citta di Treviso Palazzo Umanesimo Latino, Riviera Garibaldi 13, I-31100 Treviso, Italy *t:* +39 0422 545895 *f:* +39 0422 513526 *e:* festorganisticotv@tin.it *w:* www.organidimarca.it International organ academy with seminars, lectures, cultural exchanges

and masterclasses with international teachers.

Festival Pianistico Internazionale 'Arturo Benedetti Michelangeli' di Brescia e Bergamo c/o Teatro Grande, Via Paganora 19/A, I-25121 Brescia, Italy *t:* +39 030 293022 *f:* +39 030 2400771 *e:* info@festivalmichelangeli.it *w:* www.festivalmichelangeli.it Annual. Classical piano.

Festival Pontino Via Varsavia 31, I-04100 Latina, Italy *t:* +39 07 7360 5551 *f:* +39 07 7362 8498 *e:* campus.musica@panservice.it *w:* www.festivalpontino.it Classical and contemporary, including premieres.

Festival Puccini c/o Fondazione Festival Pucciniano, 4 Torre del Lago Puccini, I-55048, Italy *t:* +39 0584 350567 *f:* +39 0584 341657 *e:* info@puccinifestival.it *w:* www.puccinifestival.it Opera, concerts, lyric music.

Festival Spaziomusica Associazione Spaziomusica, Via Liguria 60, I-09127 Cagliari, Italy *t:* +39 070 400844, also fax *w:* www.festivalspaziomusica.it Contemporary music.

Festival Verdi Via Garibaldi 16/A, I-43100 Parma, Italy *t:* +39 0521 039393 *f:* +39 0521 206156 *e:* festivalverdi@teatroregioparma.org *w:* www.teatroregioparma.org Productions of Verdi operas plus concerts.

Grandezze & Meraviglie, Festival Musicale e Estense Via S Michele 40/42, I-41100 Modena, Italy *t:* +39 059 214 333, also fax *e:* festival@grandezzemeraviglie.it *w:* www.grandezzemeraviglie.it

Incontri Europei con la Musica Associazione Musica Aperta, Via Borgo Palazzo 31, I-24125 Bergamo, Italy *t:* +39 035 242287, also fax *e:* mabg@unibg.it *w:* www.unibg.it/mabg Classical, modern and contemporary chamber music.

Maggio Musicale Fiorentino *t:* +39 055 2779-350 *e:* relest@maggiofiorentino.com (external relations) *w:* www.maggiofiorentino.com

Musica Sacra a Roma INTERKULTUR, Am Weingarten 3, D-35415 Pohlheim, Germany *t:* +49 6403 9565 25 *f:* +49 6403 9565 29 *e:* mail@interkultur.com *w:* www.interkultur.com Choral and sacred music festival.

Rassegna di Nuova Musica CP 92, I-62100 Macerata, Italy *t:* +39 07 3326 1334 *f:* +39 07 3326 1499 *e:* info@rassegnadinuovamusica.it *w:* www.rassegnadinuovamusica.it

Ravenna Festival Via Dante 1, I-48100 Ravenna, Italy *t:* +39 0544 249211 *f:* +39 0544 36303 *e:* info@ravennafestival.org *w:* www.ravennafestival.org

Rossini Opera Festival Via Rossini 24, I-61100 Pesaro, Italy *t:* +39 07 213 800201 *f:* +39 07 213 800220 *e:* rof@rossinioperafestival.it Annual. Rossini's operas, concerts.

Settimana Musicale Senese Fondazione Accademia Musicale Chigiana, 89 Via di Citta, I-53100 Siena, Italy *t:* +39 05 772 2091 *f:* +39 05 772 88124 *e:* stampa@chigiana.it *w:* www.chigiana.it Ancient instrumental music of the Italian baroque tradition.

Settimane Musicali di Stresa e del Lago Maggiore - Festival Internazionale Via Carducci 38, I-28838 Stresa (VB), Italy *t:* +39 03 233 1095 *f:* +39 03 233 3006 *e:* info@stresafestival.eu *w:* www.stresafestival.eu Orchestras, recitals and performances by young winners of international music competitions; exhibitions.

Settimane Musicali Meranesi-Meraner Musikwochen Corso Liberta 45, I-39012 Merano, Italy *t:* +39 0473 212520 *f:* +39 0473 239043 *e:* info@meranofestival.com *w:* www.meranofestival.com Annual. Symphony orchestras and chamber music.

Sferisterio Opera Festival Via Santa Maria della Porta, 65, I-62100 Macerata, Italy *t:* +39 0733 261335 *f:* +39 0733 261499 *e:* info@sferisterio.it *w:* www.sferisterio.it

Torino Milano Festival Internazionale della Musica via Rovello 2, I-20123 Milano, Italy *t:* +39 02 88464725 *f:* +39 02 88464749 *e:* c.mitoinformazioni@comune.milano.it *w:* www.mitosettembremusica.it Music festival uniting cities of Turin and Milan.

Verona Festival Piazza Bra 28, I-37121 Verona, Italy *t:* +39 045 800 5151 *f:* +39 045 801 3287 *e:* ticket@arena.it *w:* www.arena.it

BASEL

German-speaking city, at the junction of borders with Germany and France on the river Rhine. Architecture is mix of old and new, with several buildings from prominent modern architects. The city's university is the oldest in Switzerland.

CLIMATE

Hottest month July (13-25°C), coldest month January (-2-1°C). Rainfall ranges from around 50mm in spring and autumn to around 90mm in August.

MUSICAL LIFE

Number of orchestras have their home in the town. Most prominent is Sinfonie Orchester Basel, with main venue the Stadtcasino Basel's music room but also at Theater Basel (venue for opera also); Collegium Musicum Basel another symphony orchestra. Basel Sinfonietta is an orchestra with a substantial but not exclusively contemporary music programme; Kammerorchester Basel is slightly smaller in size, and both perform concerts across the country. Also choirs such as Basler Bach-Chor and Gesangverein and strong chamber music presence. Many concerts promoted through city's music organisation, the Allgemeine Musikgesellschaft; Kammermusik.org another promoting organisation. Gare du Nord is unusual venue for new music, a converted railway station; Musical Theater Basel for lighter entertainment.

OTHER CULTURAL INFORMATION

Large number of museums and galleries, from modern art and local history to more specialist (there's a cartoon museum, design museum and doll's house museum, for example). Theatre and other performing arts in abundance covering many genres: traditional, avant-garde, satirical, cabaret; the range on offer reflects city's reputation as Swiss capital of culture.

FESTIVALS AND EVENTS

International festival of chamber music in city museums during April. Also annual jazz and Irish folk festivals, and dance festival in September.

TOURIST INFORMATION

www.basel.com, info@basel.com, +41 61 268 68 68

MUSIK-AKADEMIE DE STADT BASEL HOCHSCHULE FUER MUSIK

Leonhardsstr 6, Postfach, CH-4003 Basel, Switzerland
t: +41 61 264 57 57 *f:* +41 61 264 57 13
e: hsm@mab-bs.ch *w:* www.mab-bs.ch

Course information BA in music, BA in music and movement; MA in music pedagogy, MA in music performance; MA in specialist music performance; MA in composition and theory.

Admissions information *Application deadline* End Feb, except for MA in specialist contemporary music performance (20 Mar).

BERNE (BERN)

Swiss capital city, though not the largest, and officially German-speaking. Largely medieval city centre, located in a crook of River Aare, is a Unesco world heritage site; it features a gothic cathedral and town hall dating from the 15th century

CLIMATE

Warmest month July (12-24°C), coldest month January (-4-2°C).

MUSICAL LIFE

Camerata Bern is small flexible chamber group; Berner Kammerorchester another small orchestra with a particular reputation for commissioning and performing new works. Berner Symphonie Orchester older ensemble, based at Kultur-Casino Bern; also provide accompaniment for season of opera at Stadttheater Bern.

OTHER CULTURAL INFORMATION

Plays at Stadttheater, with smaller venues adding range to drama performance. Numerous cellar theatres staging more experimental work, comedy or puppet shows. Various museums: Zentrum Paul Klee is world's largest collection of the artist's work, but is also a wider cultural centre, housing a 300-seat concert auditorium and theatre space. Einstein's work in the city where he lived while working on special theory of relativity is recognised in the renovated Einstein-Haus.

FESTIVALS AND EVENTS

One of more unusual events is an annual festival of busking. There is a noted jazz festival every spring.

TOURIST INFORMATION

www.berninfo.com, info@berninfo.com, +41 31 328 12 12

HOCHSCHULE DER KÜNSTE BERN

Papiermühlestr 13a, CH-3014 Bern, Switzerland

EUROPE

t: +41 31 634 93 93 *f:* +41 31 634 91 71
e: musik@hkb.bfh.ch *w:* www.hkb.bfh.ch
Course information Undergrad and postgrad courses divided into 4 areas: classical, jazz, music and media art, eurythmics and music.
Admissions information *Term dates* 14 Sep -15 Jan (autumn semester); 22 Feb-4 Jun (spring semester). *Fees* CHF 719 per semester.

GENEVA (GENEVE)

French-speaking city Based on the south western end of Lake Geneva. Has an high global profile and international flavour due to presence of numerous international organisations there, such as World Trade Organisation, Red Cross/Crescent, World Health Organisation; this also means a high percentage of population comes from abroad. The city's location near mountains (Mont Salève is nearby) make it convenient for skiers.

CLIMATE

Hottest month July (13-26°C), coldest month January (-2-4°C). Rainfall is relatively consistent throughout the year, with November the wettest month (90mm).

MUSICAL LIFE

Busy classical music scene, with numerous performing organisations there. Best known is Orchestre de la Suisse Romande based at Victoria Hall but performing throughout the region as well as at main opera house, Grand Théâtre de Genève. L'Orchestre de Chambre de Genève for more reduced repertoire. Various semi-professional and occasional orchestras also. Several concert promoters arranging events at specialist and non-specialist venues. Bâtiment des Forces Motrices is an industrial building converted into an arts venue – concerts include symphonic and chamber events.

OTHER CULTURAL INFORMATION

Other art forms well catered for – dozens of theatres of various sizes in the city, and many more theatre companies. Some societies promote English-language theatre. There is a particularly thriving contemporary art scene, with the city funding a number of art centres devoted to artistic production. Various museums and exhibitions, some run by the city (and some of which offer free entry), others private concerns.

FESTIVALS AND EVENTS

Musiques en Eté festival (July-August) is an all-round music festival including classical, jazz and world music. Mai en Fanfare a series open air performances; similar kind of event in June, Fête de la Musique. Contemporary music at Archipel festival in March. Large number of non-classical music festivals (eg jazz, flamenco, hip hop) and non-music festivals throughout the year.

TOURIST INFORMATION

www.geneva-tourism.ch, +41 22 909 70 70

CONSERVATOIRE DE MUSIQUE DE GENEVE HAUTE ECOLE DE MUSIQUE

12 rue de l'Arquebuse, CH-1211 Genève 11, Switzerland
t: +41 22 319 60 60; +41 22 319 60 83 (international relations) *f:* +41 22 319 60 62
e: info@hemge.ch *w:* www.hemge.ch
Course information Bachelors and masters courses. For bachelors, students must complete 10 modules in following areas: 3 in principal study (instrument, baroque instrument, singing, composition, Dalcroze movement, school music, or music and musicology; 3 in practical training; 3 in theoretical and cultural aspect; 1 in preparatory class for masters. Masters available in interpretation, composition and theory, specialist interpretation (ie advanced performance), or pedagogy.
Admissions information *Application requirements* No age limit, but priority given to younger students. Applicants assessed on instrumental/vocal ability and general musical knowledge. See website for audition dates. *Application deadline* 15 Mar; auditions Apr-May. *Fees* CHF 80 fee must be sent with application. *No of students* Approx 550 students from around the world. *Language requirements* Classes in French only.
Facilities *Music facilities* Early music facilities; electronic music faculty. *Accommodation* Conservatoire cannot guarantee to provide accommodation, but students have access to various accommodation services.

LAUSANNE

French-speaking city on the north bank of Lake Geneva. Its location gives a spectacular panorama over the lake and mountains nearby. Lake also provides leisure opportunities, the city itself being well-appointed with green spaces adding to its high quality of life.

CLIMATE

Hottest months July and August (13-25°C), coldest month January (-1-4°C).

MUSICAL LIFE
Orchestre de Chambre de Lausanne presents various open and subscription concert series at Salle Métropole; some are chamber concerts using orchestra members. Sinfonietta de Lausanne is effectively an advanced training orchestra, giving repertoire and concert experience to young musicians. This includes pit work at city's opera, although OCL is usual accompanist. City is home to one of world's leading choral groups, the Ensemble Vocal de Lausanne, although it is often touring.

OTHER CULTURAL INFORMATION
City is home to International Olympic Committee, and there is a unique museum devoted to Olympic history. Otherwise there are various general and specialist interest museums. Art activity across the board, with several art galleries (including one at the city's art school) and sculpture spread throughout city's parks.

FESTIVALS AND EVENTS
Well-provided for festivals. Lausanne Estivale, city-wide all-round arts festival running throughout the summer; similarly Festival de la Cité (July only). City is home to Quatuor Sine Nomine who organise a biennial festival in June (odd numbered years). Bach Festival in autumn. Guitar festival in May, jazz festival in April, another in autumn; also a festival of improvised classical music in August, and a separate improvised music festival Rue du Nord in February. Other main international festival is Festival International de Danse in early autumn.

TOURIST INFORMATION
www.lausanne-tourisme.ch, information@lausanne-tourisme.ch, +41 21 613 73 73

CONSERVATOIRE DE LAUSANNE HAUTE ECOLE DE MUSIQUE
rue de la Grotte 2, CP 5700, CH-1002 Lausanne, Switzerland
t: +41 21 321 35 20 *f:* +41 21 321 35 25
e: infohem@cdlhem.ch *w:* www.cdlhem.ch
Course information Bachelors and masters courses in classical music and jazz departments; also music education.
Admissions information *Term dates* Sep-end Jun. *Application requirements* Instrumental/vocal test, theory exam and interview. School-leaving certificate or similar qualification required. *Application deadline* 31 Mar. *Fees* Audition fee CHF 80; tuition CHF 1000 for most courses except for foundation level. *Scholarships* Overseas students can apply for grants through Swiss government. See website of the Rectors' Conference of Swiss Universities www.crus.ch/information-programmes for more details.

LUGANO
Italian speaking city at the very south of the country. Popular tourist destination at a very picturesque location on the shores of the lake with the same name; ideal base for outdoor activities such as Nordic walking, mountain biking or those on the lake.

CLIMATE
Hottest month July (16-26°C), coldest month January (0-6°C). Rainfall generally quite high, especially during spring and summer with up to 200mm in May; monthly totals only fall below 100mm from December to February.

MUSICAL LIFE
Orchestra della Svizzera Italiana based in the city at the Palazzo dei Congressi. Venue also receives visits from other orchestras and performing organisations.

OTHER CULTURAL INFORMATION
Several modern art galleries, including a poster museum and a museum of photography; variety of museums, including unusual ones such as that devoted to history of smuggling in the region

FESTIVALS AND EVENTS
Lugano festival during spring sees performances from a number of visiting orchestras. Immediately followed by Progetto Martha Argerich throughout Jun, more focused on chamber music and recitals. Various jazz and blues events throughout rest of summer. Summer festival season ends with a weekend celebrating local produce.

TOURIST INFORMATION
www.lugano-tourism.ch, info@lugano-tourism.ch, +41 91 913 32 32

CONSERVATORIO DELLA SVIZZERA ITALIANA
Via Soldino 9, CH-6900 Lugano, Switzerland
t: +41 91 960 30 40 *f:* +41 91 960 30 41
e: info@conservatorio.ch *w:* www.conservatorio.ch
Contact Ellen Frau, BA and MA course administrator; Marlies Bärtschi, student officer.
Course information BA in music, BA in music &

movement, BA in music (composition & theory); MA in music pedagogy, MA in music performance, MA in specialised music performance, MA in composition and theory.
Admissions information *Term dates* Sep-Jan, Feb-Jun. *Application requirements* High school degree (Matura or equivalent); see website for details. *Application deadline* No later than 15 Apr. *Fees* c EUR 2300 pa. *Scholarships* Contact student office for details. *No of students* More than 60% of students from overseas. *Language requirements* Italian and/or English.
Facilities *Accommodation* Contact student office for details.

LUCERNE (LUZERN)

Located on Vierwaldstättersee (Lake Lucerne), official language is German. Historic city, with significant medieval presence in city centre (the Kapellbrücke bridge is a restored version of the 14th century original) and well located for tourists.

CLIMATE

Warmest months July and August (13-23°C), coldest month January (-1-2°C). Wettest period during summer with over 100mm per month from May to August.

MUSICAL LIFE

Well provided for musically. New Kultur- und Kongresszentrum Luzern built as an all-round performing arts and cultural centre, and provides home for Luzerner Sinfonieorchester. The orchestra gives its own season of concerts, and provides accompaniment at Luzerner Theater for opera and ballet. Lucerne Festival Orchestra is attached to festival, a unique group made up of the foremost chamber musicians and soloist handpicked by Claudio Abbado. Festival also runs a Festival Academy, headed by Pierre Boulez. Festival Strings Luzern another, smaller orchestra, runs its own series of concerts at the KKL independently of the festival. Plans for new flexible performance space are under way (construction due to finish in 2013).

OTHER CULTURAL INFORMATION

Luzerner Theatre also has a programme of drama on stage, plus ancillary events, discussions etc. Another cultural centre, called Boa, stages range of contemporary performance across a number of art forms. City also well provided with museums and galleries, including Richard Wagner Museum. Kulturmagazin available to subscribers to keep up to date with events.

FESTIVALS AND EVENTS

Lucerne Festival runs for 5 weeks in Aug-Sep attracts major musicians and ensembles; associated events are a week-long easter event and piano festival in Nov, with big name international classical and jazz musicians invited. Various jazz events.

TOURIST INFORMATION

www.luzern.orgm luzern@luzern.com, +41 41 227 17 17

HOCHSCHULE LUZERN - MUSIK

Zentralestr 18, CH-6003 Luzern, Switzerland
t: +41 41 226 03 70 *f:* +41 41 226 03 71
e: musik@hslu.ch *w:* www.hslu.ch/musik
Contact Silvia Boss
Course information BA (music, church music, music and movement); MA in music with majors in performance/interpretation, orchestra, chamber music, solo performance, contemporary art performance, composition, conducting (orchestral, choral, brass band), music theory, church music, jazz performance; also MA in music pedagogy. Folk music study options available.
Admissions information *Term dates* Sep-Jun. *Application requirements* Entrance exam. *Application deadline* End of Feb. *Fees* CHF 120 application fee; BA/MA/diploma studies: CHF 1000 per semester, plus CHF 100 for module exams. *Scholarships* Several available for highly talented students; please contact for details. *No of students* 502 students in total, of whom approx 75 from overseas. *Language requirements* C1 in German for BA/MA; MA solo performance possible in English or other languages.
Facilities *Performance opportunities* Lucerne Festival Academy, Luzerner Sinfonieorchester, Jazz Club Lucerne, Jazz Festival Willisau, etc. *Accommodation* StuWo Luzern runs student accommodation for various institutions in the city: www.stuwo-luzern.ch.

NEUCHATEL

Small French-speaking lakeside town at the foot of the Jura range in western Switzerland with smart old town and interesting architectural features. Ideal for many outdoor leisure activities with numerous ski resorts nearby.

CLIMATE

Hottest month July (14-24°C), coldest month January

(-2-3°C). Wettest month August (97mm), driest month April (60mm).

MUSICAL LIFE
Despite size, the town supports a decent array of music. The Ensemble Symphonique de Neuchâtel is new group formed from merger of the town's symphony and chamber orchestras, and aims to become a firm presence in region's cultural activity.

OTHER CULTURAL INFORMATION
Town's cultural centre includes a theatre.

FESTIVALS AND EVENTS
Biennial choral festival (even-numbered years) – in fact a choral competition.

TOURIST INFORMATION
www.neuchateltourisme.ch, info@ne.ch, +41 32 889 68 90

CONSERVATOIRE DE MUSIQUE NEUCHATELOIS
Avenue du Clos-Brochet 30-32, CH-2002 Neuchâtel, Switzerland
t: +41 32 725 20 53 *f:* +41 32 725 70 24
e: conservatoire.NTEL@ne.ch *w:* www.he-arc.ch/hearc/fr/musique/Annuaire/index.html
Course information Bachelors available in various specialisms: instruments, period instruments, jazz (instruments, singing or composition), singing, baroque singing, composition, Dalcroze movement and music, school music. Part of the Haute Ecole de Musique de Genève.
Admissions information *Application deadline* 30 Apr. *Fees* CHF 900 per semester, plus course and exam fees.

ZÜRICH
The country's most predominant and wealthy city with a major global importance in financial and commercial industries (Swiss stock exchange based there); its wealth helps sustain a busy Musical life. Located in German-speaking north of the country at tip of Lake Zürich.

CLIMATE
Warmest month July (12-23°C), coldest month January (-3-2°C).

MUSICAL LIFE
Principal orchestra, and one of the oldest, is the busy Tonhalle-Orchester, named after the venue it calls home (it has a main concert hall and smaller space for chamber music); also receives visits from major overseas orchestras. Several other orchestras besides, ranging from Symphonisches Orchester Zürich at larger scale to chamber orchestras like Zürcher Kammerorchester (based at its own 250-seat hall, the ZKO-Haus) and even smaller Camerata Zürich. Contemporary music and performing arts at Kunstraum Walcheturm, where you might hear city-based Ensemble für Neue Musik Zürich. Opera and ballet at Opernhaus Zürich which has own orchestra (it gives concerts in its own right outside the busy opera season).

OTHER CULTURAL INFORMATION
For more alternative style of culture, Rote Fabrik promotes various art forms. Kulturmarkt another venue with eclectic all-round programme. Very good range and variety of galleries, especially of modern and contemporary art and design. Theatre provision includes Herzbaracke, a floating variety theatre on Lake Zürich; largest theatre is Schauspielhaus Pfauen, for more conventional range of drama; Theater der Künster aims for a multi-disciplinary approach.

FESTIVALS AND EVENTS
Month-long Zürcher Festspiele in June-July features music strongly among theatre and art events. Biennial festival of site-specific performance around the city, Stromereien (odd-numbered years).

TOURIST INFORMATION
www.zuerich.com, information@zuerich.com, +41 44 215 40 00

ZÜRCHER HOCHSCHULE FÜR KUNSTE (ZURICH UNIVERSITY OF THE ARTS)
Florhofgasse 6, CH-8001 Zürich, Switzerland
t: +41 43 446 20 56 (international office)
f: +41 43 446 51 30 *e:* empfang.florhof@zhdk.ch (music); bettina.ganz@zhdk.ch (international office) *w:* www.zhdk.ch
Contact Bettina Ganz, international affairs co-ord.
Course information Bachelor and masters studies in classical music (solo, opera, orchestra, chamber music, lied-duo, piano chamber music, instrumental pedagogy); jazz pedagogy; pop pedagogy; music and movement; school music; church music (organ, choir); conducting (orchestral, choral); composition (contemporary; electro-acoustic; film, theatre and media); music theory; sound engineering.

Admissions information *Application requirements* See website for full details. *Application deadline* 28 Feb. *No of students* 40% of students from 51 overseas countries.

MUSIC FESTIVALS

ARCHIPEL. Festival des Musiques d'Aujourd'hui 8 rue de la Coulouvrenière, CH-1204 Genève, Switzerland *t:* +41 22 329 42 42 *f:* +41 22 329 68 68 *e:* info@archipel.org *w:* www.archipel.org Modern/contemporary music, video, dance, installations. Various venues.

Classic Openair Hans Roth-Str 15, CH-4500-Solothum, Switzerland *t:* +41 32 622 30 70 *f:* +41 32 621 6302 *e:* sekr.classic-openair@bluewin.ch *w:* www.classic-openair.ch Opera festival; 10 different operas with renowned singers.

Festival d'Opéra Avenches Place du Montauban 1, CH-1580 Avenches, Switzerland *t:* +41 26 676 06 00 *e:* opera@avenches.ch *w:* www.avenches.ch Open-air opera performances.

Festival de Musique Improvisée de Lausanne Association pour la Musique Improvisée de Lausanne, CP 5203, CH-1002 Lausanne *e:* info@fmil.org *w:* www.fmil.org Festival dedicated to classical improvised music.

Festival International de Musique CP 1429, CH-1950 Sion, Switzerland *t:* +41 27 323 43 17 *f:* +41 27 323 46 62 *e:* info@sion-festival.ch *w:* www.sion-festival.ch Festival encompassing range of classical music from solo recitals to orchestral concerts.

Festival Sine Nomine *w:* www.quatuorsinenomine.ch Biennial festival of chamber music in Lausanne.

Fribourg International Festival of Sacred Music Rue des Alpes 7, CP 540, CH-1701 Fribourg, Switzerland *t:* +41 26 322 4800 *f:* +41 26 322 8331 *e:* office@fims-fribourg.ch *w:* www.fims-fribourg.ch Biennial. Concerts of medieval, renaissance, baroque, romantic and contemporary music; also traditional and sacred music. W/shops and m/classes. Co-produced by Swiss radion RSR-Espace 2.

Lucerne Festival Hirschmattstr 13, CH-6002 Lucerne, Switzerland *t:* +41 41 226 4400 *f:* +41 41 226 4460 *e:* info@lucernefestival.ch *w:* www.lucernefestival.ch Classical music festival with symphony concerts, chamber music, recitals, choral concerts, serenades, musica nova, composer-in-residence.

Lucerne Festival Am Piano Hirschmattstr 13, Postfach, CH-6002 Luzern, Switzerland *t:* +41 41 226 44 00 *f:* +47 41 226 44 60 *e:* info@lucernefestival.ch *w:* www.lucernefestival.ch

Lucerne Festival zu Ostern Hirschmattstr 13, Postfach, CH-6002 Luzern, Switzerland *t:* +41 41 226 44 00 *f:* +41 41 226 44 60 *e:* info@lucernefestival.ch *w:* www.lucernefestival.ch Music for the Passion season.

Lugano Festival Via Foce 1, CH-6900 Lugano, Switzerland *t:* +41 58 866 82 40 *f:* +41 58 866 82 44 *w:* www.luganofestival.ch Numerous visiting orchestras and performers

Menuhin Festival Gstaad Postfach 65, CH-3780 Gstaad, Switzerland *t:* +41 33 748 83 38 *f:* +41 33 748 83 39 *e:* info@menuhinfestivalgstaad.com; desmondcecil@dial.pipex.com *w:* www.menuhinfestivalgstaad.com Some 40 concerts in beautiful old churches and festival tent (seating 2000). Chamber music, symphony concerts, contemporary music, violin music. Top artists and young musicians. Theme of 2010: Zwischen Himmel und Erde (Between Heaven and Earth).

Montreux Choral Festival PO Box 1526, CH-1820 Montreux, Switzerland *t:* +41 21 966 55 50 *f:* +41 21 966 55 69 *e:* montreuxchoralfestival@bluewin.ch *w:* www.choralfestival.ch Open to all choirs, offering choice of a free programme and attractive prizes.

Muséiques, Les Postfach 1650, CH-4001 Basel, Switzerland *t:* +41 61 271 24 42 *f:* +41 61 271 24 41 *e:* info@lesmuseiques.ch *w:* http://lesmuseiques.ch Chamber music in museums in Basel.

Opera St Moritz *t:* +41 81 833 55 77 *w:* www.opera-stmoritz.ch

SOLsberg Festival *t:* +41 79 322 14 34 *e:* info@solsberg.ch *w:* www.solsberg.ch 6 concerts over 2 weekends.

Verbier Festival 4 rue JJ Rousseau, CH-1800 Vevey, Switzerland *t:* +41 21 925 9060 *f:* +41 21 925 9068 *e:* info@verbierfestival.com *w:* www.verbierfestival.com Annual. Summer performing arts academy; over 200 events with internationally renowned artists, including songs, symphonic and chamber music, recitals and masterclasses.

Zürcher Festspiele c/o Opernhaus Zürich, Falkenstr 1, CH-8008 Zürich, Switzerland *t:* +41 44 269 90 90 *f:* +41 44 260 70 25 *e:* info-office@zuercher-festspiele.ch *w:* www.zuercher-festspiele.ch

Spain and Portugal

SPAIN AND PORTUGAL

Among orchestral musicians, primarily those starting out on their professional career, Portugal and, in particular, Spain have been useful sources of employment. Not only is there the attractive climate and quality of life in many places, but the increased investment in cultural activities and consequent growth in number of orchestras in Spain over the past 30 years means vacancies arose frequently.

This is not so much the case now, however; although there are still numerous performing organisations (around 50 orchestras across Spain, for example), player lists have consolidated making available positions less numerous. This is where a foot in the door at a conservatoire can help – it is not unusual for local orchestras to offer extras places to advanced students, for example. And if nothing else, a year or so in a more relaxed environment may well put things back home in perspective.

Both countries are home to styles of traditional music that are popular around the world: Portugal the distinctively mournful singing of fado; Spain has flamenco in the south, but the country's size and cultural traditions mean a range of musics can be found. In addition, both countries are significant in early music, particularly of the renaissance period.

EUROPE

SPAIN PAGE 129

Professional music training at higher education level is treated separately from the university system, although it does run parallel to the general education system with elementary, intermediate and superior levels (the latter being where professional training falls). Superior level courses can only be taught by institutions with the correct authority, whether these are private or public. In the main, national students qualify for entry to the courses by successful completion of the intermediate level of music study along with high school qualification, although the rules are not hard and fast.

Currently, conservatoires do not follow the Bologna structure, and they operate a credit system that does not relate to ECTS. In addition, they do not offer masters degrees but a single 4-year qualification (5 years for composition and conducting). Doctoral studies in musicology can be pursued at the end of this period, but only at universities (the superior level qualification gives direct access).

PORTUGAL PAGE 137

Portugal's two public conservatoires are considered as part of the polytechnic system (as opposed to the university system). Unlike Spain, the country has been quick to adopt the Bologna process structure, so students spend 4 years studying for the first Licenciado and a further 1 for masters qualification. As with Spain, doctoral studies are only available in universities. Funding comes through a combination of state funding and students' fees.

Outside the public conservatoires, music education is available elsewhere; either in private higher education institutions like Lisbon's orchestral academy (funded by student fees with some state assistance), or in universities where music teacher training goes on – professional music teachers cannot qualify at conservatoires. Music education at earlier ages is through a combination of specialised music schools (ages 10-18) or professional music schools (12-18).

BADAJOZ

City in west of Spain (and capital of the province of the same name) near border with Portugal. Its historical strategic significance, not to mention its Moorish heritage, is reflected in its buildings which include city fortifications, gates, bridge and old square.

CLIMATE

Hottest months July and August (17-34°C), coolest months January and February (4-14°C). Rainfall generally low throughout the year, with summers particularly dry.

OTHER CULTURAL INFORMATION

There is a fine arts museum in the city.

CONSERVATORIO SUPERIOR DE MUSICA DE BADAJOZ

Duque de San German 6, E-06071 Badajoz, Spain
t: +34 924 224 935 *f:* +34 924 224 771
w: www.dip-badajoz.es/cultura/conservatorio
Course information Conservatoire divided in to 5 departments: harmony, composition and theory; strings, guitar, harp, chamber music, accordeon; choral and vocal; piano; wind, brass and percussion.
Facilities *Music facilities* Various ensembles: choir, symphony and chamber orchestras, sax group, electroacoustic group, wind band.

BARCELONA

Capital of Catalunya on the Mediterranean coast towards the north east of Spain, located at the foot of a mountain range giving the city a spectacular setting; Montjuïc is a case in point, an area including various gardens. As well as examples of medieval and gothic architecture in the old part of the city, there is a unique mix of modern architectural styles, whether exotic designs of Gaudí, the Catalan version of art nouveau or more minimal style. The city's attraction to some visitors (of which there are many) is enhanced by the presence of long beaches close to the centre, and by its bustling nightlife; for some, it's the city's football club (one of the world's best known) which is the main draw.

CLIMATE

Hottest month August (20-28°C), coldest month January (-4-12°C). Rainfall generally low throughout the year, but highest in autumn (around 90mm in October).

MUSICAL LIFE

Palau de la Música Catalana is one of world's most spectacular concert halls, with distinct decorative style both inside (the concert hall itself dominated by stained glass windows) and on its exterior. It attracts major artists from all around the world, as well as Catalan performers; there's also a smaller accompanying Petit Palau built in a different style. Gran Teatre del Liceu opera house in the busy Rambla area puts on own productions (there's a resident chorus and orchestra) and acts as a receiving house. Orquestra Simfònica de Barcelona I Nacional de Catalunya is the main orchestra; it is based at the L'Auditori hall which also stages wide range of classical music performed by other groups and individuals. Orquestra de Cadaqués has HQ in Barcelona but is in fact a festival orchestra that gathers for the Cadaqués Festival and for tours.

OTHER CULTURAL INFORMATION

Extensive range of exhibitions, including galleries focusing on Picasso and Miró, on post-war Catalan and Spanish art, Catalan history etc. National Art Museum of Catalunya is particularly strong in art of the region dating back to the 11th century as well as European renaissance and baroque art. Large number of theatres.

FESTIVALS AND EVENTS

Numerous arts festivals throughout the year. Festival de Barcelona Grec (June) features flamenco and various other modern music, dance and performance. Sónar music festival, also in June, features contemporary mixed media art and music. Early music at the Festival de Música Antiga in April, organised by L'Auditori; venue also runs contemporary music event in March. More contemporary music at Festival Internacional de Música Experimental.

LOCAL PUBLICATIONS

Local daily is El Periódico de Catalunya, published in both Spanish and Catalan; La Vanguardia is Spanish-only (but is more widely read).

TOURIST INFORMATION

www.bcn.es

CONSERVATORI LICEU

La Rambla 63, E-08002 Barcelona, Spain
t: +34 93 304 11 11 *f:* +34 93 412 48 87
e: conservatori@conservatori-liceu.es *w:* www.conservatori-liceu.es
Course information Principal studies are classical

EUROPE

and contemporary music instruments and singing; composition; orchestral conducting; jazz and modern music instruments (drums, electric bass, double bass, electric guitar, percussion, piano, saxophone, keyboards, trombone, trumpet) and voice. Also department of Flamenco. Details of academic programme, including mandatory and optional courses, available on website. Postgrad specialisation includes orchestral conducting, music analysis, composition, music history and aesthetics, musicology, music education.
Admissions information *Application requirements* Admission test: performance of prepared repertoire, musical analysis, sight reading, contemporary music, *Scholarships* All students registered in a course can apply to conservatoire's scholarships programme.

ESCOLA SUPERIOR DE MUSICA DE CATALUNYA
Edicife L'Auditori, Padilla 155, E-08013 Barcelona, Spain
e: international.relations@esmuc.net
w: www.esmuc.cat
Contact Oriol Pausa.
Course information Degrees in classical music (orchestral and non-orchestral instruments), jazz and modern music, early music, conducting, musicology, sonology, theory and composition; also traditional music. Curriculum consists of core subjects, compulsory specialist subjects and options. School also arranges complementary extra-curricular activity (eg masterclasses, conferences, student concerts, professional development activity etc).
Admissions information *Scholarships* None. *No of students* Capacity of about 600, with c 150 new students accepted each year.
Facilities *Music facilities* Library with audiovisual facilities and computers with music software; instrument office offering loans and technical advice; study classrooms and rehearsal rooms; audiovisual office.

CÓRDOBA

City in Andalusia, southern Spain, and a Unesco heritage site, with an interesting history combining Spanish, Moorish and even Roman influences. Famous for its unique Mezquita Catedral, a church converted by north African conquerors to a mosque, then back to a church again (with a new Christian building built at its heart) following the Spanish reconquest. City's religious importance emphasised by the presence of its 14th century synagogue. Interesting architectural contrasts, from narrow streets of old town to its main square the Plaza de la Corredera, with a more modern area also.

CLIMATE

Some of the hottest summers in Europe (temperatures over 30°C from June to September) and mild winters (3-14°C in January). Rainfall highest in November and December (85-90mm).

MUSICAL LIFE

City has its own orchestra, Orquesta de Córdoba. Gran Teatro includes music events among its wider programming.

OTHER CULTURAL INFORMATION

Various museums, many of which result from Córdoba's importance historically.

FESTIVALS AND EVENTS

Various town events such as its Patio Festival, where houses open up their distinctive courtyards for public to look at. Main music event is the annual guitar festival in Jul.

TOURIST INFORMATION

www.turismodecordoba.org, infoave@turismocordoba.org, +34 902 201 774

CONSERVATORIO SUPERIOR DE MUSICA DE CORDOBA 'RAFAEL OROZCO'
Angel Saavedra 1, E-14003 Cordoba, Spain
t: +34 957379647 *f:* +34 957379653
e: erasmus@csmcordoba.com
w: www.csmcordoba.com
Contact Monica Marquez Carrasco (international enquiries)

DONOSTIA-SAN SEBASTIÁN

City in Basque region of Spain on north coast on the Bay of Biscay. Famed as a beach resort (La Concha is a spectacular bay setting) and overlooked by a mountain range, city is made up of several quarters of contrasting character such as the old quarter (as much of the city was destroyed by fire in 1813, this is not so old) with its fishing village and squares.

CLIMATE

Hottest month August (18-31°C), coldest month December (2-10°C).

MUSICAL LIFE
Kursaal Conference Centre has 2 concert halls and is main classical venue, although programming is not limited to classical. Casa de Okendo is another venue, a former stately home. Conciertos de Primavera is a series of concerts and music performances of various types throughout the city.

OTHER CULTURAL INFORMATION
Teatro Victoria Eugenia for plays, but some music events (eg during festival). San Telmo Museum focuses particularly on Basque art; Koldo Mitxelena cultural centre is a multi-purpose hall including exhibition spaces and rooms for other events.

FESTIVALS AND EVENTS
Quincena Musical is a month-long classical music festival running August-September; its international piano competition has events open to public (March). International jazz and film festivals (July and September respectively). Basque Week in early September celebrates Basque culture and traditions.

TOURIST INFORMATION
www.donostia.org

MUSIKENE - EUSKAL HERRIKO GOI MAILAKO MUSIKA IKASTEGIA (MUSIKENE - HIGHER SCHOOL OF MUSIC OF THE BASQUE COUNTRY)
Palacio Miramar, Mirakontxa 48, E-20007 Donostia San Sebastian, Spain
t: +34 943 316778 *f:* +34 943 316916
e: rree@musikene.net *w:* www.musikene.net
Contact Dorleta Lasagabaster
Course information Higher diploma courses for accordion, orchestral instruments, composition, voice, choral and orchestral conducting, traditional and folk instruments, jazz (various instruments), organ, music education. *Instrumental* Orchestral instruments, piano, guitar, accordion, organ. *Vocal* Vocal studies *Conducting* Orchestral and choral conducting. *Jazz/world* Jazz offered for these instruments: double bass, drums, electric bass, electric guitar, piano, saxophone, trombone, trumpet or voice. *Other* Pedagogy
Admissions information *Application requirements* Certificate of upper level secondary education, entrance exam *Application deadline* Between beginning Apr and mid May 2010. *Scholarships* Offered via Basque government and ministry of education

GRANADA
City in the far south of Spain, in Andalusia. Like other places in the region, the history and architecture of the place influenced by various factors, but have left one of Spain's most impressive monuments in the form of the hilltop Alhambra palace. Many other historic locations too. Its proximity to the Sierra Nevada mountains means visitors are attracted during winter for skiing.

CLIMATE
Hottest months July and August (17-24°C), coldest month January (2-11°C). Minimal rainfall during summer and modest throughout the year (wettest periods are spring and autumn with 40-60mm).

MUSICAL LIFE
Centro Cultural Manuel de Falla concert hall and Palacio de Exposiciones (with halls named after Falla and writer García Lorca, both of whom have strong attachment to the city), are main music venues. Teatro Alhambra has varied programme including music. Other venues, such as Teatro Municipal Isabel la Católica, also used occasionally for concerts. City's home orchestra is the busy Orquesta Ciudad de Granada which can also be heard in other nearby cities such as Sevilla.

OTHER CULTURAL INFORMATION
Flamenco is a predominant form of expression in the region with many events throughout the year; otherwise numerous cultural events organised by city council

FESTIVALS AND EVENTS
Three-week long Festival of Music and Dance runs from late June in various venues around the city. Festival Internacional de Tango de Granada in spring, and major jazz festival in November.

TOURIST INFORMATION
www.turgranada.es, +34 958 24 71 46

REAL CONSERVATORIO SUPERIOR DE MUSICA 'VICTORIA EUGENIA' DE GRANADA
Calle San Jeronimo n° 46, E-18001 Granada, Spain
t: +34 958 276 866 *f:* +34 958 276 716
e: info@conservatoriosuperiorgranada.com; internacional@conservatoriosuperiorgranada.com *w:* www.conservatoriosuperiorgranada.com
Contact Sara Ramos, contact for international enquiries
Course information Music degrees. *Instrumental*

EUROPE

Repertoire, history of music, analysis, study of musical forms, improvisation for guitar, piano accompaniment. *Vocal* Individual lessons, coaching, interpretation, phonetics and language studies for singers, choir. *Composition* Theory and analysis, electronic and electroacoustic music, composition for audiovisual media, score reduction, orchestration, contemporary music studies. *Orchestral* Symphony orchestra, wind orchestra, string orchestra, brass ensemble, percussion ensemble, *Chamber music* Wind quintet. Chamber music for piano and strings.
Admissions information *Application requirements* Entrance exam. *Application deadline* 15 May. *No of students* 350 students.

MADRID

Spanish capital, though not an old city compared with some of the urban centres in the south – it was made capital only in mid 16th century, supposedly because of its location right in the centre of the country. Famed now for its busy nightlife (a night out begins at 10pm!), a legacy of a key moment in recent history known as 'La Movida' – in the euphoria following the death of the dictator Franco, the city became the focus for an explosion of hedonistic activity particularly in the Malasaña district (it is still a popular area for going out). Despite the busy lifestyle there, however, and the large number of things to do, the city holds a number of parks and gardens for relaxation – the main park is the Retiro; there is also a botanical garden.

CLIMATE

Hottest month July (18-32°C), coldest month January (2-10°C). Wettest months April-May (45-50mm) and November-December (around 55mm).

MUSICAL LIFE

Various orchestras based in and performing in the city. Orquesta Nacionale de España (which has an associated choir) based at Auditorio Nacional de Música, but gives plenty of concerts elsewhere; Orquesta Sinfónica de RadioTelevisiónEspañola (also with an associated choir) is country's main broadcaster-subsidised orchestra; Orquesta de Cámara Reina Sofia smaller-scale group. Orquesta Sinfónica de Madrid, one of Spain's longest established orchestras, gives a substantial concert series as well as providing accompaniment at the Teatro Real (opera and ballet). Spanish popular music theatre has its own venue at Teatro de la Zarzuela; this is also home of the Orquesta de la Comunidad de Madrid. Many other concert venues, cultural centres and theatres with occasional music performance besides, not to mention jazz clubs, rock venues etc.

OTHER CULTURAL INFORMATION

City holds one of the world's finest art collections at the Prado art gallery; Reina Sofia gallery nearby, its collection predominantly of works by modern Spanish artists, especially Picasso. Apart from the big 3 (the other being the Museo Thyssen Bornemisza), plenty of others to choose from – the Real Academica de Bellas Artes has a varied collection as well as being home to the Madrid Academy of Art. For many, the chief cultural activity is provided by the Madrid football teams, Real and Atlético.

FESTIVALS AND EVENTS

Autumn festival of performing arts in Oct-Nov; Conciertos de Semana Sancta is a week of concerts in Madrid churches in the run-up to Easter. Jazz festival in Oct-Nov.

LOCAL PUBLICATIONS

InMadrid (www.in-madrid.com) is an English-language magazine containing listings, guides, reviews and employment opportunities. Madrid is the HQ of El Pais newspaper (www.elpais.com).

TOURIST INFORMATION

www.esmadrid.com

REAL CONSERVATORIO SUPERIOR DE MUSICA DE MADRID

C/ Doctor Mata 2, E-28012 Madrid, Spain
t: +34 915392901 *f:* +34 915275822
e: infosecre@real-conserv-madrid.es *w:* www.educa.madrid.org/web/csm.realconservatorio.madrid/
Admissions information *Term dates* 1 Oct-10 Jun.

MURCIA

City traversed by river Segura in south east of Spain in region of the same name, close to Mediterranean coast. Has a mix of architectural styles – even the cathedral was built over 3 different periods – though has remained relatively undeveloped in past few years compared with other coastal cities not so far away.

CLIMATE

Hottest months July and August (19-34°C), coldest month January (4-10°C). Low rainfall throughout the year, with a maximum of 4 rainy days per month (spring and autumn).

MUSICAL LIFE

The region has an orchestra, the Orquesta Sinfónica de la Région de Murcia, and concert hall, the Victor Villegas auditorium and congress centre where it gives most of its concerts; hall also receives visting orchestras, chamber music, choral events etc, and non-classical performers.

OTHER CULTURAL INFORMATION

Romea Theatre for theatre and dance, also music theatre and flamenco events. A number of the city's museums touch on religious themes (eg the Salzillo Museum, or Cathedral Museum), echoing the city's tradition as manufacturer of nativity scenes; art galleries also present, as well as a museum charting city's history. Bullfighting is a particular tradition in southern Spanish regions, and Murcia has its own bullring and bullfighting museum.

FESTIVALS AND EVENTS

Like many Spanish cities, has popular processions during religious festivals. Also Murcia Tres Culturas, a festival of cultural activities focusing on interaction between Islam, Christianity and Judaism. Week-long jazz festival in May

TOURIST INFORMATION

www.murciaciudad.com, promocionturistica@ayto-murcia.es, +34 968 358600.

CONSERVATORIO SUPERIOR DE MUSICA DE MURCIA

Paseo del Malecon 9, E-30004 Murcia, Spain
t: +34 968 29 47 58 *f:* +34 968 29 47 56
e: info@csmmurcia.com; erasmus@csmmurcia.com *w:* www.csmmurcia.com

Admissions information *Application requirements* Courses in orchestral instruments, accordion, singing, harpsichord, guitar and flamenco guitar, baroque instruments; also composition, choral and/or orchestral direction, musicology, music education. Courses made up of obligatory modules to give all students a common musical base and optional choices to complement students' specialisms. All instrumental students give recitals as part of course.

OVIEDO

City in north west Spain on the Bay of Biscay with pre-Romanesque architectural style predominant. At its heart is an old town whose layout still reflects the city's medieval heritage, and includes a striking 13th century cathedral.

CLIMATE

Hottest month July (17-28°C), coldest month January (5-11°C). Wettest month January (130mm), driest months July (25mm).

MUSICAL LIFE

2 orchestras based in the city: Oviedo Filarmonia and regional Orquesta Sinfónica del Principado del Asturias. Both perform at the new Auditorio Príncipe Felipe, a flexible 3-hall venue (the biggest hall seats well over 2000, the chamber hall 400) that is part of a congress centre complex. The Oviedo Filarmonia (one of Spain's newest, founded in 1999) also providing orchestra for opera at the Teatro Campoamor. Opera includes important Zarzuela season. A little confusingly, it is not based at the town's Teatro Filarmonica, the stage being too small for full size orchestra concerts, although musical events do feature as part of its programming. Also Oviedo Filarmonia Youth Orchestra, invites young musicians from different countries. Some music events at the university (advertised on its website).

OTHER CULTURAL INFORMATION

Handful of galleries and museums: the fine arts museum is the largest.

FESTIVALS AND EVENTS

Jazz festival in July. Numerous religious processions, and city carnival in February.

TOURIST INFORMATION

www.ayto-oviedo.es, oficina.turismo@ayto-oviedo.es

CONSERVATORIO SUPERIOR DE MUSICA EDUARDO MARTINEZ TORNER

Corrada del Obispo S/N, E-33003 Oviedo, Spain
t: +34 985217556 *f:* +34 985203720
w: www.consmupa.es

Course information Majors in accordion, composition, guitar, organ, percussion, piano, saxophone, singing, string instruments, brass instruments, woodwind instruments.

Admissions information *Term dates* Sep 1-Jun 30 *Application requirements* Theoretical and practical entrance exam; completed secondary level education. *Application deadline* EUR 700-800 per year. *No of students* 85% national and EU, 15% non-EU. *Language requirements* Spanish

Facilities *Music facilities* Ensembles includes symphony and chamber orchestras, percussion ensemble, sax ensemble, symphonic wind band and various chamber ensembles. *Performance opportunities* Around 200 concerts per year (solo recitals, chamber music, symphonic ensembles, etc). *Accommodation* Private halls of residence.

SALAMANCA

City in western Castille y León region of Spain, home to the country's oldest university (early 13th century); today the city is a popular student destination giving it a lively nightlife that contrasts with its quieter daytime character. Old town, with its square and numerous old buildings of varying styles and the Plaza Mayor square, is a Unesco world heritage site. Nicknamed the 'golden city' due to the colour its sandstone buildings take as the sun sets.

CLIMATE

Hottest month July (12-29°C), coldest month January (-1-8°C). Rainfall is low throughout the year although winter and late spring are slightly wetter (around 50mm in May, 40mm in November-December).

MUSICAL LIFE

Palacio de Congresos y Exposiciones is main venue. Watch out for 'tuna', songs sung all around the city, typically by students dressed in medieval costume. Also concerts at various cultural centres and theatres.

OTHER CULTURAL INFORMATION

Houses a Filmoteca, a cinema which, as well as putting on various film season, allows you to watch your own choice of filmArchive of Spanish Civil War based in the city. Museums include a museum of art nouveau and art deco, and a small fine arts museum, with contemporary art at the Centro Internacional de Arte.

FESTIVALS AND EVENTS

All-round arts festival, as well as a festival of flamenco, runs in June. Contemporary music at Festival SMASH in October; also Salamanca Solotech festival of electronic music in the same month. Jazz festivals in spring and summer. Festival of religious music during run-up to Easter.

TOURIST INFORMATION

www.salamanca.es

CONSERVATORIO SUPERIOR DE MUSICA DE SALAMANCA
C/ Lazarillo de Tormes 54-70, E-37005
Salamanca, Spain
t: +34 923 28 21 15 *f:* +34 923 28 28 78
e: info@consuperiorsal.com; erasmus@consuperiorsal.com
w: www.consuperiorsal.com

Course information Courses in the following departments: musicology/ethnomusicology; conducting, composition and music theory; early music; strings, voice, woodwinds; brass and percussion. Full list of courses available on website.

SEVILLE (SEVILLA)

One of the main cities in southern Spain, capital of Andalusia, with a history dating back to Roman times and before. For a significant period of its history, the city lay in the Moorish empire and there is much of this civilisation echoed in the city's appearance today, most particularly in the Real Alcázar (royal palace; it also includes extensive gardens) but also in its cathedral (predominantly gothic but with a converted minaret as its bell tower), churches and other buildings. Seville's historical importance is also demonstrated by the fact it is home to a university founded in the 15th century. A favourite among young people due to its thriving nightlife, it is also renowned for its tapas.

CLIMATE

Hottest months July and August (19-35°C), coolest month January (5-16°C). Wettest during winter (95mm in December), but very dry during summer with virtually no rainfall in July and August.

MUSICAL LIFE

Real Orquest Sinfónica de Sevilla plays a substantial season at the Theatre of La Maestranza, a venue which also shows opera, dance and the traditional Spanish popular musical form, Zarzuela.

OTHER CULTURAL INFORMATION

The fine arts museum focuses particularly on Spanish art of the region (the style known as the School of Seville was operating during the 16th and 17th centuries). Well known (or perhaps notorious) for being a centre of bullfighting, as depicted in the opera Carmen.

FESTIVALS AND EVENTS

Seville is known for its devout Easter week

processions which give way to a week of somewhat less sober festivities, the Feria de Abril.

TOURIST INFORMATION

www.sevilla.org

CONSERVATÓRIO SUPERIOR DE MUSICA MANUEL CASTILLO

t: +34 954915630 *f:* +34 954374373 *e:* luismarin@csmsev.es; internacional@csmsev.es *w:* www.csmsev.es; www.erasmus.csmsev.es

Admissions information *Term dates* Dec-May. *Scholarships* Scholarships from ministry of education and Erasmus. *Language requirements* Courses in English and Spanish at the language institute, University of Seville.

Facilities *Music facilities* Own building equipped with classroom insts. *Accommodation* Accommodation available through www.sacu.us.es.

VALÈNCIA

Port city on the Mediterranean coast in the east of Spain (there are beaches within reach of city centre). Charcaterised by a range of architectural styles, with narrow winding streets, Gothic cathedral and churches but also numerous buildings in more modern style. Culinary speciality is a particular variety of paella; crowds also drawn in by the annual Tomatina, at which locals throw huge quantities of the fruit at one another throughout the nearby town of Buñol.

CLIMATE

Hottest month August (21-26°C), coldest month January (7-12°C). Modest rainfall throughout the year, although October tends to be rainier (around 70mm).

MUSICAL LIFE

Home to recently opened Ciutat de les Arts i de les Ciènces, an enormous complex that includes the Palau de les Arts Reina Sofia; this itself houses 4 performance spaces. Alongside its construction came creation of a brand new orchestra, the Orquestra de la Comunitat Valenciana. Palau de la Música has several concert halls, and is home to the Orquesta de València; several concert series involving international artists run here. A more local musical tradition is for brass bands.

OTHER CULTURAL INFORMATION

As well as music venues, City of Arts and Sciences holds Europe's largest aquarium and a science museum. Other exhibitions throughout the city: modern art institute, fine arts museum, museum of bullfighting etc; also a huge aquarium.

FESTIVALS AND EVENTS

Contemporary performing arts festival in February. Annual and long-standing brass band festival; several other events spotlighting local traditional music. Las Fallas is a noisy series of celebrations in March featuring giant papier mâché structures, street parties with characteristic firecrackers and firework displays.

TOURIST INFORMATION

www.turisvalencia.es, turisvalencia@turisvalencia.es, +34 963 606 353

CONSERVATORIO SUPERIOR DE MUSICA DE VALENCIA

Cami de Vera 29, E-46022 Valencia, Spain
t: +34 963605316 *f:* +34 963605701
e: info@csmvalencia.es *w:* www.csmvalencia.es

ZARAGOZA

City in Aragon, north east Spain. Its 16th century university attracts over 40,000 students each year, including numerous overseas students. Some of its buildings reflect its past as an Arab-run city, notably the Moorish castle, the Aljafería; but there are also several churches dating back to the 14th century. In fact, there are influences from all kinds of European cultures in the city – city takes its name from Caesar Augustus.

CLIMATE

Hottest months July-August (17-31°C), coldest month December (2-10°C). Wettest month October; very little summer rain.

MUSICAL LIFE

Classical music at the Auditorio de Zaragoza, from visiting orchestras and soloists as well as resident performers Orquesta de Cámara del Auditorio and Coro Amici Musicae; also resident is Al Ayre Español early music ensemble.

OTHER CULTURAL INFORMATION

Teatro Principal Zaragoza for classical theatre. Large collection of tapestries at La Seo cathedral; Museo del Foro an exhibition of life in the city during Roman times. History centre at the San Agustin convent has archaeological findings from throughout city's history.

FESTIVALS AND EVENTS
Pilar Festival, with mixture of events from rock and folk music to handicraft fair as well as classical music concerts, takes over the town in October. Like many Spanish cities, has a carnival event in February. Jazz festival in November, folk music and art festival in September.

TOURIST INFORMATION
www.zaragoza.es, turismo@zaragoza.es, +34 902 14 2008

CONSERVATORIO SUPERIOR DE MUSICA DE ARAGON
Via Hispanidad 22, E-50009 Zaragoza, Spain
t: +34 976 716980 *f:* +34 976 716981
e: informacion@csma.es; erasmus@csma.es
w: www.consersup.com
Contact Hector Fouce, Erasmus co-ordinator

MUSIC FESTIVALS

Contemporary Music Festival of Valencia - ENSEMS C/ Grabador Esteve 5-1-2a, E-46004 Valencia, Spain *t:* +34 96 316 3723 *f:* +34 96 316 3724 *e:* ensems@ivm.gva.es *w:* www.ivm.gva.es Contemporary music. Conferences, composers, meetings, installations, etc.

Deia Festival Festival Internacional de Deia, Davall es Penya, E-07179 Deia, Mallorca, Spain *t:* +34 971 639178, also fax *w:* www.dimf.com Chamber music only.

Festival de Barcelona Grec Institut de Barcelona, La Rambla 99, E-08002 Barcelona, Spain *t:* +34 93 316 1112 *f:* +34 93 316 1110 *e:* bcnfestival@mail.bcn.es *w:* www.barcelonafestival.com Annual. Contemporary, flamenco and rock music.

Festival de Música Antiga Auditori de Barcelona, c/ Lepant 150, E-08013 Barcelona, Spain *e:* info@auditori.cat *w:* www.auditori.cat

Festival de Musica de Calonge Plaza de Castell Medieval 1, E-17251 Calonge (Girona), Spain *t:* +34 97 265 0311 *f:* +34 97 265 0673 *e:* info@festivalscalonge.net *w:* www.festivalscalonge.net Orchestral, jazz, flamenco. Summer season of concerts held in the medieval castle of Calonge, followed by autmun/winter season of piano concerts.

Festival de Musica de Canarias Avda de Canarias, 8 Trasera Edf Tucan, E-35002 Las Palmas de Gran Canaria, Spain *t:* +34 928 247 442 *f:* +34 928 276 042 *e:* info.festival@canariasculturaenred.com *w:* www.festivaldecanarias.com Annual. Classical, symphonic, choral, chamber music concerts and recitals, including premieres of works commissioned by the festival. Located on Gran Canaria, Tenerife and throughout the Canary Islands.

Festival de Musiques Religioses i del Mon Girona Passeig de la Devesa 35, E-17001 Girona, Spain *t:* +34 872 08 07 09 *w:* www.girona.cat/musiquesreligioses/

Festival de Opera de Las Palmas de Gran Canaria Alfredo Kraus Plaza de San Bernardo 8, E-35002 Las Palmas de Gran Canaria, Spain *t:* +34 928 37 01 25 *f:* +34 928 36 93 94 *e:* artistico@operalaspalmas.org *w:* www.operalaspalmas.org

Festival Internacional de Música Contemporánea de Tres Cantos C/Saturno 23, E-28760 Tres Cantos (Madrid), Spain *t:* +34 918040571, also fax *e:* festivaltc@terra.es *w:* www.festivaltrescantos.com

Festival Mozart Caixagalicia a Corun Palacio de la Opera, Glorieta de America, 3, E-15004 A Coruna, Spain *t:* +34 981 252 021 *f:* +34 981 277 499 *e:* info@festivalmozart.com *w:* www.festivalmozart.com

Granada International Festival of Music and Dance Aptdo Correos 64, E-18080 Granada, Spain *t:* +34 95 827 6200 *f:* +34 958 286 868 *e:* info@granadafestival.org *w:* www.granadafestival.org Annual. Classical music, flamenco, opera, ballet, recitals, workshops, fringe.

International Festival Andres Segovia C/ Fuerte de Navidad 2-6d, E-28004 Madrid, Spain *t:* +34 91 470 2655, also fax *e:* pablocconcejal@hotmail.com *w:* www.pablodelacruz.net Annual international guitar festival. Includes new music, and a new work each year for solo guitar and strings. Includes exhibition of early and new guitars in Jardín Botánico de Madrid.

Musica Antigua Aranjuez Cimbalo Producciones SL, C/Apodaca 9, Bajo derecha, E-28004 Madrid, Spain *t:* +34 91 447 64 00 *f:* +34 91 447 96 99 *e:* cimbalo@cimbalo.es *w:* www.musicaantiguaaranjuez.net

Operadhoy Campomanes, 3-3 Izda, E-28013 Madrid, Spain *t:* +34 91 548 73 48 *f:* +34 91 548 33 93 *w:* www.musicadhoy.com

Quincena Musical Avd Zurriola 1, E-20002 San Sebastian, Spain *t:* +34 94 300 3170 *f:* +34 94 300 3175 *w:* www.quincenamusical.com Annual. Classical music.

LISBON (LISBOA)

Portuguese capital on the river Tagus at the Atlantic coast. City has varied history, being successively conquered by Romans, Moors and eventually Portuguese again in 12th century. This history occasionally reflected in general architecture of the city, however following famous earthquake in 1755 (not the only one to have struck the city), major rebuilding took place in more contemporary style; the Alfama quarter is one that survived the disaster. Among various modern architectural structures is the longest bridge in Europe, the Vasco da Gama Bridge across the Tagus.

CLIMATE

Hottest months July and August (18-28°C), coolest month January (8-12°C). Winter months are markedly wetter, with over 100mm in November and December.

MUSICAL LIFE

Gulbenkian Foundation is a major musical presence (named after the philanthropist Calouste Gulbenkian, well known in other countries for his acts of charity in the cultural field), supporting both an orchestra and choir as well as programming various concert series in the three halls it houses. Other concert venues include Centro Cultural de Belém which stages all kinds of performing arts events from opera and classical music (Orquestra Metropolitana de Lisboa is a regular visitor) to theatre and dance. Teatro Nacional de São Carlos is the city's opera house, staging a full season plus symphony concerts by its house orchestra, the Orquestra Sinfónica Portuguesa (sometimes with the opera chorus). City closely associated with Fado, a unique, melancholy style of singing; there are numerous venues (bars and suchlike) where it can be heard.

OTHER CULTURAL INFORMATION

Modern art gallery at Gulbenkian Foundation; also Museu Calouste Gulbenkian, an exhibition of his private collection. Various museums devoted to Lisbon's and Portugal's history, customs and crafts; unusual museum of royal horse-drawn carriages. City's variety of theatres include a few either for or of interest to children.

FESTIVALS AND EVENTS

Alkantara is a biennial performing arts event (even years) that started out as dance-focused but now has a wider scope. Not far outside city is Sintra Music Festival, a classical music event running June-July. Jazz festival in August.

TOURIST INFORMATION

www.visitlisboa.com, atl@visitlisboa.com, +351 210 312 700

ACADEMIA NACIONAL SUPERIOR DE ORQUESTRA

Associação Música-Eudcaçao e Cultura, Travessa da Galé, 36, P-1349-028 Lisboa, Portugal
t: +351 21 361 73 20 *f:* +351 21 362 38 33
e: metropolitana@metropolitana.pt *w:* www.metropolitana.pt
Course information Bachelors and masters level qualifications for training in orchestral instruments or orchestral conducting. Also degree in piano accompaniment / piano in chamber music.
Admissions information *Fees* 1st cycle: EUR 2750 (orchestral conducting), EUR 2420 (orchestral instruments), EUR 2530 (piano); 2nd cycle: EUR 2420 (orchestral conducting), EUR 2420 (orchestral instruments), EUR 2530 (piano).

ESCOLA SUPERIOR DE MUSICA DE LISBOA

Rua do Ataide 7A, P-1200 Lisboa, Portugal
t: +351 21 3224940 *f:* +351 21 347 1489
e: esml@esml.ipl.pt *w:* www.esml.ipl.pt
Contact José João Gomes dos Santos, dir; Cecilia de Almeida Gonçalves, deputy dir/external relations co-ord
Course information 1st cycle: music (composition, choral conducting, instruments, voice); community music; musical communication (programming, production & stage techniques, audio & musical technology). 2nd cycl: masters in music.
Admissions information *Term dates* Sep-Jan; Feb-Jun. *Application requirements* 1st cycle: general or musical secondary education, audition and written test. 2nd cycle: a 1st cycle or equivalent qualification. *Application deadline* 2nd cycle: Feb; 1st cycle: May. Further details available on website. *Fees* 1st cycle: to be decided; 2nd cycle: EUR 1600 per year. *No of students* Approx 300 national students. *Language requirements* Portuguese, for attending theoretical lectures.
Facilities *Music facilities* Concert halls, electroacoustics studio, open-air auditorium *Accommodation* Students' residence available.

OPORTO (PORTO)

Portugal's second city, in the north of the country on the Atlantic coast. Its centre, with its baroque and Romanesque architecture, is an Unesco world heritage site. Sometimes nicknamed 'city of bridges' due to the number crossing the river Douro – the

Ponte Maria Pla was designed by Gustave Eiffel, and is a clear precursor of the Eiffel Tower in its design. City's pre-eminent role in export of fortified wine to Britain gave the drink port its name; there are numerous port cellars in the city where examples can be tried.

CLIMATE

Hottest months July and August (15-25°C), coolest month January (5-13°C). Winter rainfall is substantial (nearly 160mm November-January).

MUSICAL LIFE

Casa da Música, its unusual polyhedric design by Rem Koolhaas, is the prestigious music venue and home for Orquestra Nacional do Porto, a full-size symphony orchestra with interesting range of programming. Three other groups resident there: chorus; a baroque music ensemble; and Remix Ensemble, an internationally renowned contemporary music group. Coliseu do Porto, an art deco concert hall with a varied programme of classical music and other events.

OTHER CULTURAL INFORMATION

Main museums are Soares dos Reis museum (art, ceramics, furniture etc) and Museu de Serralves (modern and contemporary art). City is home to an unusual artistic co-operative with a troubled history, Árvore, a place dedicated to artistic creation and display.

FESTIVALS AND EVENTS

Annual cartoon festival running over the summer months. Various city festivities such as Festa da São João (June) or the Queima das Fitas (May), traditionally the last hurrah of the city's students before exams begin.

TOURIST INFORMATION

www.portoturismo.pt, turismo.central@cm-porto.pt, +351 223 393 472

ESCOLA SUPERIOR DE MÚSICA, ARTES E ESPECTÁCULO DO PORTO (PORTO SUPERIOR SCHOOL OF MUSIC AND PERFORMING ARTS)

Rua da Alegria 503, P-4000-045 Porto, Portugal
t: +351 22 519 37 60 *f:* +351 22 518 07 74
e: international@esmae-ipp.pt
w: www.esmae-ipp.pt
Contact Bruno Pereira.
Course information Music courses: instrumental, composition, music production and technology, jazz, early music; also courses in theatre (acting, sound and light design, costumes, scenography, stage management) and image arts (photography, audiovisual and multimedia).
Admissions information *Term dates* Sep-Jul *Application requirements* See website for details of application requirements. *Application deadline* Mar-April *Fees* approx EUR 900pa. *No of students* 680 national students, 40 from overseas

MUSIC FESTIVALS

Alkantara Rua do Forno do Tijolo, 54 - 5o Esq, P-1170-138 Lisbon, Portugal *t:* +351 213 152 267 *f:* +351 213 151 368 *e:* alkantara@alkantara.pt *w:* www.alkantara.pt Biennial performing arts festival.
Festival do Estoril Galerias Estoril, Rua de Lisboa 5, Lj 12, P-2765-240 Estoril, Portugal *t:* +351 21 468 5199 *e:* festivaldoestoril@sapo.pt *w:* www.estorilfestival.net Symphonic, chamber, recitals, master courses, competition, seminars, conferences, composers meeting.
Festival Internacional de Musica da Povoa de Varzim Rua D Maria I - 56, P-4490-538 Povoa de Varzim, Portugal *t:* +351 52 5261 4145 *f:* +351 52 5261 2548 *e:* auditorio@cm-pvarzim.pt *w:* www.cm-pvarzim.pt/go/festivalinternacionalmusica Medieval, renaissance, baroque, classical, romantic and contemporary music.
Ponte de Lima Festival of Opera and Classical Music Associacao Cultural do Norte Portugal, Quinta de Igreja, Feitosa, P-4990-341 Ponte de Lima, Portugal *t:* +351 258 931 141 *f:* +351 258 931 143 *e:* teatrodb@cm-pontedelima.pt *w:* www.operalima.com
Sintra International Choir Festival *t:* +351 21 916 26 28 *e:* sintrachoirfestival@gmail.com *w:* www.sintrachoirfestival.com

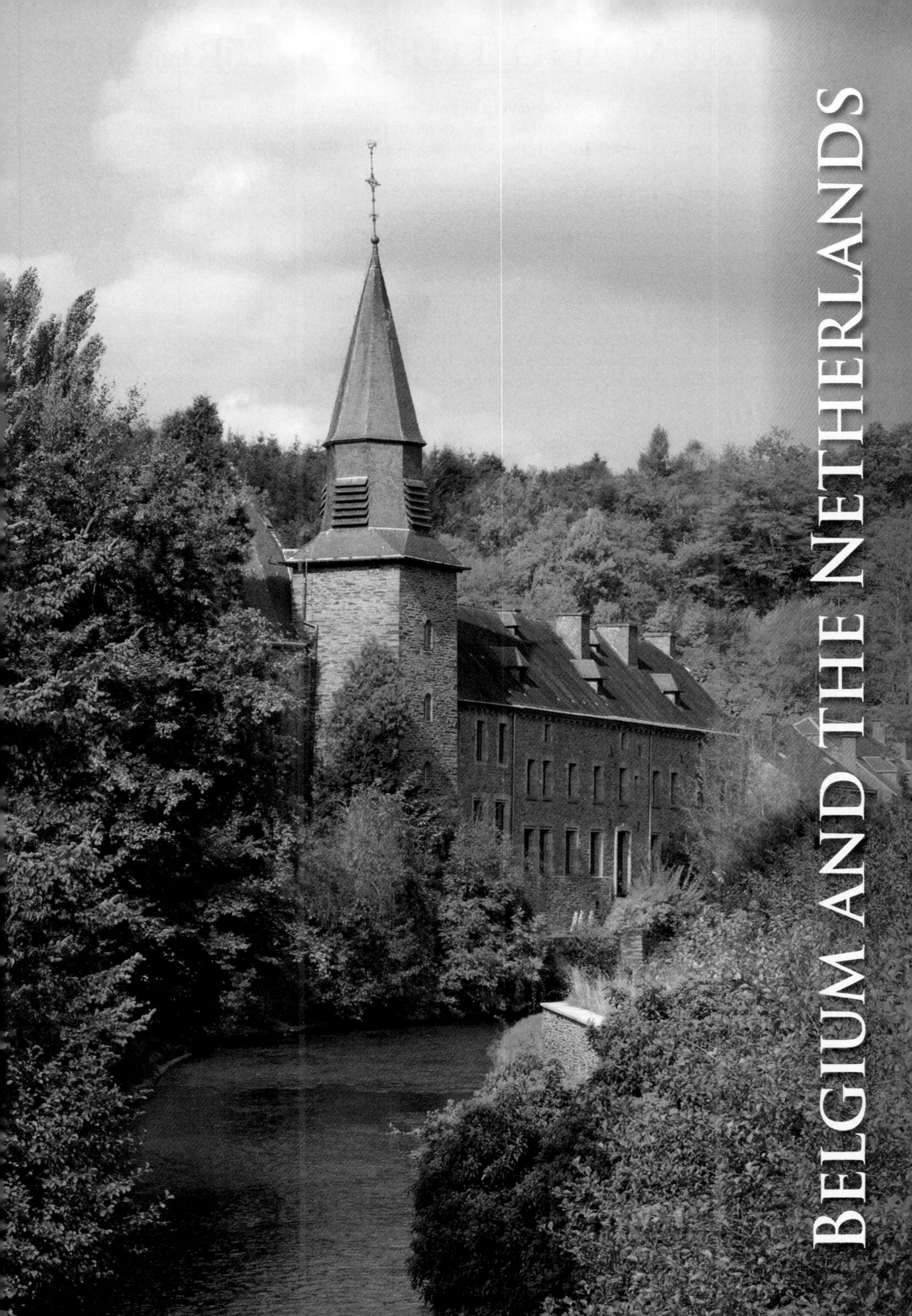
BELGIUM AND THE NETHERLANDS

Belgium and The Netherlands

Students intending to apply to institutions in Belgium will need to bear in mind the dual-language constitution of the country. Flanders is to the north (it includes the cities of Antwerp, Gent and Leuven) and is Dutch-speaking; the south (the part of the country known as Wallonia and whose main city is Liège) is French-speaking. The anomaly is the capital Brussels (Brussel in Dutch, Bruxelles in French) which lies in the southern part but is officially bilingual, a situation complicated by the fact that increasingly French has come to predominate. For various reasons, such as the relative wealth of the north compared to the south, this is quite a contentious issue in Belgian politics and society, and visitors should be aware of it before arriving. In the Netherlands, English is widely understood (though not universally) in the main cities.

Leaving the language issue to one side, both countries offer much to the visitor wishing to spend a reasonable period of time there. For instance, both countries have long histories with periods of great prosperity and influence and this has left its mark in town planning and architectural styles – think gothic town halls, cobbled streets and market places. Both are well-connected, with Amsterdam airport a major European hub and Brussels one of the homes of the European parliament.

BELGIUM PAGE 141

The situation in Belgium is somewhat complicated for those coming from overseas because of the two cultural systems.

Both systems have adopted the Bologna system of 3 (bachelors or 1st cycle) + 2 (masters or 2nd cycle) year levels, although there are slight differences between the systems.

In French-speaking institutions, for instance, students can supplement their studies with a further 60 ECTS credits to gain a 'specialist artist' masters. The curriculum in the French-speaking institutions is to a large extent determined centrally, with all institutions teaching the same courses; only one third of the curriculum is set by the individual conservatoires.

In the Flemish system, degrees are offered by the conservatoires (officially known as Hogescholen, or high schools) in association with universities, and quality assurance is undertaken on the same basis as academic degrees. Institutions are at liberty to design their own courses, although the nature of advanced musical studies in many areas means there are inevitably similarities. The one slightly unusual exception is the Gent-based Orpheus Instituut, a specialist music academy operating at postgraduate level only.

In both Flemish and Walloon/Brussels systems, earning a bachelors automatically qualifies a student to progress to masters level.

THE NETHERLANDS PAGE 146

Bachelors courses in the Netherlands are 4 years, with an additional 2 for masters studies, and institutions have a great deal of flexibility in the modules they can offer – the Utrecht college offers a degree in bell-ringing, for instance. However, they are required to ensure courses are designed in such a way that certain stipulated competencies for that course are met.

Tuition fees for non-EU/EEA students have been considerably increased in recent years, and event students from within the European area now must expect to pay some fees (probably at least EUR 1500, depending on course and location). This is a result of changes in the Dutch government's allocation of its education resources; in the case of non-EU/EEA students, government funding has ceased, forcing Dutch universities and other institutes of higher education to introduce tuition fees.

ANTWERP (ANTWERPEN)

A city in the Dutch-speaking part of Belgium (Flanders) on the river Scheidt at the North Sea, it came into prominence during the 16th century thanks to its success as a trading port and as one of the principal cities in Europe at the time. Its wealth at that time has left a legacy in the city's distinctive architecture, such as that around the main square – the city hall and guild houses being some of the most spectacular – although there has been modern development around the river and its quays. Now also famous as a centre for the diamond trade.

CLIMATE

Warmest months July and August (12-23°C), coldest month January (0-6°C); wettest months also in summer, although the weather can be changeable throughout the year.

MUSICAL LIFE

Large amount of musical performance. Vlaamse Opera performs some of its season at the opera house (other shows are in Gent), its orchestra giving occasional concerts too. Similarly the Symfonieorkest Vlaanderen, which has bases in cities around Flanders. A third orchestra, and one of the busiest, is de Filharmonie, performing at de Singel arts centre or the Queen Elizabeth Hall.

OTHER CULTURAL INFORMATION

Significant in fine art due to the style of painting known as the Antwerp School (Rubens, Van Dyck and so on). This is well represented in city's galleries, such as the Rubenshuis, or the Royal Museum of Fine Arts

FESTIVALS AND EVENTS

Under the umbrella of Flanders Festival-Antwerp is a small event, Laus Polyphoniae, in August focusing on period music. Larger scale Antwerp Summer Festival features all kinds of music as well as circus, theatre, dance and other performances. Various outdoor events during summer. City hosts an annual book fair in November. Slightly more unusual is annual Laundry Day, a street party whose name refers to the custom in earlier times of women gossiping while hanging out laundry in the street.

TOURIST INFORMATION

www.antwerpen.be, toerisme@stad.antwerpen.be, +32 3 232 01 03

ARTESIS HOGESCHOOL ANTWERPEN - KONINKLIJK CONSERVATORIUM

Desguinlei 25, B-2018 Antwerpen, Belgium
t: +32 3 244 18 00 *f:* +32 3 238 90 17
e: conservatorium@artesis.be *w:* www.artesis.be/conservatorium

Contact Wilma Schneider, international relations co-ord; Birgit Soil, head of the student admin.

Course information Bachelors degrees (180 ECTS) in instrumental studies, vocal studies, theory of music/harmony and counterpoint, jazz and popular music. Masters degrees (120 ECTS) in instrumental studies, vocal studies, conducting, composition, music pedagogy, jazz and popular music. Also postgrad course (1 year, 60 ECTS) specialising as instrumental or vocal concert soloist, in composition, accompaniment, chamber music or orchestra.

Admissions information *Term dates* Sep-Jul. *Application requirements* Appropriate diploma and artistic entrance exam. Overseas students may be admitted on the basis of a DVD/video recording (not CD). *Application deadline* Mid May (first session); end Aug/beginning Sep (second session). Exact dates to be confirmed. *Fees* Approx EUR 540 for undergraduate; EUR 2500-5700 for postgraduate, depending on course and nationality. *Scholarships* None. *No of students* 400 national students; about 80 from overseas. *Language requirements* Level A1 for theory of music/harmony.

Facilities *Music facilities* Library inc scores, reference works, online reference (inc Grove Online)

BRUSSELS (BRUSSEL / BRUXELLES)

Belgian capital, and centre for European politics (it holds the headquarters of the European Commission). Although located in the (wealthier) Dutch-speaking part of the country, most residents have French as their first language and it has taken over as lingua franca (!). In fact, both languages have official status. This is, perhaps understandably, a cause of some tension, particularly among the Dutch community. At the centre of the city is one of Europe's most spectacular squares, the medieval Grote Markt / Grand Place, although as a whole it does not have the historic feel of other Flemish cities.

CLIMATE

Warmest months July and August (13-22°C), coldest month January (0-6°C). Rainfall fairly uniform throughout the year, ranging between 50 and 80mm per month.

La Monnaie / De Munt is the city's opera house,

EUROPE

and apart from the opera orchestra, 2 other main groups based there: National Orchestra of Belgium, performing about 70 concerts a year at Palais des Beaux-Arts / Paleis voor Schone Kunsten, around Belgium and abroad; Brussels Philharmonic is new name for the Flemish Radio Orchestra, and has a new home, the multi-space Flagey building. Orchestra still associated with Flemish Radio Choir. Various concert series run through the year.

OTHER CULTURAL INFORMATION
Several museums and galleries; the museum complex Musées Royaux des Beaux Arts / Koninklijke Musea voor Schone Kunsten houses several in one place. Brussels a notable contributor to Art Nouveau, and the home of Art Nouveau architect Victor Horta is open to public. Musical instrument museum (located in a Horta building) is one of the most comprehensive in the world. The Atomium is one of the most recognisable landmarks; built for Expo 58, its interconnected spheres now contain various science-related exhibits, some permanent.

FESTIVALS AND EVENTS
Specialist contemporary music festival, Ars Musica, in spring. Early music festival at the Grand Sablon church, also in spring. KlaraFestival begins at end of August and runs for 2 weeks. Free concerts in all kinds of music styles during Brussels Summer Festival and classical music at Royal Parc festival in July; jazz during Jan festival at Théâtre Marni, during weekend in May (Brussels Jazz Marathon) as well as July (Brosella Folk and Jazz Festival).

TOURIST INFORMATION
www.brusselsinternational.be; tourism@brusselsinternational.be; +32 2 513 89 40

CONSERVATOIRE ROYAL DE BRUXELLES
Rue de la Régence 30, 1000 Bruxelles, Belgium
t: +32 2 500 87 17 *f:* +32 2 512 69 79
e: secretariat@conservatoire.be; erasmus@conservatoire.be *w:* www.conservatoire.be
Contact Vincent Heylen, erasmus co-ord.
Course information 2-cycle structure leading to either bachelors or masters. Specialisms in orchestral instruments, period instruments, singing, music theory, jazz.
Admissions information *Term dates* 3 terms: mid Sep-late Jan, late Jan-mid May, mid May-mid Sep. Last term includes summer holiday and 2 exam sessions. Full details of mid-term holidays available on website. *Application requirements* By application and audition (timetable of auditions available on website)

KONINKLIJK CONSERVATORIUM BRUSSEL
Regentschapsstraat 30, B-1000 Brussel, Belgium
t: +32 2 513 45 87 *f:* +32 2 513 22 53 *e:* kcb@kcb.be *w:* www.kcb.be
Course information Bachelors in academic music or professional music training. Full or part time study, flexible degree programmes.
Admissions information *Application requirements* Downloadable application form. All students must comply with entrance requirements and pass an exam. See website for full details. *Fees* 2009-10 fees: EUR 567.80 (EU, Norway, Iceland, Liechtenstein); EUR 6072 (all other countries).
Facilities *Music facilities* Practice rooms, unique 19th century concert hall, library. *Performance opportunities* Opportunities for ensemble playing, lunchtime concerts, seminars and masterclasses.

GENT (GHENT)
City in the Dutch-speaking part of Belgium whose centre has a very distinctive medieval flavour thanks to the predominance of its architecture of the period. The rivers (it is on the confluence of the Lys and Scheidt rivers) and canal flowing through it add to its authentic charm – the canal, which links to the coast, also means the city can accommodate sea-going vessels.

CLIMATE
Warmest month August (14-23°C), coldest month January (1-6°C). As with much of the country, rainfall is relatively uniform throughout the year.

MUSICAL LIFE
Home to one of the world's great vocal ensembles, the Collegium Vocale Gent; city is also the main base for Vlaamse Opera. Bijloke Gent Music Centre is a medieval infirmary converted into a smart concert hall putting on classical, jazz and world music concerts.

OTHER CULTURAL INFORMATION
Many museums and galleries. Museum of Fine Arts for old masters, including the work of Flemings such as Hieronymus Bosch; also contemporary art gallery (SMAK), design museum, textile museum, even a museum of psychiatry. Vooruit Arts Centre for contemporary performance; Capitole (a former cinema) for musicals, comedy, cabaret and so on. Brand new museum, the Museum of the City of Gent,

is due to open in 2010.

FESTIVALS AND EVENTS
Gentse Feesten, a 10-day festival of music and theatre including many street events, begins in July.

TOURIST INFORMATION
www.visitgent.be, visit@gent.be, +32 9 266 56 60

HOGESCHOOL GENT CONSERVATORIUM
Hoogpoort 64, B-9000 Gent, Belgium
t: +32 9 269 20 00 *f:* +32 9 269 20 08
e: cons@hogent.be; katrien.vanacker@hogent.be (foreign relations) *w:* http://cons.hogent.be
Contact Katrien VanAcker, foreign relations.
Course information Majors in performing music (instrumental, vocal; classical, jazz or pop); creative music (composition, music production); music theory/ harmony and counterpoint; also instrument making. Post-masters in orchestral conducting, composition, contemporary music solo performance.
Admissions information *Application requirements* Entrance exam; details of exam requirements and application form available on website. *Language requirements* Dutch or English (MMus offered in English)
Facilities *Music facilities* 2 concert halls (Salle Miry, 504 seats; Salle Mengal, 96 seats); theatre hall, recording studio, library, study facilities.

ORPHEUS INSTITUUT
Korte Meer 12, B-9000 Gent, Belgium
t: +32 9 330 40 81 *f:* +32 9 330 40 82
e: info@orpheusinstituut.be
w: www.orpheusinstituut.be
Course information Only postgrad studies, all musical styles and trends. Laureate programme, tailor-made to student's artistic choices and personal background; doctoral programme 'docARTES' starts with 2 year curriculum, title awarded to musicians/ composers who can combine artistic performances at the highest level with systematic theoretical reflection.
Admissions information *Term dates* Duration of study period determined once candidate is accepted for enrolment. *Application requirements* For laureate programme, application by portfolio (see website for details of requirements), interview and possible admission exam; for doctoral programme 'docARTES', see www.docartes.be. *Application deadline* Anytime during year (laureate programme); 1 Oct or 1 Apr (docARTES programme). *Fees* EUR 2500 enrolment fee (laureate and doctoral programmes). *No of students* 32 overseas students on doctoral programme.
Facilities *Music facilities* 120 seat concert hall (converted cinema) with Steinway and harpsichord, audiovisual equipment; conference room, study rooms, library, recording studio

LEUVEN (LOUVAIN)
Small Flemish city with a large student population (it is the location for the world's oldest Catholic university and a number of other higher education institutions). The city includes a number of characteristic northern European gothic buildings, like the towering town hall and St Peter's Church across the square. Also has an architectural feature common to a number of places in Belgium, a béguinage, a collection of apartments built originally for a religious community of women, that in Leuven is more like a village – the Leuven grand béguinage has been restored having fallen into decline by the mid 20th century. The city is considered by many Belgium's beer capital because of the close association between brewing and the city.

MUSICAL LIFE
Base for internationally renowned early music group La Petite Bande

OTHER CULTURAL INFORMATION
A new museum, M, opened in 2009 – forward-looking institution dedicated to various visual arts including photography, video, architecture as well as painting and sculpture.

FESTIVALS AND EVENTS
International organ festival in May; Afrika Filmfestival is another event.

TOURIST INFORMATION
www.leuven.be, tourism@leuven.be, +32 16 20 30 20

LEMMENSINSTITUUT LEUVEN HOGESCHOOL VOOR WETENSCHAP & KUNST (FACULTY OF MUSIC, PERFORMING ARTS AND EDUCATION)
Herestraat 53, B-3000 Leuven, Belgium
t: +32 16 23 39 67 *f:* +32 16 22 24 77
e: info@lemmens.wenk.be
w: www.lemmens.wenk.be
Contact K Wittevrongel.

EUROPE

Course information Bachelors and masters in composition, conducting (orchestral and choral), music education, music therapy, instrumental and vocal music, jazz; also drama.
Admissions information *Term dates* Sep-Jan; Feb-Jun. *Application requirements* Admission test or proof of degree equivalence. *Fees* EUR 635 (EU members); EUR 5700 (non-EU members). *No of students* 450 students. *Language requirements* English and French language facilities (1st and 2nd year); Dutch from 3rd year onwards.
Facilities *Music facilities* Free entrance to weekly concerts in the Lemmensinstituut. *Accommodation* 80% of students live in private accommodation; assistance available through University of Leuven housing service.

LIEGE

Historic old city in the French speaking part of Belgium on the river Meuse and near the borders of Germany and the Netherlands.

MUSICAL LIFE

L'orchestre Philharmonique de Liège is a well regarded orchestra which performs a full season at the Salle Philharmonique (and across Belgium), a venue which also stages recitals and other concerts. Opera from the Opéra Royal de Wallonie at the city's opera house.

OTHER CULTURAL INFORMATION

Galleries include a museum of modern and contemporary art, a gallery of Walloon art plus smaller spaces; various museums on particular subjects (eg lighting, or transport) as well as more general – the Ansembourg museum and its portrayal of aristocratic life, or the Museum of Walloon Life; the Grand Curtius museum, with its striking redbrick construction, is another exhibition of artefacts and decorative arts.

FESTIVALS AND EVENTS

Festival de Liège (January-February) showcases contemporary theatre, dance and music. Festival of crime film in April; annual jazz festival in May.

TOURIST INFORMATION

www.liege-leodium.be

CONSERVATOIRE ROYAL DE LIÈGE

Boulevard Piercot, 29, B-4000 Liège, Belgium
t: +32 4 222 03 06 *f:* +32 4 222 03 84 *e:* info@crlg.be *w:* www.crlg.be

Course information Bachelors and masters in accompaniment, lyric arts, singing, composition, strings, orchestral and choral conducting, theory of music, guitar, organ, percussion, piano, woodwind and brass.
Facilities *Music facilities* Library. *Performance opportunities* Orchestra, jazz band.

MONS

City in the French-speaking part of Belgium. Although it has a long history, reflected in the central square with its town hall, it is known more for its more recent industrial past.

MUSICAL LIFE

Orchestre Royal de Chambre de Wallonie is based in Mons, although it performs across the region.

OTHER CULTURAL INFORMATION

manège.mons and the Conseil Culturel Participatif are both Mons-based organisations promoting cultural activity in the city. Various small local institutions such as a Maison du Design, a theatre company, dance company and museums.

FESTIVALS AND EVENTS

The Doudou is a festival specific to Mons, a street celebration of a 14th century religious procession taking place over a week over Trinity Sunday.

TOURIST INFORMATION

www.mons.be

CONSERVATOIRE ROYAL DE MONS

7 rue de Nimy, B-7000 Mons, Belgium
t: +32 6534 7377 *f:* +32 6534 9906 *e:* crm.mons@sup.cfwb.be *w:* www.conservatoire-mons.be

Course information Bachelors (3 years) and masters (2 years) music teaching, theory (with option in composition), keyboard instruments, string instruments, percussion, woodwind and brass instruments, singing, early music (various instruments), electroacoustic music, piano accompaniment, composition, conducting (orchestral and choral).

NAMUR

City in French-speaking Belgium with a history dating back to medieval times. Its most striking feature is its citadel, a hill-top fortress built then to protect the city, a function it fulfilled right up to World War II.

 **OTHER CULTURAL INFORMATION**

Various small museums.

ⓘ **TOURIST INFORMATION**

www.namurtourisme.be

INSTITUT SUPÉRIEUR DE MUSIQUE ET DE PÉDAGOGIE

28 rue Juppin, B-5000 Namur, Belgium
t: +32 81 73 64 37 *f:* +32 81 73 95 14
e: info@imep.be; erasmus@imep.be
w: www.imep.be
Contact Christian Croufer, Erasmus exchange admin.
Course information Institute based in Christian educational tradition. Courses offered in keyboard instruments (piano, organ, accompaniment, accordion), strings (incl guitar and harp), wind, brass, percussion, singing, early music (recorder, lute, harpsichord, viola da gamba), composition and conducting.
Admissions information *Application requirements* Entrance exam; application form available online. *Fees* See website for details of course material and inscription fees.
Facilities *Accommodation* Bulletin board listing local & available accommodation.

WATERLOO

Town on the outskirts of Brussels, famous as the location for the British general Wellington's victory over Napoleon in 1815.

 **TOURIST INFORMATION**

www.waterloo-tourisme.be, info@waterloo-tourisme.be, +32 2 352 09 10

CHAPELLE MUSICAL REINE ELISABETH ASBL

445 Chaussée de Tervuren, B-1410 Waterloo, Belgium
t: +32 2 352 01 10 *f:* +32 2 351 10 24
e: info@cmre.be; jmtom@wanadoo.fr
w: www.cmre.be
Contact Jean-Marie Tomasi, international consultant
Course information Four areas of study: preparatory class for exceptional young talents aged 8-15 (piano, violin, singing); class for advanced musicians aged 16-22 (piano, violin, singing); 'Master after Master' diploma for students at post-conservatoire level (piano, violin, singing, chamber music); Opera Studio.
Admissions information *Application requirements* Application form available on website. Applicants should include any documentation likely to give an indication of their ability, copies of diplomas obtained, prizes won in competitions, recent recommendations or written favorable opinions, etc. *Application deadline* Early Mar. *Fees* EUR 25 application fee; EUR 12,500pa tuition fee.
Facilities *Music facilities* Library and record collection. *Accommodation* Study bedrooms including pianos.

MUSIC FESTIVALS

Le Clavecin en Fête *t:* +32 16 48 08 36 *f:* +32 16 49 06 90 *e:* betty.bruylants@cyclone.be *w:* www.amisduclavecin.be Festival of harpsichord performances.
Festival Ars Musica 203/1 Galerie Louise, B-1050 Bruxelles, Belgium *t:* +32 2 219 2660 *f:* +32 2 219 8814 *e:* info@arsmusica.be *w:* www.arsmusica.be Annual festival of contemporary music. Concerts, conferences, masterclasses, multidisciplinary activities (exhibitions, films), opera.
Festival de Wallonie Rue de l'Armée, Grouchy 20, B-5000 Namur, Belgium *t:* +32 81 733781 *f:* +32 81 742503 *e:* info@festivaldewallonie.be *w:* www.festivaldewallonie.be
International Acousmatic Festival: L'Espace du Son Musiques & Recherches, Place de Ransbeck 3, B-1380 Ohain, Belgium *t:* +32 23 544368 *f:* +32 2 351 0094 *e:* musiques.recherches@skynet.be *w:* www.musiques-recherches.be 4-day festival, acousmatic music.
KlaraFestival Rue Ravensteinstraat 36, B-1000 Brussels, Belgium *t:* +32 2 548 95 95 *f:* +32 2 548 95 90 *w:* www.klarafestival.be
Laus Polyphoniae 12 Everdijstraat, B-2000 Antwerpen, Belgium *t:* +32 3 202 46 69 *f:* +32 3 202 46 64 *w:* www.festival.be Festival focusing on historically informed performance.
MAfestival Concertgebouw, t Zand 34, B-8000 Brugge, Belgium *t:* +32 50 33 22 83 *f:* +32 50 34 52 04 *e:* info@MAfestival.be *w:* www.festival.be/brugge Competition and exhibition for instrumental and vocal soloists. Lunchtime and evening concerts. 2008 themes: London in Musica Antiqua; viola da gamba.
Les Nuits de Septembre rue des Mineurs 17, B-4000 Liège, Belgium *t:* +32 42 236674 *f:* +32 42 221540 *e:* jmlg@jeunessesmusicales.be *w:* www.festivaldewallonie.be Baroque music.
Zomeropera Alden Biesen Kasteelstr 6, B-3740 Bilzen, Belgium *t:* +32 89 79 41 27 *e:* info@zomeropera.be *w:* www.zomeropera.be Festival production of Il Barbiere di Siviglia; production for children of Haensel und Gretchen.

EUROPE

THE NETHERLANDS

ALKMAAR

City on the Noord Holland peninsula in the west of the country characterised by canals and architecture dating back to the 17th century and beyond. It has a celebrated traditional cheese market, a legacy of the city's historic role as an agricultural marketplace.

MUSICAL INFORMATION

The city is noted for the variety of organs in its churches.

OTHER CULTURAL INFORMATION

Stedelijk Museum regional museum is in the city. Cheese museum at the city's landmark Waag – 'weighing house'; there is also a beer museum in the city.

FESTIVALS AND EVENTS

Biennial 10-day organ festival (odd-numbered years).

TOURIST INFORMATION

www.alkmaar.nl

CONSERVATORIUM HOGESCHOOL INHOLLAND ALKMAAR

PO Box 403, NL-1800 AK Alkmaar, The Netherlands
t: +31 72 518 35 55; +31 72 518 34 56 (international office) *f:* +31 72 518 35 54
e: Intoffice.Alkmaar@inholland.nl (international office) *w:* www.inholland.nl
Admissions information *Term dates* Sep-Jun *Fees* EUR 1620 (Dutch and EU/EEA students); EUR 6500 (non-EU/EEA). *Language requirements* Some courses can be taught in English but Dutch language courses and/or transition year are available.

AMSTERDAM

Capital of the Netherlands, though not the seat of government, and a major tourist destination. Historically prominent due to its importance as a trading port in the 17th century, at which time the first of the canals which run around it and for which it is now famous were built. The historic centre is at the heart, with 5 rings of canals surrounding it. Architecturally mixed, with renaissance, baroque, neo-gothic examples, but also more modern style from art nouveau and art deco and after; it gave its name to a style of brick-based modern architecture, the Amsterdam School. The city is ideal for cyclists as the city has a strong culture of cycle riding, aided by its lack of hills.

CLIMATE

Warmest month August (12-21°C), coldest month January (1-6°C). Rainfall fairly uniform throughout the year, but slightly wetter in autumn and early winter.

MUSICAL LIFE

Royal Concertgebouw Orchestra, one of the world's best, performs at the hall from which it takes its name; the building encompasses 3 performance spaces, from the Grote Zaal for orchestral concerts to the ornate, oval Spiegelzaal. Opera at Muziektheater, a modern building in keeping with surroundings, home to De Nederlandse Opera. Various orchestras provide accompaniment here, including the Amsterdam-based Netherlands Philharmonic. Amsterdam Symphony Orchestra also travels to Den Haag and Rotterdam as well as playing at the Concertgebouw. Nieuw Ensemble is an Amsterdam-based contemporary music group; Orchestra of the Eighteenth Century a period classical ensemble. Jazz and improvised music have their own specialist venue, the Bimhuis, next to a specialist contemporary music venue, the Muziekgebouw aan 't IJ. Concerts happen in numerous other venues too, such as Oude Kerk (the city's cathedral and a major landmark), and the city is popular destination for touring amateur choirs, youth orchestras etc.

OTHER CULTURAL INFORMATION

The city has a Museum Square, with the main Rijksmuseum (Dutch art in particular, especially Rembrandt – there is also a Rembrandt museum elsewhere), the Van Gogh Museum and Stedelijk Museum (modern art, currently undergoing expansion and renovation) the main institutions. Away from the square, many will pay a visit to Anne Frank's House; many other small museums and exhibitions too. Famous Russian Hermitage museum opened a new branch in the city in 2009. The architectural style of the Amsterdam School is explored in a museum dedicated to it.

FESTIVALS AND EVENTS

Holland Festival (June) is largest event in the city, featuring music and opera as part of wider performing arts programme. August sees a festival celebrating city's canals, Grachtenfestival, with concerts in various venues, private buildings, restaurants and churches as well as concert halls.

LOCAL PUBLICATIONS
Amsterdam Spoke (www.amsterdam-spoke.com) is a magazine covering events, enterainment, leisure activities and local news.

TOURIST INFORMATION
www.iamsterdam.com, info@atcb.nl, +31 20 2018800

CONSERVATORIUM VAN AMSTERDAM
Oosterdokskade 151, Postbus 78022, NL-1070 LP Amsterdam, Netherlands
t: +31 20 527 7550 *f:* +31 20 676 1506 *e:* info@ahk.nl *w:* www.conservatoriumvanamsterdam.nl
Contact Rita Spin, international relations office.
Course information Bachelors and masters in classical music, bachelors and masters in jazz, bachelors in pop, masters in opera, bachelors in music in education.
Admissions information *Term dates* See website for course dates. *Application requirements* Entrance exam consisting of practical part and general part (ear tests, musical knowledge); sample test available on website. For exchange students a recording is sufficient. *Application deadline* 1 Apr; entrance exam in May/Jun, early exam in Jan possible. *Fees* EUR 1300-2000, depending on nationality and course. Further details on website. *No of students* 50% of student intake from overseas. *Language requirements* English or Dutch.
Facilities *Music facilities* New conservatory building contains c 100 teaching rooms, 4 concert halls, 60 study rooms, library, internet café, 2 recording studios with channels to the concert halls. *Accommodation* No campus accommodation; some advice on finding housing is provided

ARNHEM
Eastern Dutch city, and location of a notorious World War II battle. Noted for its green spaces and smart city centre.

CLIMATE
Hottest months July and August (11-22°C), coldest month January (-1°-4°C). Wettest month December (92mm), driest month April (50mm).

MUSICAL LIFE
Main performing arts venue is Musis Sacrum Schouwberg, featuring classical music among its wider programme. Het Gelders Orkest performs there, and elsewhere in the region.

OTHER CULTURAL INFORMATION
Several museums, like the Arnhem Museum for Modern Art which has its own collection of modern and contemporary art, decorative art and design; it also houses temporary exhibitions and a sculpture garden. The National Heritage Museum is an open air display feature various aspects Dutch history, and the country's National Park can be found nearby. The Liberation Route reflects the city's part in the end of WWII.

FESTIVALS AND EVENTS
Annual outdoor summer art festival (the Sonsbeek Festival). More unusually, there is an annual international festival/competition for human statues.

TOURIST INFORMATION
www.vvvarnhemnijmegen.nl

ARTEZ SCHOOL OF MUSIC
Utrechtsestraat 85, PO Box 49, NL-6800 AA Arnhem, Netherlands
t: +31 26 35 35 643 *f:* +31 26 35 35 637
e: conservatorium.arnhem@artez.nl *w:* www.artez-conservatorium.nl; www.artez.nl
Contact Thom Koldenhof, dir of Arnhem location.
Course information Classical music, jazz and pop, music theatre.
Admissions information *Term dates* Aug-Jul. *Application requirements* Entrance exam and practical test; see website for full details. *Application deadline* 1 May. *Fees* EU/EEA: EUR 1805 (full time), EUR 996 (part time); non-EU/EEA: EUR 7763. Loans may be available; see website for more details. *Scholarships* Scholarships for non-European students only. *No of students* 900 students; 45% from overseas. *Language requirements* Dutch is official language, alhough some bachelors programmes are bilingual (Dutch/English). Most masters courses in English. Intensive language courses for non-Dutch speakers.
Facilities *Music facilities* Concert auditoria, studios, mediatheques, variety of workshops for audio-visual productions, graphics, music and sound. *Accommodation* Website gives details of accommodation agencies in each location.

DEN HAAG (THE HAGUE)
City on the North Sea, Seat of Dutch government, home of royal family although not the country's capital city. Also home to various international political organisations such as International Court

EUROPE

of Justice and other judicial institutions. Apart from the conservatoire and an applied sciences institute, there is no university so student life not as extensive as elsewhere. Architecture and built environment atypical of the country without prominent canals or narrow streets encountered elsewhere. City has two popular beaches nearby.

CLIMATE

Warmest months July and August (13-21°C), coldest months January and February (1-6°C). Rainfall tends to be heaviest during summer and autumn, although in general, weather is changeable throughout the year.

MUSICAL LIFE

The Residentie Orkest is the main orchestra, performing at the Anton Philipszaal, next door to a specialist dance venue, Lucent Danstheater.

OTHER CULTURAL INFORMATION

City houses a substantial collection of art by Piet Mondriaan (Gemeentemuseum); numerous other galleries and museums such as the Mauritshuis Museum with its collection of Dutch and Flemish masters.. Panorama Mesdag an unusual, large 360 degree painting of a late 19th century landscape; Beelden aan Zee is collection of outdoor sculptures. Numerous theatres also, ranging from the classical Royal Theatre to circus and theatre in a converted swimming baths (Theatre de Regentes)

FESTIVALS AND EVENTS

Jazz festival in May. A major festival celebrating Indonesian and European culture, the Pasar Malam Besar, reflects the city's and country's role in historical trading with Indonesia (May-Jun).

TOURIST INFORMATION

www.denhaag.com, +31 900 3403505

KONINKLIJK CONSERVATORIUM, DEN HAAG (ROYAL CONSERVATOIRE, THE HAGUE)

Juliana van Stolberglaan 1, NL-2595 CA Den Haag, The Netherlands
t: +31 703151515 *f:* +31 703151518 *e:* e.eijken@koncon.nl *w:* www.koncon.nl
Contact Eugene Eijken, international students adviser
Course information Bachelor of music and master of music, in classical music, early music, jazz, sonology, art of sound, composition, music pedagogy, opera; also dance (ballet).
Admissions information *Term dates* 1 Sep-30 Jun. *Application requirements* See website for full details, including set works for auditions. *Application deadline* 1 May. *Fees* EUR 3194. *No of students* Approx 800 students, inc c 500 from overseas.

ENSCHEDE

City in east Netherlands near Germany, former mainstay of the Dutch textile industry and currently undergoing a number of urban renewal projects to help reverse years of decline – there is a distinct modern feel to the place as a result. Science and technology predominates in city's educational background, but there is an arts academy too.

CLIMATE

Warmest months July and August, temperatures ranging between 14° and 22°C.

MUSICAL LIFE

City has its own opera company, Nationale Reisopera and the Netherlands Symphony Orchestra is based there. Podium Twente manages concerts at 3 venues – Muziekkwartier, Muziekcentrum and Grote Kerk

OTHER CULTURAL INFORMATION

Rijksmuseum Twenthe has its own collection of art, particularly 17th and 18th century, and has space for temporary exhibitions on a variety of themes.

FESTIVALS AND EVENTS

Location for the Enschede Music Festival; there is also a Festival of Jewish music in December; Cross-Linx is a festival focusing on cross-over music in March. International circus festival in December.

TOURIST INFORMATION

www.visitenschede.nl

ARTEZ SCHOOL OF MUSIC

Van Essengaarde 10, NL-7511 PN Enschede, The Netherlands
t: +31 53 48 28 130 *f:* +31 53 43 01 689
e: conservatorium.enschede@artez.nl *w:* www.artez.nl/conservatorium
Contact Juul Diteweg, dir of Enschede location.
Course information Bachelor degree: classical music, jazz & pop, academy of pop music, media music, music therapy, music education. For more details see under Arnhem.

GRONINGNEN

Small northern Dutch city with a city centre dating to the medieval period; its architecture often described as having an Italian flavour. Population fluctuates depending on academic term dates – it has a large number of students attending the university or fine art academy as well as the music school, consequently a relaxed atmosphere and busy nightlife.

CLIMATE

Warmest month August (11-22°C), coldest month January (-1-5°C).

MUSICAL LIFE

Main formal venues are the Martini Plaza (musicals), De Oosterpoort and De Stadsschouwburg (classical, pop, jazz and world music). The city has its own orchestra in the shape of Noord Nederlands Orkest, although many of its performances are outside the city in other towns in the region. Wide variety of music on offer in the city in informal venues thanks in part to the thriving student atmosphere.

OTHER CULTURAL INFORMATION

Groninger Museum a highly regarded contemporary art gallery; also comic museum and graphic museum.

FESTIVALS AND EVENTS

Outdoor festival, Noorderzon, in August features theatre and a range of music.

TOURIST INFORMATION

http://toerisme.groningen.nl, info@vvvgroningen.nl, +31 900 2023050

PRINCE CLAUS CONSERVATOIRE

Veemarktstraat 76, NL-9724 GA Groningen, The Netherlands
t: +31 50 595 13 01 *f:* +31 50 595 13 99
e: prinsclausconservatorium@org.hanze.nl; j.kruger@pl.hanze.nl (international affairs)
w: www.hanze.nl

Contact Jan-Gerd Kruger, international affairs
Course information Music BA (jazz, classical, composition, conducting); music education BA; art education MA; music MA (performing, teaching, joint programme).Music BA (jazz, classical, composition, conducting); music education BA; art education MA; music MA (performing, teaching, joint programme) from September 2010. *Conducting* Choral and brass band. *Historical performance* Harpsichord and organ. *Composition* Music and studio production *Chamber music* Twice-yearly chamber music week. *Opera* Several opera productions per year. *Choral* Compulsory choir class for classical students. Jazz choir. *Jazz/world* Special jazz programme: 8 New York based teachers visit Groningen on a rotating scheme as well as Dutch teachers. See www.newyorkgroningen.com for details.
Admissions information *Term dates* Early Sep-mid Jul. *Application requirements* See website for details. *Application deadline* Sep 2010. *Fees* Approx EUR 1600 per year. *Scholarships* Scholarships available, applications required well before deadline; see website for full details. *No of students* 380 students. *Language requirements* Dutch or English (TOEFL 5.5).
Facilities *Music facilities* Fully equipped practice rooms, most with grand pianos; 3 concert venues (40-200 seats); studio facilities. *Performance opportunities* Orchestral and opera performances throughout the year at several venues across the city; own booking agent for performances/concerts. Peter the Great summer festival with summer school; collaboration with Slovenian jazz summer camp Jazzinty. *Accommodation* Overseas students can apply for accommodation for up to 12 months through www.housingoffice.nl.

MAASTRICHT

Attractive city straddling the river Meuse in the south of the country almost on the border with Belgium. Historically important as a fortress (remnants of the city walls are still present in parts) as well as a trading city, and claims to be oldest city in the Netherlands. Large number of students due to university and other higher education institutes.

CLIMATE

Warmest month August (13-23°C), coldest month January (0-5°C). Wettest months Jun-July (71mm), driest month February (54mm).

MUSICAL LIFE

Opera Zuid a small company putting on a small number of productions each year, using orchestras from elsewhere. Other opera companies also visit from out of town. Home orchestra is Limburgs Symfonie Orkest which performs at Theater aan het Vrijthof, a venue with its own concert series (chamber music, choral music, children's concerts etc)

OTHER CULTURAL INFORMATION

Theater an het Vrijthof programme goes beyond

music, with theatre and fringe type events. Bonnefanten Museum the pick of the museums and galleriesl it features a range of art, particularly contemporary; it runs a loans scheme enabling subscribers to display works at home.

FESTIVALS AND EVENTS
Musica Sacra Maastricht, a short festival in September focusing on religious music. Jazz Maastrich festival in October. The KunstTour is an annual springtime art exhibition.

LOCAL PUBLICATIONS
Week In, Week Uit (www.maastrichnet.nl) has details of events and other leisure activities.

TOURIST INFORMATION
www.vvv-maastricht.eu

CONSERVATORIUM MAASTRICHT
Bonnefantenstr 15, NL-6211 KL Maastricht, The Netherlands
t: +31 43 3466 680 *f:* +31 43 3466689
e: info.conservatorium@hszuyd.nl *w:* www.conservatoriummaastricht.nl

Course information Bachelors and masters courses in classical music, including composition, orchestral and wind band conducting, opera singing and specialist options; also jazz/pop and music in education courses.

Admissions information *Term dates* See website for up-to-date details. *No of students* 70% international students from c 48 countries, 30% Dutch. *Language requirements* Dutch or English.

Facilities *Music facilities* Music library including books and scores. 3 concert halls in 2 buildings; studio equipped with Pro Tools equipment; practice rooms.

ROTTERDAM
Dutch city at the Rhine/Meuse delta, the largest port in Europe and second largest city in the country. Its biggest historical development came at the end of the 19th century; consequently, the architecture of the city is more modern in feel than elsewhere in the country, including some striking developments like the Erasmus bridge or the Euromast; perhaps most striking are the distinctive, lopsided 'Cube Houses' residential accommodation, one of which is open to public.

CLIMATE
Warmest month August (15-20°C, coldest month January (1-4°C). Rainfall relatively even throughout the year, though wettest in late autumn and early winter.

MUSICAL LIFE
Rotterdam Philharmonic Orchestra is one of most respected in the world. Its home is De Doelen convention centre, a complex with one large and two smaller concert halls (programme not limited to classical music).

OTHER CULTURAL INFORMATION
Usual range of museums and galleries, a few reflecting Rotterdam's history (such as the Maritime Museum). Architecture Institute reflects the city's unique culture of modern design; modern art also prominent in city's numerous smaller galleries.

FESTIVALS AND EVENTS
Festivals feature variety of music: as well as rock and pop, and summer carnival event, North Sea Jazz Festival (July) features a wide range of jazz genres. For classical the Gergiev Festival (Valery Gergiev was chief conductor of the Rotterdam Philharmonic) runs for a week from August to September. Also a film festival at the beginning of the year and an international poetry festival in June.

TOURIST INFORMATION
www.rotterdam.info, info@rotterdam-store.com, +31 10 271 01 20

CODARTS HOGESCHOOL VOOR DE KUNSTEN
Kruisplein 26, NL-3012 CC Rotterdam, The Netherlands
t: +31 10 2171100 *f:* +31 10 2171101
e: codarts@codarts.nl; rc@codarts.nl *w:* www.codarts.nl

Course information Bachelors, preparatory and masters courses in musical theatre, pop, jazz/fusion, composition/arranging, music production, Argentinean tango, Indian music, Flamenco, Latin/Latin jazz/Brazilian, Turkish music and classical music

Admissions information *Application requirements* Online application via Studielink, audition and interview. *Fees* Approx EUR 1620 per year for bachelors. EUR 60 application fee. *Scholarships* Some reimbursements available for EU/EES countries under certain circmstances. *No of students* 1200, half of whom come from overseas (from around 60 countries). *Language requirements* Dutch

(compulsory for BMus in education programme), or English for overseas students.
Facilities *Music facilities* Music auditorium, theatre room, ensemble room, recording studio, 10 dance studios, media libary (over 15,000 items of sheet music), 40 practice/teaching rooms, 16 study cells; instruments include 74 pianos, drum kits and audio sets. *Accommodation* Institution has an agreement with Stadswonen (city housing) to help house 1st year students; foreign students given priority.

UTRECHT

City in centre of Netherlands on the river Rhine with medieval, previously walled, centre exemplified in the Dom tower (part of a planned cathedral which was never completed). The city centre is criss-crossed by Dutch canals which are an integral, historical part of the city's design – originally they played a key role in its trade significance.

CLIMATE

Warmest months July and August (12-22°C); coldest month January (-1-5°C).

MUSICAL LIFE

Muziekcentrum Vredenburg is the main concert hall – programming goes beyond classical music. Utrecht is the base for the Netherlands Bach Society, although this is a predominantly touring group.

OTHER CULTURAL INFORMATION

Several museums on a range of themes. Centraal Museum displays art and cultural artefacts from different periods; mechanical musical instrument museum; museum of Australian aboriginal art; there is even a museum dedicated to Utrecht resident and creator of the children's cartoon character Miffy, Dick Bruna.

FESTIVALS AND EVENTS

Early Music Festival (August-September) includes many concerts in churches across Utrecht. Festival aan de Werf is a platform in May for young artists, musicians and other performers to show off new work in indoor and outdoor locations. Netherlands Film Festival takes place in Utrecht (September-October).

TOURIST INFORMATION

www.utrechtyourway.nl

UTRECHTS CONSERVATORIUM

Utrecht School of the Arts, Mariaplaats 28, NL-3511 LL Utrecht, The Netherlands
t: +31 30 2314044 *f:* +31 30 2314004
e: info@muziek.hku.nl *w:* www.hku.nl/english
Course information Bachelor of music, bachelor of music in education and master of music.
Admissions information *Term dates* Sep-Aug *Application requirements* Entrance exam and suitable educational qualifications required; see website for full details. *Application deadline* Apr. *Fees* 2010-11 fees: EUR 1672 (EUR 7622 for non-eu students). *Scholarships* For more information contact marijke.arnold@muziek.hku.nl (scholarships co-ordinator). *No of students* 605 students in total; approx 170 from overseas. *Language requirements* Dutch and English.
Facilities *Music facilities* Various concert halls, chapel, studio, library, music software/ICT support etc. *Performance opportunities* Many projects and concerts throughout the year, working closely with local, regional and national venues. *Accommodation* Through student service centre

ZWOLLE

Attractive city in the east of the country. Its old city walls, together with a striking gatehouse, are still in evidence.

TOURIST INFORMATION

www.zwolle.nl

ARTEZ SCHOOL OF MUSIC

Aan de Stadsmuur 88, NL-8011 VD Zwolle, The Netherlands
t: +31 38 42 70 500 *f:* +31 38 42 70 565
e: conservatorium.zwolle@artez.nl *w:* www.artez.nl/conservatorium
Contact Wim Fiselier, dir of the Zwolle location.
Course information Bachelor degree: classical music, jazz & pop, education in music. For more details see under Arnhem. Master of music.
Admissions information *Term dates* Aug-Jul *Application requirements* Entrance exam and practical test. *Application deadline* 1 May 2010 *Fees* Fees payable for EU/EEA and non-EU/EEA students; see www.artez.nl for current details. *No of students* 900 students; 45% from overseas. *Language requirements* Dutch is the official language of education although some of the bachelors programmes are bilingual (English/Dutch). Most of the masters lectures are in English. Students who do not speak Dutch can register for an intensive ArtEZ language course.
Facilities *Music facilities* Concert auditoria, studios,

media studios and a variety of workshops for audio-visual productions, graphics, music and sound. *Accommodation* See www.artez.nl/housing for details.

MUSIC FESTIVALS

Delft Chamber Music Festival Herengracht 453, NL 1017 BS Amsterdam, Netherlands *t:* +31 20 6404666 *f:* +31 20 6403961 *e:* contact@delftmusicfestival.nl *w:* www.delftmusicfestival.nl International chamber music festival.

Europa Cantat Haus der Kultur, Weberstr 59a, D-53113 Bonn, Germany *t:* +49 228 912 5663 *f:* +49 228 912 5658 *e:* info@europacantat.org *w:* www.europacantat.org Triennial singing festival, next in Turin.

Festival aan de Werf Boorstr 1007, NL-3513 SE Utrecht, Netherlands *t:* +31 30 231 58 44 *e:* info@festivalaandewerf.nl *w:* www.festivalaandewerf.nl Festival showcasing work of young artists, musicians and other performers at indoor and outdoor venues.

Festival Early Music Utrecht Organisatie Oude Muziek, PO Box 19267, NL-3501 DG Utrecht, Netherlands *t:* +31 30 232 9000 *f:* +31 30 232 9001 *e:* info@oudemuziek.nl *w:* www.oudemuziek.nl Annual early music festival.

Holland Festival Piet Heinkade 5, NL-1019 BR Amsterdam, The Netherlands *t:* +31 20 788 21 00 *f:* +31 20 788 21 02 *e:* info@hollandfestival.nl *w:* www.hollandfestival.nl

International Chamber Music Festival Utrecht / Janine Jansen 217 Groot Hertoginnelaan, NL-2517 ES Den Haag, The Netherlands *t:* +31 70 2539 271 *f:* +31 70 3659 021 *e:* info@kamermuziekfestival.nl *w:* www.kamermuziekfestival.nl

International Gaudeamus Music Week Music Center the Netherlands, Rokin 111, NL-1012 KN Amsterdam, Netherlands *t:* +31 20 3446060 *f:* +31 20 6733588 *e:* info@mcn.nl *w:* www.gaudeamus.nl Annual in Amsterdam. Contemporary music; performances of works by winners of the International Gaudeamus Composers' Competition prize. International selection of approx 40 works in very different musical styles by composers aged 30 and under.

International Organ Festival Haarlem PO Box 1091, NL-1000 BB Haarlem, Netherlands *t:* +31 20 488 04 79 *f:* +31 2 488 04 78 *e:* office@organfestival.nl *w:* www.organfestival.nl Biennial. Various recitals (organ, choir, instrumental).

Musica Sacra Maastricht Vrijthof 47, NL-6211 Maastricht, Netherlands *t:* +31 43 350 55 23 *f:* +31 43 350 55 22 *e:* info@musicasacramaastricht.nl *w:* www.musicasacramaastricht.nl

Orgelfestival Holland in Alkmaar Clarissenbuurt 9, NL-1811 GB Alkmaar, The Netherlands *t:* +31 72 5113915 *e:* ericahoorn@hetnet.nl; jf.seijdell@quicknet.nl *w:* www.alkmaarorgelstad.nl International organ competition, organ academy, symposia and concerts, primarily in Grote St Laurenskerk in Alkmaar.

Orlando Chamber Music Festival Piet Heinkade 5, NL-1019 BR Amsterdam, Netherlands *t:* +31 20 519 1870 *f:* +31 20 519 1871 *e:* info@orlandofestival.nl *w:* www.orlandofestival.nl International chamber music festival.

The Big Bang Stichting Het Schlagwerkfestival, Postbus 550, NL-3500 AN Utrecht, Netherlands *w:* www.thebigbang.nl Percussion festival in various cities across the Netherlands.

CENTRAL EUROPE

CENTRAL EUROPE

There are certain places so imbued with a musical atmosphere that this becomes as much a reason to visit as city's architecture or art gallery. This is especially so in central Europe, and Poland, Hungary and the Czech Republic in particular.

All three countries here have strong musical traditions, each with its own particular flavour. In the Czech Republic, classical music is often associated with Prague. Mozart lived there for a while (there is a 'Prague' symphony; Don Giovanni was written for the Estates Theatre there); its river Vltava, as immortalised by Smetana in Ma Vlast, is a strong symbol of Czech nationhood. But the Czech music is not just an urban phenomenon – it is not hard to see how the emergence of Czech classical music is closely linked with the country's folk music.

The same could be said of Hungary, although the folk influences there seem to point more to the future, notably in the work of Kodály and Bartók, two figures who dominate the Hungarian musical imagination. Then there is Poland, whose musical sensibility combines something of the two: the intimacy of Chopin and romantic expression of a Wieniawski on the one hand; uncompromising modernity, more recently, on the other.

CZECH REPUBLIC PAGE 155

Students attending the two university level specialist music institutions will in most cases be the cream of those having passed through one of the lower music schools (lower in terms of students' age and educational level). In the Czech system, these schools are known as 'conservatories' (the higher education institutions are 'academies'); they also offer vocational training courses to those choosing not to follow a performance path.

HUNGARY PAGE 158

Professional training in Hungary is relatively straightforward in that there is only one independent institution providing specialist tuition of this kind, although there are music departments at universities where performance studies are part of the curriculum. Diplomas are awarded after 10 semesters of study, equating to a masters degree under the Bologna Process, with the ECTS grading adopted; indeed the first Bologna-compliant 2-cycle courses have recently been introduced. Music teacher training qualifications are achieved after 8 semesters.

The highest level of training is at the pyramid of a music education system that begins at elementary school, and is much influenced by the work of Zoltan Kodály. Pre-conservatoire training is via 21 secondary music schools, plus the junior department at the Liszt Academy.

POLAND PAGE 160

Poland has been one of the most keen to adopt the 2-cycle system, with all 8 of its conservatoires running degree courses according to the 3+2 scheme; indeed, certain of them also offer a doctoral level 3rd cycle. In addition, all academies are government funded institutions; one outcome of this is that a certain degree of curriculum consistency can be maintained between them – approx one third of conservatoires' curriculum is determined as core, with the remainder left to their discretion. Part of the core training is given over to music teacher training, meaning that conservatoire graduates have some experience in this field as well as in performing.

As with Hungary, music training begins at an early age, with state institutions taking children from the age of 7. However, these are not specifically music schools; rather, they offer general education (graduates of the Music Lyceums, around age 18 or 19, are not obliged to study music at higher education level, but can choose from the full range of degree courses offered).

BRNO

City in Moravian region of south eastern Czech Republic, the country's second largest city. Surrounded by forests it is characterised by a distinctive central European architectural styles and dominated by the city centre cathedral of St Peter and St Paul, although the city's more recent industrial heritage has led to a more functional modern element. Overlooked by hilltop Spilberk castle, now a museum but formerly active as a fort.

CLIMATE

Hottest month August (12-24°C), coldest months December and January (-4-1°C). Winter is the driest period (around 25mm); wetter during early summer (70mm in June).

MUSICAL LIFE

Brno Philharmonic gives public and subscription concerts at its base, the Besední dům, as well as at the Janáček Theatre in the National Theatre, a venue for opera and ballet also. National Theatre encompasses other buildings too: Mahen Theatre is primarily a venue for drama, but has a smaller associated space, Theatre on the Wall, for chamber music and recitals; Reduta Theatre a mixture of drama, music theatre and opera. Though principally an art gallery of Czech artists, the Wannieck Gallery hosts occasional concerts by the Brno Philharmonic and the Czech Philharmonic Brno choir.

OTHER CULTURAL INFORMATION

Brno Cultural Centre houses a number of small galleries with changing exhibitions; City Museum one of several providing historical information about the city and the region; mechanical musical instruments part of the various exhibitions at the Technical Museum. Other cultural exhibitions include the Museum of Gypsy Culture.

FESTIVALS AND EVENTS

Brno International Music Festival is largest music event, running for 3 weeks in autumn. Associated with other spin-offs such as Exposition of New Music (March) and Easter Festival of Sacred Music. Plenty of other events besides: Spilberk Festival features Brno Philharmonic in concerts during August; musical theatre festival in June; also theatre and dance festivals at various points throughout the year.

TOURIST INFORMATION

www.brno.cz, info@ticbrno.cz, +420 542 211 090

JANACKOVA AKADEMIE MUZICHYCH UMENI V BRNE (JANACEK ACADEMY OF MUSIC AND PERFORMING ARTS)

Faculty of Music, Komenskeho nam 6, CZ-662 15 Brno, Czech Republic
t: +420 542 591 607 *f:* +420 542 591 633
e: konarkova@jamu.cz *w:* http://hf.jamu.cz
Contact Petra Konarkova.

Course information Bachelor's degree programmes in composition, orchestral/choral conducting, church music, music management, opera direction, voice, orchestral instuments; all available for master's degrees, except church music. Doctoral programmes in interpretation and the theory of interpretation, composition and theory of composition.

Admissions information *Application requirements* CV and copy of academic qualifications. *Application deadline* 15 Dec (BA study), 15 Apr (MA study), 15 Jun (PhD study) *Fees* None for degree programmes; fees charged for lifelong learning programmes. All applicants must pay entrance admission fee. *No of students* 66 overseas students. *Language requirements* Czech language exam for non-Czech or Slovak students. Lifelong learning programmes may be taught in English or German.

Facilities *Music facilities* Library, inc music and students' work, also films; studies and reading rooms. Chamber opera studio, concert hall; various classrooms and practice rooms. Music faculty students may qualify for discounts and free tickets for certain events. *Accommodation* Hall of residence near music faculty building; shared rooms. Applications for accommodation must be received by 15 May.

PRAGUE (PRAHA)

Czech capital situated on the river Vltava in Bohemian region of the country. City has had a dominant role in central European history, and this is reflected in its magnificent city architecture whether the hilltop castle that envelops St Vitus cathedral in the old town, the Charles Bridge, any number of buildings around Wenceslas Square and throughout the city. As well as having political importance over the years, the city is also a significant musical city, absorbing musical influences from various surrounding countries. This legacy has made it one of the world's most visited destinations generally, but also among music lovers in particular.

CLIMATE

Hottest months July and August (14-25°C), coldest

month January (-4-2°C), with temperatures dropping significantly in November and rising in April. Wettest month May (77mm), driest months December-February (around 25mm). Snow is common during winter

MUSICAL LIFE

City has extremely active musical life with numerous orchestras (Czech Philharmonic Orchestra, Prague Symphony Orchestra, Prague Philharmonic Orchestra, Prague Radio Symphony Orchestra, Czech National Symphony Orchestra); opera (Prague National Theatre, Estates Theatre and Prague State Opera); the city is also home to plenty of early music and chamber ensembles. Various concert series either at specific venues or arranged by concert promoters such as EuroArt's chamber music series. City is popular touring destination for choirs, orchestras and chamber groups from all over the world.

OTHER CULTURAL INFORMATION

Various galleries and museums such as the National Gallery and the City Museum; modern culture celebrated also, at Museum of Czech Cubism, the Centre for Modern and Contemporary Art and the Franz Kafka Museum. Unofficial 'ball season' takes over during Jan-Feb at various locations such as the Palace Lucerna.

FESTIVALS AND EVENTS

City hosts a number of festivals: Prague Spring Festival in May is one of the most prestigious European festivals but there are also events in summer and autumn. Summer festival of sacred music includes a choir competition. Various festivals of local or traditional music and folklore from Feb Bohemian Carnival to a festival of Roma culture in May.

TOURIST INFORMATION

www.pis.cz, tourinfo@pis.cz, +420 221 714 444

AKADEMIE MUZICKYCH UMENI V PRAZE

Malostranske nam 13, CR-118 00 Praha 1, Czech Republic
t: +420 234 244 136 (international office)
f: +420 257 530 698 *e:* studijni@hamu.cz
w: www.hamu.cz
Contact Ing Lea Motlova, head of student dept; Jiri Kucmas, international office
Course information 3-year BA, 2-year MA, PhD programme. Study at both levels in orchestral instruments, conducting, opera direction, organ, harpsichord, guitar, music theory, music direction, music management, sound production, chamber music (some courses not offered every year). Options also available in areas such as music history, music aesthetics, cultural education, languages, as well as teaching courses. PhD programme covers composition and compositional theory, interpretation and interpretational theory, music theory, sound production, music production.
Admissions information *Term dates* End Sep-end Jun. *Application requirements* For BA, entrance exams end Jan covering individual specialism, music history and theory, and practical piano. See website for specific details of exam contents (specific for each course). For MA, an outstanding BA degree is required. *Application deadline* 30 Nov (BA); 31 Mar (MA) *Fees* CZK 599 admin fee *Scholarships* No. *No of students* 360 national students and 40 from overseas. *Language requirements* Good knowledge of English.
Facilities *Music facilities* Music library and sound archive, sound studio for electro-acoustic compositions, acoustic research laboratories; opera studio, contemporary music studio and chamber music room. *Performance opportunities* Martinu Hall, Gallery concert hall. *Accommodation* Halls of residence.

MUSIC FESTIVALS

Brno International Music Festival Hybesova 29, CR-602 00 Brno, Czech Republic *t:* +420 543 420 955 *f:* +420 543 420 950 *e:* mhfb@arskoncert.cz *w:* www.mhf-brno.cz
Emmy Destinn Music Festival A Barcala 404/38, CR-370 05 Ceske Budejovice, Czech Republic *t:* +420 38 644 4448, also fax *e:* fked@volny.cz *w:* www.festival-ed.cz Operatic, oratorio and chamber music repertoire.
International Jazz Festival Prague Pragokoncert Arts Agency, U Bulhara 3, Praha 1, Czech Republic *t:* +420 224 235 340 *f:* +420 224 234 340 *e:* Letov@pragokoncert.com Jazz, from traditional to modern.
International Music Festival Janacek May 28 Rijna 124, CR-702 00 Ostrava, Czech Republic *t:* +420 597 489 421 *f:* +420 597 489 422 *e:* festival@janackuvmaj.cz *w:* www.janackuvmaj.cz Classical music festival.
Mahler-Jihlava International Festival Mahler 2000, Balbinova 14, CR-120 00 Praha 2, Czech Republic *t:* +420 224 238 673 *f:* +420 224 238

619 *e:* arcodiva@arcodiva.cz *w:* www.arcodiva.cz Annual. Classical music (chamber, symphonic) festival in Jihlava, southern Czech Republic.

Prague Spring International Music Festival Hellichova 18, CR-118 00 Praha 1, Czech Republic *t:* +420 257 320 468 *f:* +420 257 313 725 *e:* info@festival.cz *w:* www.festival.cz Classical music festival, also competition.

Prague Winter Festival *e:* dublin@ifbarts.com *w:* www.praguewinterfestival.com

Smetana's Litomysl Smetanova Litomysl ops, Jiraskova 133, CR-570 01 Litomysl, Czech Republic *t:* +420 603 801 740 *e:* helpdesk@smetanaoperafestival.com *w:* www.smetanaoperafestival.com Open air opera festival with more than 20 concert performances (mainly opera, classical music concerts, ballet, opera programme for children etc) at the Unesco-listed Litomysl renaissance castle.

Spilberk Festival Komenskeho namesti, CR-302 00 Brno, Czech Republic *e:* info@filharmonie-brno.cz *w:* www.filharmonie-brno.cz

Summer Festivities of Early Music Melantrichova 971/19, CR-110 00 Prague, Czech Republic *t:* +420 224 229 462 *f:* +420 224 233 417 *e:* info@collegiummarianum.cz *w:* www.collegiummarianum.cz Festival programmes presented by renowned soloists and ensembles demonstrate variations and connection between European cultures.

XXI Festival Forfest Czech Republic 2009 Artistic Initiative of Kromeriz, Kojetinska 1425, CR-767 01 Kromeriz, Czech Republic *t:* +420 573 341316, also fax *e:* forfest@quick.cz; forfest@seznam.cz *w:* www.forfest.cz International festival of contemporary arts with spiritual orientation. Concerts, exhibitions, workshops and lectures with local and foreign artists. Presentation of young composers and creative artists; portraits of well-known artists.

HUNGARY

BUDAPEST

Capital of Hungary on the river Danube, originally two towns (Buda and Pest) separated by it. Since the end of the Cold War it has become a popular destination for tourists attracted by its distinctive mid-European atmosphere and architecture such as the dramatic riverfront parliament building and the vast hilltop castle area on the opposite bank. Much of this atmosphere is down to city's prominent position in late 19th century Austria-Hungary.

CLIMATE

Hottest month July (16-28°C), coldest month January (-3-2°C). Rainfall fairly consistent throughout the year at around 40mm, though slightly wetter during summer (65-70mm in May and June).

MUSICAL LIFE

State opera house, ornate late 19th century building with stunning interior on city's Andrássy avenue, stages Hungarian State Opera and Ballet companies. Budapest Philharmonic Orchestra is the country's oldest still in operation and gives its concerts at the opera house; other orchestras based in the city include Hungarian National Philharmonic Orchestra, Hungarian Radio Symphony Orchestra; particularly noteworthy is Budapest Festival Orchestra, a group that has high international reputation. Various chamber orchestras and ensembles as well: Franz Liszt Chamber Orchestra is one of the better known.

OTHER CULTURAL INFORMATION

Millenáris is a modern cultural centre incorporating theatre, exhibitions and exhibition spaces. Városliget park encompasses a number of attractions, such as botanical gardens, medicinal baths and Vajdahunyad Castle. City has a national gallery and fine arts museum. Unusual among capital cities in being renowned for its thermal baths, with many visitors treating.

FESTIVALS AND EVENTS

Budapest Spring Festival is country's biggest music event with performers coming from all over the world; performances not limited to classical music. International choir festival runs during easter, centred round a competition. Budafest is summer music festival event with gala performances, opera etc; Autumn Festival has classical music component but features wide range of performing arts and film.

TOURIST INFORMATION

www.budapestinfo.hu, +36 1 266 0479

LISZT FERENC MUSIC ACADEMY

Liszt Ferenc ter 8, HU-1061 Budapest, Hungary *t:* +36 1 462 4615, also fax (international office) *e:* hars.borbala@lisztakademia.hu; pandi.zita@lisztakademia.hu *w:* www.lisztakademia.hu; www.lisztacademy.hu

Contact Borbála Hárs, Zita Pándi.

Course information 3-year BA and 2-year MA courses in several faculties: piano (inc other keyboard instruments and harp), church music, music education, wind and percussion instruments, chamber music, solo singing and opera, strings, music theory, composition, choral and orchestral conducting, musicology, jazz, folk music, Kodaly Pedagogy. Part time study available.

Admissions information *Term dates* Mid Sep-Jan; 1 Feb-end Jun. *Application requirements* Min age 18. Students must have secondary school diploma; MA applicants must have BA in the area they wish to study. Entrance exam is compulsory for all applicants and is held end Jun/beginning Jul in Budapest. Exam covers solfege/theory, piano test and audition on main instrument (see website for specified works). MA students must also take a theory test and pass an audition. *Application deadline* 15 Feb (full-time); 30 Apr (part-time or preparatory course). *Fees* Annual fees vary according to course; EUR 3000-9000 for BA and MA; EUR 60 application fee (non-refundable); EUR 60 registration fee at beginning of studies. *Scholarships* None. *No of students* 550-600 national students, 90-100 international students per year. *Language requirements* Hungarian or English.

Facilities *Music facilities* Library, multimedia library, audio-visual studio. *Performance opportunities* Student concerts and graduation concerts. *Accommodation* No student housing facilities, but international registrar's office can assist in finding rental accommodation.

MUSIC FESTIVALS

Budafest VIP Arts Manager & Production Office, Hajos ut 13-15, H-1065 Budapest, Hungary *t:* +36 1 302 4290 *f:* +36 1 332 4816 *e:* viparts@viparts.hu *w:* www.viparts.hu

Budapest Autumn Festival Budapest Festival Center, Szervita ter 5, H-1052 Budapest, Hungary *t:* +36 1 486 3322 *f:* +36 1 486 3310 *e:* bof@festivalcity.hu *w:* www.bof.hu Contemporary arts: music, dance, theatre, performance art, jazz, exhibitions, film, open-air programmes.

Budapest Spring Festival Budapest Festival

Center, Szervita ter 5, H-1052 Budapest, Hungary *t:* +36 1 486 3300 *f:* +36 1 486 3310 *e:* info@festivalcity.hu *w:* www.festivalcity.hu Opera, orchestral and chamber concerts, dance, jazz, theatre, open-air programmes, folk music.

Esztergom International Guitar Festival and Seminar Szendrey-Karper Laszlo International Guitar Festival Foundation, PO Box 8, H-2501 Esztergom, Hungary *t:* +36 22 460267, also fax *w:* www.guitarfestival.hu Concerts, masterclasses, guitar competition, exhibition of guitars, guitar orchestra.

International Bartok Seminar and Festival Filharmonia Concert Agency, Kazinczy u 24-26, H-1075 Budapest, Hungary *t:* +36 1 266 1459 *f:* +36 1 302 4962 *w:* www.filharmoniabp.hu; www.bartokfestival.hu Annual. 20th C, Bartók and contemporary music.

International Choir Festival & Competition Budapest INTERKULTUR, Am Weingarten 3, D-35415 Pohlheim, Germany *t:* +49 6403 956525 *f:* +49 6403 956529 *e:* mail@interkultur.com *w:* www.interkultur.com Performances in the famous concert halls of Budapest.

International Kodály Festival POB 188, H-6001 Kecskemet, Hungary *t:* +36 76 481 518 *f:* +36 7 632 0160 *e:* office@kodaly.hu *w:* www.kodaly.hu Chamber concerts and recitals, exhibitions, introduction of prize-winning young artists. Works of Kodály and contemporary Hungarian music.

International Opera Festival Miskolc *t:* +36 46 504060 *f:* +36 46 504068 *e:* operami@t-online.hu *w:* www.operafesztival.hu

Summer on the Chain Bridge Budapest Festival Center, Szervita ter 5, H-1052 Budapest, Hungary *t:* +36 1 486 3300 *f:* +36 1 486 3310 *e:* info@festivalcity.hu *w:* www.festivalcity.hu Free open air programmes.

POLAND

BYDGOSZCZ

City towards the north of Poland on Brda and Vistula rivers. Its development began in 15th century and town's architecture encompasses various styles from that time on; today there are various plans to develop and expand the city further. Home to several higher education institutions apart from music academy.

MUSICAL LIFE

Filarmonia Pomorska is home base for Pomeranian Philharmonic Orchestra. Opera Nova is a modern design opera house putting on a range of productions from opera to music theatre and operetta; also orchestral concerts.

OTHER CULTURAL INFORMATION

Teatr Polski for all kinds of theatre production, plus a range of music events (concerts, cabaret, pop and traditional music). There is a regional Culture Centre has courses and events in various art forms. Several small art galleries and museums.

FESTIVALS AND EVENTS

Opera Nova hosts an annual opera festival in April featuring performances from Polish and foreign companies. Filarmonia hall holds an early music festival in autumn.

TOURIST INFORMATION

www.visitbydgoszcz.pl, bylot@op.pl, +52 58 58 702

AKADEMIA MUZYCNA IM F NOWOWIEJSKIEGO W BYDGOSZCZY (ACADEMY OF MUSIC BYDGOSZCZ)

ul Slowackiego 7, PL-85-008 Bydgoszcz, Poland
t: +48 052 321 05 82 *f:* +48 052 321 23 50
e: rektor@amuz.bydgoszcz.pl *w:* www.amuz.bydgoszcz.pl

Course information Several departments: composition (including theory of music and sound engineering), instrumental, vocal studies/acting, and choral conducting and music education. As well as performance specialism, options available in complementary subjects, eg ear training, history and literature of music, foreign languages, philosophy, music aesthetics, history of culture. Postgraduate studies for choirmasters, instrumentalists and singers.

Facilities *Music facilities* 2 faculty buildings in city centre: 53 lecture/practice rooms with pianos, 140-seat concert hall, 100-seat hall, recording studio. Many rooms have audio-visual recording equipment. Instruments available for rent. Concert series arranged, plus student ensembles such as symphony orchestra, chorus and chamber choir,

GDANSK

City on Baltic coast with a strategic importance, thanks to its port location, dating back to medieval times – it was part of the Hanseatic League trading guild that encompassed various countries along north European coastline. Its shipyards were the epicentre of the popular Solidarnosc (Solidarity) trade union movement which eventually helped lead to fall of communism in the country. Despite this modern association with heavy industry, many attractive buildings from earlier periods can be found throughout the centre. A major education centre, with over 60,000 students at its higher education institutions.

CLIMATE

Warmest month July (13-21°C), coldest month January (-4-2°C), although these averages can be significantly surpassed. Wettest month July (80mm), driest month January (33mm).

MUSICAL LIFE

Polska Filharmonia Baltycka based at its own concert hall, as is Opera Baltycka at its opera house.

OTHER CULTURAL INFORMATION

Gdansk Archipelago of Culture a city-wide cultural network of buildings promoting cultural and performance activities of many kinds. Showcase for modern art at Łazni Centre for Contemporary Art. Baltic Sea Cultural Centre another multi-art organisation based in 2 buildings including a converted church for concerts and other performances.

FESTIVALS AND EVENTS

International Festival of Organ Music over summer until early autumn, held at Oliwa cathedral. Classical concerts organised over summer.

TOURIST INFORMATION

www.got.gdansk.pl, itpkp@got.gdansk.pl, +48 58 348 13 68

AKADEMIA MUZYCZNA W GDANSKU

Lakowa 1-2, PL-80-743 Gdansk, Poland
t: +48 58 300 92 01 *f:* +48 58 300 92 10
e: muzyczna@amuz.gda.pl; brydak@amuz.gda.

pl *w:* www.amuz.gda.pl
Contact Wojslaw Brydak, foreign enquiries.
Course information Faculties: composition and music theory; instrumental; vocal and acting; choral conducting, music education, eurythmics and church music
Admissions information *Term dates* Early Oct-early Feb (winter semester); early Feb-end Sep (summer semester) *Fees* Free on regular courses; postgrad fees EUR 233-440 per semester, depending on course. *Scholarships* Some financial aid may be available. *No of students* Approx 450 students.
Facilities *Music facilities* Academic library with approx 80,000 scores and books etc; sound recording studio *Accommodation* Student dormitory on campus (2 or 3 bed rooms).

KATOWICE

City in an upland area in the southern Polish region of Silesia, with an economy traditionally based on heavy industry. Prevalent architectural feel is modern, with some art nouveau influences among Bauhaus-era modernism and more functional post-war designs.

CLIMATE

Warmest months July and August (18-23°C), coldest month January (-4-2°C). Summer is wettest period (75mm in July), winter driest (around 30mm December-February).

MUSICAL LIFE

Silesian Philharmonic Symphony Orchestra is regional orchestra based in the city, performing at the Philharmonic Hall. National Polish Radio Symphony Orchestra Katowice also based in the city, performing for the most part at the Silesian Theatre. Spodek is a huge arena hosting rock concerts.

OTHER CULTURAL INFORMATION

City has a number of theatres, ranging from the standard Silesian Theatre to several more experimental companies. Several galleries and museums.

FESTIVALS AND EVENTS

Conducting competition named after Polish conductor Grzegorz Fitelberg, held every four years.

TOURIST INFORMATION

www.um.katowice.pl, ciom@um.katowice.pl, +448 32 259 38 08

AKADEMIA MUZYCZNA IM KAROLA SZYMANOWSKIEGO (KAROL SZYMANOWSKI ACADEMY OF MUSIC)
ul Zacisze 3, PL-40-025 Katowice, Poland
t: +48 32 779 2112; +48 32 779 2222 (international relations) *f:* +48 32 256 44 85
e: TokStudiow@am.katowice.pl (rector's office); J.Mentel@am.katowice.pl (international relations)
w: www.am.katowice.pl
Course information The academy offers full-time as well as part-time BA and MA studies aligned to the European Credit Transfer System (ECTS). Full-time and part-time BA or MA in several division: composition; conducting and music theory; music education; choral conducting; piano; string instruments; organ and harpsichord; wind, brass and percussion; chamber music; accordion; guitar and harp; vocal; composition and music arrangement; jazz instrumental and vocal.
Facilities *Music facilities* New 480-seat concert hall *Performance opportunities* Each year the Academy holds variety of artistic events such as concerts, master classes, international and national competitions and conferences. The artistic activity of the school is also connected with the Karol Szymanowski Academic Symphony Orchestra.

KRAKOW (CRACOW)

Located in the south of the country Krakow's several hundred years of history (it was the country's capital until the 17th century, and counts significant Roman and Jewish influences in its past) have left a rich architectural and cultural legacy, and its city centre has been registered on Unesco's world heritage list. Today, a thriving city with an exciting array of cultural activities including a busy nightlife, its network of underground cellars providing a unique venue for unusual entertainment.

CLIMATE

Hottest month July (19-25°C), coldest month January (-6-1°C). Wettest (but also sunniest) month July (90mm), driest months December-January (35mm).

MUSICAL LIFE

One of country's musical centres with very active musical life. The Karol Szymanowski Philharmonic building has a resident orchestra (and several chamber groups drawn from its ranks) and choir; Sinfonietta Cracovia a smaller group that performs there also. Several choirs in the city, plus Krakow Opera and Ballet (which have their own orchestra). Busy city for jazz.

EUROPE

OTHER CULTURAL INFORMATION
City houses a number of cultural centres covering a variety of areas: Rotunda Cultural Centre a popular student hangout (jazz, cabaret, film club, venue for bands); Institute of Art Association promotes young performers as part of programme of cultural events; Dworek Białoprądnicki has a strong music presence among its cultural programme. Plentiful art galleries, many of which focus on Polish art (eg Piano Nobile Contemporary Art Galler, Marian Gołogórski Gallery, Sukiennice Gallery, or the Krakow Poster Gallery).

FESTIVALS AND EVENTS
Large festival of Jewish culture in summer.

TOURIST INFORMATION
www.krakow.pl, simratusz@infokrakow.pl, +48 12 433 73 10

AKADEMIA MUZYCZNA W KRAKOWIE
ul Sw Tomasza 43, PL-31-027 Krakow, Poland
t: +48 12 422 04 55 *e:* zbmszlez@cyf-kr.edu.pl (international affairs); zbjanik@cyfronet.pl
w: www.amuz.krakow.pl
Contact Mieczyslaw Szlezer, prorector for international affairs.
Course information Courses in instrumental music, vocal music, conducting, theory, composition, education.
Admissions information *Term dates* 1 Oct-10 Jun. *Application requirements* Abitur diploma or equivalent; musical knowledge and skills equal to conservatory higher level diploma. *Application deadline* 25 May. *Fees* Up to EUR 1000 per semester (Polish & EU students); EUR 4000 (non EU students). *Scholarships* Scholarships provided by the state and private sponsors. *No of students* 500 national students, plus 35 from overseas.
Facilities *Music facilities* 3 concert halls; library with 50,000 items including audio-visual recordings. *Accommodation* Student dormitory with 146 places in 2, 3 or 4 bed rooms.

ŁÓDŹ
Central Polish city with a largely industrial background, particularly textiles. Its people suffered during World War II, particularly its substantial Jewish who were forced for several into a ghetto before its destruction in 1944. The city is home to the country's national film school and is closely associated with the Polish film industry.

CLIMATE
Hottest months July and August (12-23°C), coldest month January (-1--6°C). Snow common during winter

MUSICAL LIFE
City's orchestra is Łodz Philharmonic, which has its own strikingly designed concert hall; classical music recitals and other events staged there too.

OTHER CULTURAL INFORMATION
Modern art gallery has a substantial collection; also city art gallery. Textile museum reflects city's industrial past.

FESTIVALS AND EVENTS
Film music festival has been running for over 10 years; also ballet festival.

TOURIST INFORMATION
www.cityoflodz.pl, cit@uml.lodz.pl, +48 42 638 59 55

AKADEMIA MUZYCZNA IM GRAZYNY I KIEJSTUTA BACEWICZOW (THE GRAZYNA AND KIEJSTUT BACEWICZ ACADEMY OF MUSIC)
32 Gdanska St, PL-90-716 Lodz, Poland
t: +48 42 662 16 00; +48 42 662 16 15 (international relations) *e:* international@amuz.lodz.pl *w:* www.amuz.lodz.pl
Contact Dorota Rossowska, international relations contact.
Admissions information *Term dates* Oct-early Feb (winter semester); mid Feb-mid Jun (summer semester).

POZNAN
City in western Poland, one of the country's oldest – its gothic cathedral is the oldest in the country although it has been much renovated and rebuilt. Location for an anti-Stalin uprising that is celebrated in various ways in the city. City falls into 5 districts, with the old town and its various interesting historic buildings covering many different styles and periods at the centre. Popular student city with over 130,000 students.

CLIMATE
Hottest months July and August (19-24°C), coldest month January (-5-2°C). Wettest month July (70mm) with around 13 rainy days (though generally restricted to brief downpours), driest month February (23mm). Snow is common during winter.

MUSICAL LIFE
Poznan Philharmonic is city's main orchestra; chamber orchestra provided by Amadeus Chamber Orchestra of the Polish Radio performing in the main hall of the city's Adam Mickiewicz university. Regular opera performances at Theatr Wielki Stanisława Moniuszki.

OTHER CULTURAL INFORMATION
Art and sculpture museum has a collection of European art from various countries; museum of applied arts features various artefacts and items of decorative art. Among numerous other museums and exhibitions is a musical instrument museum on old market square; both classical instruments and folk instruments from around the world.

FESTIVALS AND EVENTS
Open air events throughout the city during July and August. Sacred music festival in February-March. Home to quinquennial Henryk Wieniawski Violin Competion and biennial festival of contemporary Polish music (April). Annual Malta theatre festival (June) – the name refers to the artificial lake in the city, rather than the Mediterranean country.

TOURIST INFORMATION
www.poznan.pl, it@cim-poznan.pl, +48 61 852 61 56

AKADEMIA MUZYCZNA IM IGNACEGO JANA PADEREWSKIEGO
ul Swiety Marcin 87, PL-61-808 Poznan, Poland
t: +48 61 856 89 00 *f:* +48 61 853 66 76
e: amuz@amuz.edu.pl *w:* www.amuz.edu.pl
Course information 3-year BA and 2-year MA. Faculties of composition, conducting, theory and eurhythmics; instruments; vocal studies; choral conducting, music education and church music. Only Polish academy with course in violin-making. Also faculties in Szczecin.
Admissions information *Application requirements* B1 certificate in Polish, secondary school qualification. For MA students, audition at end Sep. *Application deadline* Mid May *Fees* BA students from EU/EFTA countries study free; for non-EU/EFTA, EUR 5500, payable mid-Oct. MA fee is EUR 3000, payable by mid Oct. *Language requirements* Polish.
Facilities *Accommodation* Academy has its own dormitory with double and triple rooms.

WARSAW
Polish capital with a history dating back over seven centuries, little of which remains visible due to massive destruction during World War II bombing, although there have been some restoration projects (notably in the old town area). Its revived Jewish quarter, with its own institute, is a reminder of the Nazi imposed ghetto. City attracts large numbers of students (over a quarter of a million in higher education institutions of varying types and specialisms).

CLIMATE
Hottest months July and August (14-24°C), coldest month January -6-0°C). Wettest month July (73mm), much drier in winter.

MUSICAL LIFE
City is musically very active. Main institutions: Teatr Wielki is the grand home for Polish National Opera company; Sala Filharmonii (Philharmonic Hall) home of the historic orchestra (and choir) of the same name has a main concert hall and chamber music room. Sinfonia Varsovia a smaller but equally busy group, based in one of the city's most prominent buildings, the Pałac Kulturny. Polish Radio Symphony Orchestra based at Lutosławski Concert Hall in the city. Chamber opera company, Warszawska Opera Kameralna runs several projects, including annual baroque opera festival, and annual Mozart festival (company claims to be the only one featuring the complete Mozart operas in its repertoire). Beethoven festival at easter. Various concert series, such as the summer concerts at the Royal Castle, or those arranged by the Chopin Society based in the city.

OTHER CULTURAL INFORMATION
Centre for Contemporary Art features various exhibitions and performances. Among the usual range of art galleries and museums are a poster gallery (Galeria Plakatu) and the Museum of Cartoon and Caricature. Theatre covers the range of genres – for instance, among more serious establishments, Teatr Studio Buffo puts on revues.

FESTIVALS AND EVENTS
Numerous music events including, early, sacred and contemporary music; Warsaw Autumn the main example of the latter, running for over a week in September since 1950s. Chopin Piano Competition takes place every 5 years. Film festival in October, as well as the Jazz Jamboree; street art festival in the summer.

TOURIST INFORMATION
www.warsawtour.pl, info@warsawtour.pl, +48 22 94 31

AKADEMII MUZYCZNEJ IM FRYDERYKA CHOPINA (THE FREDERIK CHOPIN ACADEMY OF MUSIC)

2 Okolnik Str, PL-00-368 Warsaw, Poland
t: +48 22 827 72 41; +48 22 827 83 08 (international office) *f:* +48 22 827 83 06
e: foreign@chopin..edu.pl; irenapodobas@chopin.edu.pl *w:* www.chopin.edu.pl
Contact Irena Podobas, international relations; Justyna Zayac, ERASMUS co-ord.

Course information Level 1 (bachelor's) and level 2 (graduate) courses in several departments: composition, conducting and music theory; piano, harpsichord and organ; instrumental studies (inc accordion and chamber music); vocal studies; music education; sound engineering. Also individual postgrad training in orchestral and keyboard instruments (classes in English, Spanish, German, Italian).

Admissions information *Term dates* 1 Oct-end Jan (winter semester); early Feb-end May (spring semester); exam sessions may fall outside these dates. *Application requirements* EU nationals required to pass Polish as a Foreign Language exam, level B1. Requirements vary depending on course; for more details, see website. *Application deadline* 31 May. *Scholarships* None offered by academy; contact Polish embassies or consulates for information about government grants.

Facilities *Music facilities* Three-storey building with a 170-seat concert hall, 80-seat chamber music hall (80 seats), recording studio, 60-seat organ room, library and sound library.

WROCŁAW

Historic city in south west Poland on the river Oder and tributaries – in fact the city is a collection of islands joined together by numerous bridges (over 100). Has a busy, architecturally distinctive market square; city's thousand years of history have left a legacy of mixed architectural styles (baroque, gothic etc). Many students attracted to city's baroque university, but many other institutes besides.

CLIMATE

Hottest months July and August (15-24°C), coldest month January (-4-0°C). Wettest months are during summer (around 70mm per month June-August); drier in autumn and winter (around 30mm).

MUSICAL LIFE

Several instrumental groups based in the city, ranging from Witold Lutosławski Philharmonic Orchestra and Wrocław Chamber Orchestra Leopoldinum to chamber and early music ensembles. Ferenc Liszt Society based in the city but organises concerts throughout Poland.

OTHER CULTURAL INFORMATION

Several museum exhibitions on various themes (architectural, archaeological, art and ethnography); a number of contemporary art galleries. Notable artwork is the Racławice Panorama, a 19th century battle depiction created by several artists and housed in its own rotunda building. Plenty of theatres.

FESTIVALS AND EVENTS

City hosts a number of music festivals. Wratsilavia Cantans is not just singing festival but features performances of all kinds of classical music (one week in Jun, one in September). Musica Polonica Nova is a festival of contemporary Polish music every other year; early music at Maj z Muzyką Dawną in May. Guitar and organ festivals (autumn and summer respectively). Various jazz events, and festivals focusing on traditional Polish music .

TOURIST INFORMATION

www.itwroclaw.pl; info@itwroclaw.pl; +48 71 344 31 11

AKADEMIA MUZYCZNA IM KAROLA LIPINSKIEGO (THE KAROL LIPINSKI ACADEMY OF MUSIC)

pl Jana Pawla II nr 2, PL-50-043 Wroclaw, Poland
t: +48 71 355 5543 *f:* +48 71 355 2849
e: info@amuz.wroc.pl *w:* www.amuz.wroc.pl

Course information 3-year BA programme, 2-year MA programme. 4 depts: composition, conducting, theory and music therapy; instrumental studies (inc early music and chamber music); vocal studies; music education. Details of course requirements on website. *Vocal* song/oratorio or stage singing. *Composition* Computer composition and film music.

Admissions information *Term dates* Early Oct- mid Jan, with exams end Jan-early Feb (winter semester); mid Feb-end May, with exams early Jun (summer semester). *Application requirements* Admission criteria, procedures and application dates vary depending on course; full details available on website. *Application deadline* 15 May (EU citizens); 23 Aug (non-EU citizens). *Fees* EUR 2000, plus EUR 200 pa (bachelors and masters

studies), EUR 3000, plus EUR 200 (doctoral studies); non-EU citizens only. *No of students* 600 national, 7 overseas students. *Language requirements* All group classes in Polish; some individual teaching in English and German to overseas students. Language classes available at University of Wroclaw
Facilities *Music facilities* Chamber music hall, ballet hall, library (over 100,000 titles), audio-visual studio, computer composition studio. Over 200 concerts arranged per year.

MUSIC FESTIVALS

Bydgoszcz Opera Festival ul Marszalka Focha 5, PL-85-070 Bydgoszcz, Poland *t:* +48 52 3251510 *f:* +48 52 3251639 *e:* dryekcja@opera.bydgoszcz.pl *w:* www.opera.bydgoszcz.pl
Gaude Mater: International Festival of Sacred Music Gaude Mater Centre of Culture Promotion, Dabrowskiego 1, PL-42-200 Czestochowa, Poland *t:* +48 34 324 3638, also fax; +48 34 365 17 60, also fax *e:* biuro@gaudemater.pl *w:* www.gaudemater.pl Promotes the meeting of cultures and religions through the presentation of music from various religions and denominations. Each year over 1000 performers invited to take part including orchs, choirs, chamber music ensembles and soloists, giving about 20 festival concerts.
International Festival Wratislavia Cantans Rynek 7, PL-50-106 Wroclaw, Poland *t:* +48 71 3427257 *f:* +48 71 330 52 12 *e:* office@wratislavia.art.pl *w:* www.wratislavia.art.pl
Jewish Culture Festival in Krakow ul Jozefa 36, PL-31-056 Krakow, Poland *t:* +48 12 431 15 17 *f:* +48 12 431 24 27 *e:* office@jewishfestival.pl *w:* www.jewishfestival.pl Music from synagogue, klezmer, Hasidic, classical and Jewish folk music; also films and other presentations.
Ludwig van Beethoven Easter Festival Chmielna 15/10 St, PL-00-021 Warszawa, Poland *t:* +48 22 331 91 91 *f:* +48 22 313 00 05 *e:* biuro@beethoven.org.pl *w:* www.beethoven.org.pl Festival featuring music of Beethoven and others.
Maj z Muzyka Dawna ASK WAGANT, skr poczt 2372, PL-50-131 Wroclaw 3, Poland *e:* biuro@muzykadawna.pl Festival of early music.
Mozart Festival in Warsaw, The Warsaw Chamber Opera, ul Nowogrodzka 49, PO-00-695 Warszawa, Poland *t:* +48 22 628 3096 *f:* +48 22 627 2212 *e:* tickets@wok.pol.pl *w:* www.operakameralna.pl Annual. Features Mozart's stage works.
Musica Polonica Nova ul Mazowlecka 17, PL-50-412 Wroclaw, Poland *t:* +48 71 344 69 66 *f:* +48 71 344 39 45 *e:* biuro@MusicaPolonicaNova.pl *w:* www.musicapolonicanova.pl Biennial festival of contemporary music, focusing on Polish composers.
Music in Old Cracow Ul Zwierzyniecka 1, PL-31-103 Krakow, Poland *t:* +48 12 421 45 66 *f:* +48 429 43 28 *e:* info@capellacracoviensis.pl *w:* www.capellacracoviensis.pl Symphonic, vocal, chamber music, recitals.
Organ Days c/o Philharmonic Orchestra Karol Szymanowski, Zwierniecka 1, PL-31-103 Krakow, Poland *t:* +48 12 422 0958, also fax *e:* fk@filharmonia.krakow.pl *w:* www.filharmonia.krakow.pl Organ recitals, oratorio concerts.
Sacrum Profanum ul Olszanska 7, PL-31-513 Krakow, Poland *t:* +48 12 4249650 *f:* +48 12 4249652 *w:* www.sacrumprofanum.pl
Song of Our Roots Rynex 6, PL-37-500 Jaroslaw, Poland *t:* +48 16 621 64 51, also fax *e:* earlymusic@poczta.onet.pl *w:* www.jaroslaw.pl/festiwal Early and traditional music, especially liturgical. Workshops in Gregorian chan, traditional dances, festival choir. Concerts performed by artists and participants together. Lodging in old abbey.
Warsaw Autumn International Festival of Contemporary Music c/o Polish Composers' Union, Rynek Starego Miasta 27, PL-00-272 Warszawa, Poland *t:* +48 22 831 1634 ext 32; +48 22 635 91 38; +48 22 8310607, also fax *e:* festival@warsaw-autumn.art.pl *w:* www.warsaw-autumn.art.pl Annual. Contemporary music: symphony and chamber music, solo recitals, electronic and computer music, multimedia project.

 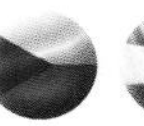   

SLOVAKIA

AKADEMIA UMENI V BANSKEJ BYSTRICI (ACADEMY OF ARTS IN BANSKA BYSTRICA)

Jana Kollara 22, SK-974 01 Banska Bystrica, Slovakia
t: +421 48 4320 317 *f:* +421 48 4145 109 *e:* information@aku.sk; vitko@aku.sk (international co-operation) *w:* www.aku.sk
Contact Peter Vitko (international enquiries).
Course information Courses for piano, accordion, voice, composition, conducting, orchestral instruments, harpsichord, saxophone.
Admissions information *Term dates* 1 Oct 2009-31 Jan 2010; 12 Feb-30 Jun 2010. *Application requirements* Audition in front of panel of professors; school-leaving exam (for bachelor degree study), bachelor diploma (for masters degree study), masters diploma (for doctoral study). *Application deadline* 30 Nov 2008 (bachelor degree); 31 Mar 2009 (masters); 30 Jun 2009 (doctorate). *Fees* Currently no fee for EU students; under review. *No of students* 130 music faculty students.

VYSOKA SKOLA MUZICKYCH UMENI (ACADEMY OF MUSIC AND DRAMATIC ARTS)

Zochova 1, SK-813 01 Bratislava, Slovakia
t: +421 254419346 *f:* +421 254412056 *e:* rektorat@vsmu.sk *w:* www.vsmu.sk

SLOVENIA

LJUBLJANA

AKADEMIJA ZA GLASBO (ACADEMY OF MUSIC)

Stari trg 34, SI-1000 Ljubljana, Slovenia
t: +386 1 242 73 01 *f:* +386 1 425 48 57
e: intern.office@uni-lj.si (international office); dekanat@ag.uni-lj.si (music faculty)
w: www.uni-lj.si
Contact Katya Cerjak, head of international relations; Jerneja Čelofiga, incoming students co-ord.
Admissions information *Scholarships* Some are available to foreign students. *Language requirements* All lectures and practical classes are held in Slovenian.
Facilities *Accommodation* University housing dept can help students to find local accommodation. Foreign students are not eligible for dormitory accommodation.

EASTERN EUROPE

ALBANIA

TIRANA (TIRANE)

AKADEMIA E ARTEVE

Sheshi Nene Tereza, Tirane, Albania
t: +355 4 2247596 *f:* +355 4 225488 *e:* petritmalaj@hotmail.com; iscmal@abcom-al.com
w: www.artacademy.al
Contact Petrit Malaj, rector; Sokol Shupo, dean of music faculty.
Course information study programs on: musicology, conducting, composition, piano, violin, viola, cello, double bass, guitar, flute, oboe, clarinet, trombone, trumpet, accordion, bassoon, horn, tuba, singing and pedagogy.
Admissions information *Language requirements* Albanian language required.

BELARUS

MINSK

BELARUSIAN STATE ACADEMY OF MUSIC

Internatsionalnaya str 30, 220030 Minsk, Belarus
t: +375 17 328 55 02 *f:* +375 17 328 55 01
e: international@tut.by *w:* www.bgam.edu.by
Contact Natalia Ganul, head of international relations.
Course information Main undergrad course lasts 5 years. 1-yr MA and 3-yr PhD in Musicology can also be undertaken. Short-term tailored courses are also a possibility.
Admissions information *Term dates* Sep-Jan (winter semester); Feb-Jun (spring semester) *Application requirements* All overseas students take 1-year preliminary course studying Russian and a special course in line with their intended specialisation, and are required to pass an exam at the end. Details of audition requirements available on website. *Fees* $2960-4460pa depending on course (inclusive of accommodation).

BOSNIA HERZEGOVINA

SARAJEVO

ACADEMY OF MUSIC AT THE UNIVERSITY OF EAST SARAJEVO

Vuka Karadzica 30, 71 123 Isocno Sarajevo, Bosnia Herzegovina
t: +387 57 342 125, also fax *e:* makss@spinter.net *w:* www.muzickaakademija.net
Zoran Rakic, contact.
Course information Bachelors (4 yrs) and masters (1 yr) degrees; artist diploma. *Instrumental* accordion, piano, flute, guitar, violin, viola. *Vocal* Solo singing. *Conducting* On in the departments of composition, general music pedagogy and church music. *Composition* Courses available. *Chamber music* Subject in the department of vocal and instrumental studies. *Choral* For all students, except violin, viola and flute. *Other* Department of church music and chanting; general music pedagogy.
Admissions information *Term dates* Mid Sep-end Dec (winter semester); Feb-mid Jun. *Application deadline* Jun and Sep. *Fees* Approx EUR 2000 per year; please contact for full details. *No of students* 263 students in total. *Language requirements* Serbian, Croat, Bosnian.
Facilities *Music facilities* Town facilities used by students. *Performance opportunities* Various concert series run by the academy. Some students are engaged in the opera and orchestra in Sarajevo and are members of different choirs. *Accommodation* Student hostel and other on-campus accommodation available.

UNIVERZITET U SARAJEVU MUZICKA AKADEMIA

Music Academy, Josipa Stadlera 1/II, 71000 Sarajevo, Bosnia and Herzegovina
t: +387 33 200 299 *f:* +387 33 444 896 *e:* info@mas.unsa.ba *w:* www.mas.unsa.ba
Contact Ivan Carlovic, dean.
Course information Departments for composition, conducting, solo singing, piano and percussion, woodwind, string, musicology and music theory and teaching.

BULGARIA

PLOVDIV

ACADEMY OF MUSIC, DANCE AND FINE ARTS

2 St Todor Samoudomov, PO Box 117, BG-4025 Plovdiv, Bulgaria
t: +359 32 601 441 *f:* +359 32 631 668 *e:* amti_sekretar@evrocom.net *w:* www.artacademyplovdiv.com
Contact Prof Luben Dosev, vice rector of academy
Course information Courses in various departments: Piano and Accordion, Orchestral Instruments, Folk Music, Ethnomusicology, Music Theory and History, Music Education. See website for more details of course content and structure. *Instrumental* Piano, clarinet, acoustic guitar, flute, bagpipe, fiddle, mandolin. *Vocal* Folk singing, musical theatre. *Chamber music* Folk music chamber ensembles.
Admissions information *Language requirements* English, Bulgarian
Facilities *Accommodation* None.

CROATIA

ZAGREB

MUZICKA AKADEMIJA SVEUCILISTA U ZAGREBU

Gunduliceva 6, HR-10000 Zagreb, Croatia
t: +385 1 48 10 200 *f:* +385 1 48 72 380 *e:* referada@muza.hr (admissions) *w:* www.muza.hr
Contact Rosanda Zimmermann, international office.
Course information Music academy is split into 8 depts: composition/theory, musicology, conducting/harp/percussion, voice, keyboard instruments, strings/guitar, wind, music education.
Admissions information *No of students* Approx 500 total students; 150 professors.
Facilities *Performance opportunities* 300 concerts, performances and productions per year; 2 concerts per year at the Vatroslav Lisinski concert hall and in various other concert series; possibility of performance with the Zagreb Philharmonic or at the national theatre.

ROMANIA

BUCHAREST (BUCURESTI)

UNIVERSITATEA NATIONALA DE MUZICA BUCURESTI

Str Stirbei Voda nr 33, Sector 1, RO-010102 Bucuresti, Romania
t: +40 21 313 58 89, also fax *e:* international@unmb.ro *w:* www.unmb.ro
Contact Lucia Costinescu, dir of international relations dept
Course information Undergraduate, masters and doctoral studies in performing, singing, composition (classical and jazz), musicology, music pedagogy, conducting (orchestral and choral), Byzantine music.
Admissions information *Term dates* Oct-Feb (1st semester); Feb-June (2nd semester). *Application requirements* Admission exam. *Application deadline* 1 May. *Scholarships* Government scholarships available. *No of students* 1300 students.

CLUJ-NAPOCA

ACADEMIA DE MUZICA GHEORGHE DIMA

25 Ion IC Bratianu St, RO-400079 Cluj-Napoca, Romania
t: +40 264 591241; +40 264 591242 int 118 (international relations) *f:* +40 264 593879 *e:* facultateademuzica@yahoo.com; oana.balan@amgd.ro (international relations) *w:* www.amgd.ro

LASI

UNIVERSITATEA DE ARTE 'GEORGE ENESCU' IASI

Str Horia 7-9, RO-700126 Iasi, Romania
t: +40 232 212548; +40 232 225333 (international office) *f:* +40 232 216637 *e:* fgrigoras@arteiasi.ro *w:* www.arteiasi.ro
Contact Florin Grigoras, international office

SERBIA AND MONTENEGRO

BELGRADE (BEOGRAD)

FAKULTET MUZICKE UMETNOSTI
Univerzitet umetnosti u Beogradu, Kralja Milana 50, 11000 Beograd, Serbia
t: +381 11 2659466
e: fmuinfo@fmu.bg.as.yu
w: www.fmu.bg.ac.yutIRANE

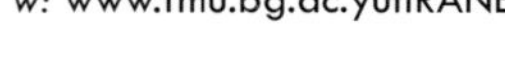

EUROPE

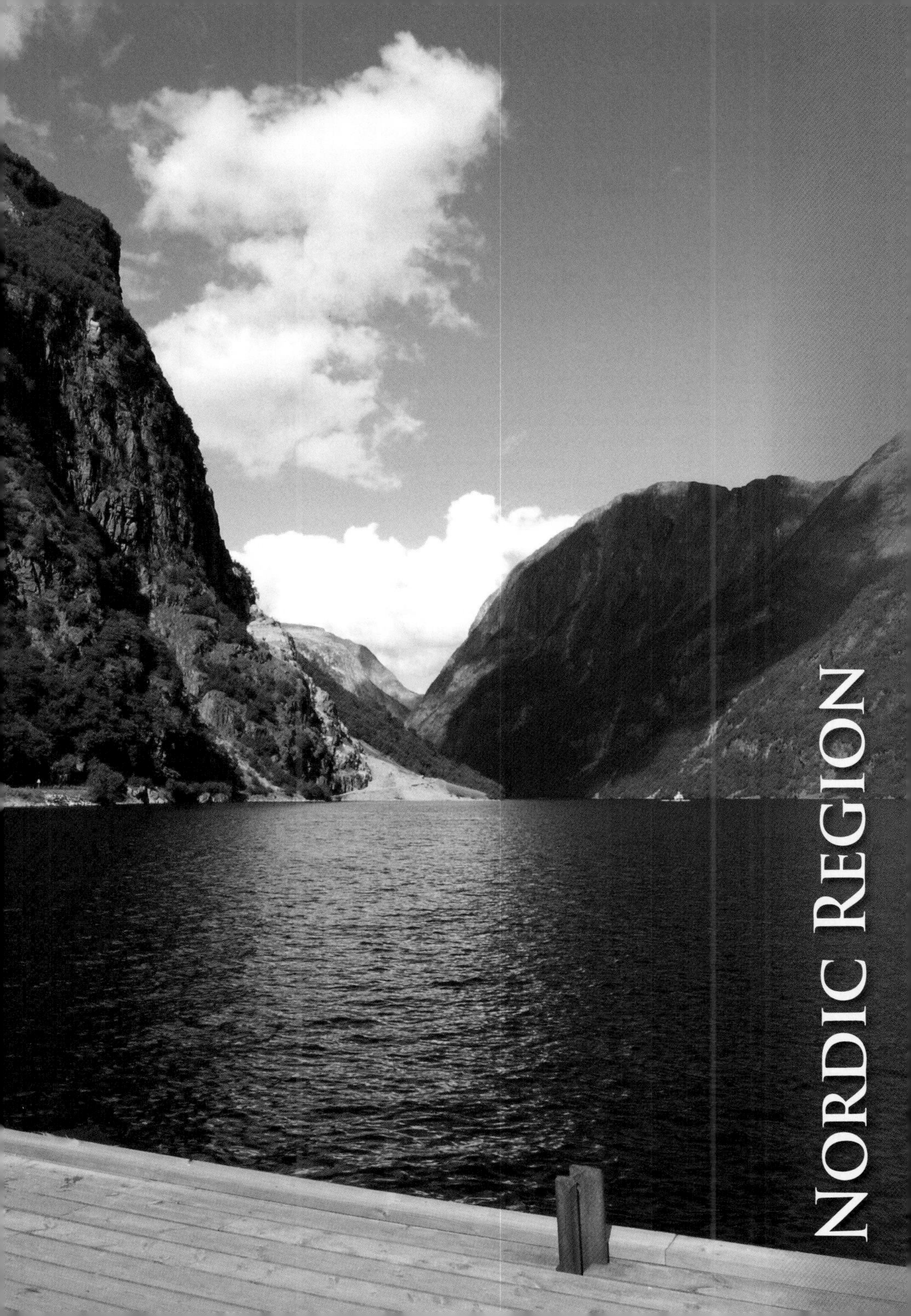
NORDIC REGION

NORDIC REGION

Although the countries in the far north of Europe may seem to be distant from the continent's musical heart, geography should not be confused with importance. All five of the countries in this section have thriving classical music scenes. Iceland supports a professional orchestra and has proved a useful place for young professionals from other countries to get orchestral experience, for instance; Finland has an enormous number of music festivals for a country of just over 5 million people (music was a significant part of the country's sense of national identity in the run-up to its independence in the early 20th century, and the legacy remains. They also offer something a little different in terms of the experience of living there – Norway's most northern music academy is within the Arctic Circle, offering the prospect of midnight sun in summer and months where the light levels don't rise above twilight For outdoor types, Sweden and Norway offer dramatic scenery. Denmark is a gateway to both north and south, now connected to Sweden by bridge, while remaining a place worth exploring in its own right.

DENMARK PAGE 173

Professional training in Denmark has followed the Bologna recommendations for several years now (since 2004), so the system is well established there. Education takes place in specialist music institutions that run parallel to the country's universities, with a degree structure that is the same, save for the fact that a Konservatorium cannot offer PhDs. They may have input into PhDs offered by universities, but it will be the latter who verify and administer them. Around 90% of students progress to the 2nd cycle of studies at masters level. The level of government funding is such that, for EU/EEA students at least, there are no tuition fees.

FINLAND PAGE 177

Although advanced music training in Finland is provided by institutions running a Bologna-compliant system, only one, the Sibelius academy in Helsinki currently offers masters level as well as the BMus. As a result, graduates of that institution have an advantage in their progression to that higher level – they are automatically accepted without having to take an entrance exam. In terms of qualification, the masters degree is considered the appropriate level certificate for professional performing; the bachelors, however, does entitle a graduate to teach music in schools. All higher education institutions in Finland are state-funded, but the level is higher for music conservatoires (up to 95% of funding).

ICELAND PAGE 181

The 2 advanced level training institutions in Iceland are run on slightly different lines since, by law, the older College of Music is not able to award degrees for the training it gives. In order to rectify this, the Academy of Arts was set up as a private concern (though government-funded) to offer artistic training in performing and visual arts. Its various curricula are designed by the departments themselves, so are not set down by the government. The majority of pre-professional training begins in specialist music schools, partly funded by local government, partly through fees.

NORWAY PAGE 183

There are 3 kinds of higher education institutions providing music training: fully independent state-funded music academy (there is one, the Norwegian Academy of Music), university-affiliated institutions, or private institution such as the Barratt-Due institute. Unlike other degree courses, these institutions are not obliged to provide degrees according to Bologna, so some 4-year 1st cycle degrees are offered; curricula are also independent of central control, with each establishment deciding course content and structure.

SWEDEN PAGE 187

Advanced music training is Sweden is simple to understand since all establishments follow the same degree structure (3 years undergrad + 2 years second cycle); all conservatoires, as with higher education more generally, are centrally funded, with students required to contribute for student welfare and small administration fees only. It has been found that graduates of Swedish conservatoires have good employment prospects, with many able to pursue at least part of their professional career in the field.

AARHUS (ÅRHUS)

Port on Denmark's east coast (Jutland peninsula) and surrounded by forests. Dates back over 1000 years, and the city today still features many old buildings – the dramatic cathedral, one of the tallest in Europe, is 13th century, for example – but also more modern architecture (the harbour area is currently being redeveloped). A big student town, with 35,000 at the university alone – it has been estimated that one in five people in the city is a student.

CLIMATE

Warmest month August (12-22°C), coldest months December and January (-1-3°C).

MUSICAL LIFE

Musikhuset Århus is a striking glass dominated concert hall; main hall seats over 1500, chamber hall over 300. Home to Danish National Opera and Aarhus Symoniorkester; another orchestra is Aarhus Sinfonietta. Also venues featuring rock, alternative music etc such as VoxHall.

OTHER CULTURAL INFORMATION

Studenterhus in the harbour area is a building/organisation specifically for the city's students – it aims to provide a meeting place, networking possibilities and promote events. Among the range of exhibitions are several reflecting on city's past: a recreation of an old Danish town, a Viking museum, a museum documenting the changing lives of Danish women, and a museum of the occupation. Also modern art gallery and thriving theatre scene.

FESTIVALS AND EVENTS

Aarhus Festival (August-September) features different kinds of music and various art forms; jazz festival runs for a week in July. Nordic choir festival in July also promotes aspects of Nordic culture; Spor festival focuses on contemporary classical music. Various rock festivals and events.

TOURIST INFORMATION

www.visitaarhus.com, +45 8731 5010

DET JYSKE MUSIKKONSERVATORIUM (ROYAL ACADEMY OF MUSIC)

Skovgaardsgade 2C, DK-8000 Arhus C, Denmark
t: +45 8713 3800 *f:* +45 8712 3840 e: mail@musikkons.dk *w:* www.musikkons.dk
Contact Keld Hosbond.
Course information All levels: classical, rhythmic, electronic; also adult education/refresher courses. All orchestral instruments offiered, voice, contemporary music, composition, opera and musical theatre,
Admissions information *Term dates* Aug/Sep-June. *Application requirements* Tests on main instrument/voice plus minor subjects (theory, ear tests), as well as piano. Full details of application procedure and requirements for each course are available on website. *Application deadline* 1 Dec (1st Apr for exchange students) *Fees* Fees apply to non-EU/EEA students and for the adult education/refresher courses. For details, see website. *Scholarships* None. *No of students* 400 students, inc 30 international students. *Language requirements* English.
Facilities *Music facilities* 120-seat recital hall; hall for rhythmic music (465 seats/1000 standing); symphonic hall and 2 other halls within the Aarhus Concert Hall (320-1600 seats). More expansion of facilities planned. *Accommodation* Help finding accomodation available.

EUROPE

COPENHAGEN (KØBENHAVN)

Danish capital based on Zealand island at the east of the country, connected to Jutland and Sweden by Oresund Bridge. Characterised by large number of parks and gardens (the most famous being the Tivoli Gardens) and an attractive mixture of architectural styles from the medieval old town to a number of new developments, with baroque churches and 18th century town houses in between.

CLIMATE

Warmest months July and August (13-20°C), coldest months January and February (-2-2°C). Rainfall is moderate but consistent throughout the year (in the range 24-60mm per month), with late winter/early spring being the driest

MUSICAL LIFE

Brand new concert hall opened in 2009 to house DR Radiosymfoniorkest, currently in the DR/Copenhagen Concert Hall along with the broadcaster's other music ensembles (choir, chamber orchestra, big band). Several other venues: dramatic waterfront opera house with main stage and studio theatre puts on range of opera, plus children's shows and concerts; also experimental music theatre at Musikteater Plex. Tivoli Concert Hall puts on concerts and stage events. The Queen's Hall is a medium-sized concert hall with its own chamber ensemble at the Royal Library's Black Diamond building; smaller is Rundetaarn which stages range of recitals and chamber music from various artists. Copenhagen Philharmonic (Sjællands Symfoniorkester) performs at various venues, including those mentioned. Athelas Sinfonietta a chamber orchestra concentrating on contemporary music. City has a strong jazz tradition.

OTHER CULTURAL INFORMATION

National Museum and National Gallery both in the city. Modern art in particular at Louisiana museum of modern art; Ny Carlsberg Glyptolek, which houses varied collection of philanthropist Carl Jacobsen; Ordrupgaard Museum. The Round Tower is an unusual feature, an observatory dating back to the 17th century which still functions, although it is also used for exhibitions and events.

FESTIVALS AND EVENTS

City's Golden Days festival, which promotes its cultural activity, includes diverse musical performances; annual jazz festival in July. The famous Tivoli Gardens holds music events from classical to rock during summer. Nearby Roskilde is one of Europe's biggest outdoor rock festivals.

TOURIST INFORMATION

www.visitcopenhagen.com, touristinfo@woco.dk, +45 7022 2442

DET KONGELIGE DANSKE MUSIKKONSERVATORIUM

Rosenørnsallé 22, DK-1970 Frederiksberg, Denmark
t: +45 7226 7226 *f:* +45 7226 7272
e: dkdm@dkdm.dk *w:* www.dkdm.dk

Course information Bachelors and masters programmes available in 9 departments: strings; woodwind and harp; brass, percussion, orchestral conducting; singing; piano, guitar, accordion; church and consort music; educational theory and aural studies; composition/theory; recording. Also 3 year soloist programme at Opera Academy. 2-yr advanced postgraduate diploma.

Admissions information *Application requirements* Entrance exam; details and contents of exam available on website. Academy may take into account possibilities for appropriate combination of instruments/voices for ensembles. *Application deadline* 1 Mar for Erasmus/Nordplus applications (through home institution); 1 Dec for full degree students from EU/EEA-countries. 1 Feb for Advanced Postgraduate Diploma and Opera Academy. 1 Apr for full degree non-EU/EEA students applying for bachelor or master. *Fees* See website: www.dkdm.dk/Saadan_soeger_du/Non_eu_applicant.aspx?sc_lang=en *Scholarships* Non-EU students can apply for scholarships from The Royal Danish Academy of Music to cover part of the living expenses. *No of students* 352 students in total, about half of whom are international. *Language requirements* Most classes in both Danish and English; all students expected to have some knowledge of English. Danish language course available through DKDM.

Facilities *Music facilities* 6 concert halls in different sizes (1 big, 1 medium, 4 small); library with modern AV-facilities, places for reading and soft sofas; classrooms and practise rooms; electronic booking system for practice rooms; IT laboratory; recording facilities; instruments. *Performance opportunities* Large and small scale performance projects. *Accommodation* Information and guidance provided for finding accommodation in Copenhagen.

RYTMISK MUSIKKONSERVATORIUM

Leo Mathisens Vej 1, Holmen, DK-1437 København K, Denmark
t: +45 32 68 67 00 *f:* +45 32 68 67 66
e: aah@rmk.dk *w:* www.rmc.dk

Contact Aage Hagen, head of international relations.

Course information Degree programmes predominantly geared towards contemporary music; music education, music and movement education, music performance, music technology, music management, song writing (eg pop, jazz etc). Masters offered in music education, music and movement education, music performance (including european jazz); also postgraduate diplomas and certificates in performance or composition.

Admissions information *Term dates* 2 semesters, Aug-Dec & Jan-Jun. *Application requirements* Online application form through www.musikuddannelser.dk; entrance exam. *Application deadline* 1 Dec. *Fees* None for EU/EEA residents. DKK350 application fee may be required. *Scholarships* None. *No of students* 196 students.

ESBJERG

Small, relatively modern city (development began in late 19th century) on the west coast of Denmark's Jutland peninsula. Its location makes it good for outdoor activities, from cycling to birdwatching.

CLIMATE

Warmest month August (12-21°C), coldest months

EUROPE

December and January (-1-3°C).

MUSICAL LIFE
Musikhuset Esbjerg is the city's main venue, with 2 auditoriums (one for chamber performances), staging all music genres. Tobakken a large venue for popular and alternative music, jazz etc.

OTHER CULTURAL INFORMATION
Art museum a recently renovated gallery housing its own collection, plus special exhibitions – it also includes an 'aesthetic laboratory' and interactive displays. City museum tells the story of the city, with a focus on its association with amber. Other institutions include a printing museum, local history museum (the Bramming Museum) and a museum concentrating on Denmark under German occupation in World War II.

TOURIST INFORMATION
www.visitesbjerg.dk, kls@visitesbjerg.dk, +45 76136101

VMK - ACADEMY OF MUSIC AND MUSIC COMMUNICATION
Kirkegade 61, DK-6700 Esbjerg, Denmark
t: +45 76 10 43 00 *f:* +45 76 10 43 10
e: info@vmk.dk *w:* www.vmk.dk
Contact Jesper Asp, international co-ord.
Course information Courses in ensemble music (rhythmic or classical), music communication, church music, electronic music.
Admissions information *Term dates* Aug-Jun. *Application requirements* Entry exam, application form and CD. *Application deadline* Previous Dec. *Fees* Amount depends on nationality. *Scholarships* None. *No of students* 110 students in total. *Language requirements* Danish or English.
Facilities *Music facilities* Concert hall, music library, recording studio, rehearsal rooms etc. All-Steinway academy. *Accommodation* Student housing guaranteed.

ODENSE
City based on the island of Funen in the east of Denmark, one of the oldest in the country and birthplace of Hans Christian Andersen. The city combines characteristic Danish architecture with plenty of green space.

CLIMATE
Warmest month August (12-22°C), coldest months December and January (-1-3°C)

MUSICAL LIFE
Odense Symfoniorkester plays a full season of concerts at its home, the Odense Koncerthus.

OTHER CULTURAL INFORMATION
Hans Christian Andersen commemorated with a museum and an exhibition at his childhood home. Art galleries include Kunsthallen Brandts has changing exhibitions focusing on contemporary Danish and international art; Funen Art Museum has a permanent collection of Danish art from 18th century onwards.

FESTIVALS AND EVENTS
Main classical festival is Musikhøst (Music Harvest); contemporary music festival at end of November; Bach Week in March. Folk music festival in May. City is venue for Carl Nielsen competitions (violin, clarinet, flute in rotation). Hans Christian Andersen festival in summer; also film and blues festivals.

TOURIST INFORMATION
www.visitodense.com, otb@visitodense.com, +45 63 75 75 20

DET FYNSKE MUSIKKONSERVATORIUM (CARL NIELSEN ACADEMY OF MUSIC ODENSE)
Islandsgade 2, DK-5000 Odense C, Denmark
t: +45 6611 0663 *f:* +45 6617 7763 *e:* dfm@adm.dfm.dk; ib@adm.dfm.dk (international relations) *w:* www.dfm.dk
Contact Inge Brauke, international co-ord.
Course information Bachelor degree in classical/contemporary music or jazz or folk music, 3-year course including main specialism, ensemble playing and general subjects (eg ear training, piano playing, theory, music history, computer technology). MA in classical/contemporary music or jazz or folk music, 2-year course qualifying students for professional career. Advance postgrad diploma, special additional 2-year course for exceptional students.
Admissions information *Term dates* Aug-Dec (1st semester); Jan-Jun (2nd semester) *Application requirements* Entrance exam (see website for full requirements and set audition items); MA students must have BA degree and recommendation; advanced postgrad diploma students need MA, plus entrance exam. International students accepted as regular students, as exchange students or as guest students with Danish government grant. *Application deadline* 1 Dec (1 Feb for advanced postgrad diploma). *Fees* None for EU/EEA nationals.

No of students 150 students *Language requirements* All tuition is in Danish. Individual lessons may be conducted in English.

Facilities *Performance opportunities* Possibility of taking part in several local festivals. *Accommodation* Furnished accommodation in hall of residence available for all exchange students.

MUSIC FESTIVALS

Aalborg Opera Festival Godthabsgade 8, DK-9400 Norresundby, Denmark *t:* +45 9931 4166 *e:* gft-kultur@aalborg.dk *w:* www.aalborgoperafestival.dk Mainly indoor opera festival with about 40 performances and concerts all over town.

Aarhus Festival Officersbygningen, Vester Alle 3, DK-8000 Aarhus C, Denmark *t:* +45 87 30 83 00 *f:* +45 87 308 319 *e:* mail@aarhusfestuge.dk *w:* www.aarhusfestival.com Annual festival, largest single collection of cultural events in Scandinavia. Theatre, cabaret, opera, ballet and dance, classical and new music, rock, jazz and folk music. Exhibitions, film and media, sports, symposia, seminars and events for children.

Music Harvest Festival Det Fynske Musikkonservatorium, Islandsgade 2, DK-5000 Odense, Denmark *t:* +45 66 110663 *f:* +45 66 177763 *e:* musikhost@adm.dfm.dk *w:* www.musikhost.dk Annual. Held in Odense, concerts and seminars on contemporary music.

Opera Hedeland Hobjergvej 15 - Trorod, DK-2950 Vedbaek, Denmark *e:* info@operahedeland.dk *w:* www.operahedeland.dk Annual open-air production in 3500 natural arena between Copenhagen and Roskilde.

Selso Summer Concerts Langs Hegnet 39, DK-2800 Lyngby, Denmark *t:* +45 45 930778, also fax *e:* koncert@flutist.dk *w:* www.flutist.dk Annual. Classical music festival.

Susaa Festival Skovmarksvej 52, Vetterslev, DK-4100 Ringsted, Denmark *t:* +45 57 649164 *w:* www.susaafestival.dk Works by Danish composers, including world premieres. Held at Kulturcentret Grönnegade, Nästved.

HELSINKI

Finland's capital, located on the Baltic coast. Although dating back to mid 16th century, biggest developments came in second half of 19th century and post-World War II.

City's architecture a mixture of neo-classical and art nouveau styles; there are many distinctive buildings, either civic (such as art nouveau railway station) or religious (Helsinki cathedral, or the Uspenski orthodox cathedral). Coastal location an added attraction: visitors can take trips to the archipelago's various islands, for instance, not to mention the ferry services to Estonia and Sweden.

CLIMATE

Warmest month July (13-21°C), coldest month January (-7--1°C). Wettest months August-October (around 70-80mm), although snowfall is frequent in winter.

MUSICAL LIFE

Finlandia Hall, with its marble exterior also a distinctive building, in different style; is the home of the Helsinki Philharmonic Orchestra, but receives visits from other orchestras such as the Finnish Radio Symphony Orchestra, a group that plays in various venues. Kulttuuritalo one such place, a flexible mixed repertoire venue. Good choice of opera: as well as Helsinki City Opera and other small companies, the Finnish national company based in the city. New venue, Helsinki Music Centre, under construction now and will be more focused on classical music. Neighbouring districts of Espoo and Vantaa also have thriving music scenes.

OTHER CULTURAL INFORMATION

Good collection of museums and galleries, covering all periods of art and city's history; the Design Museum shows off Finland's strong tradition in this field. Children have their own cultural venue, Annantalo Arts Centre.

FESTIVALS AND EVENTS

Helsinki Festival runs for a fortnight in August, featuring classical, popular and world music. Musica Nova (February) has a more eclectic musical outlook, taking in various styles of modern music at venues across the city. More traditional range of classical music at Avanti! Festival in June. Again, children are well served with several theatre, dance and arts festivals at different points in the year.

TOURIST INFORMATION

www.visithelsinki.fi, tourist.info@hel.fi, +358 9 3101 3300

HELSINGIN KONSERVATORIO (HELSINKI CONSERVATORY OF MUSIC)

Ruolahdentori 6, FI-00180 Helsinki, Finland
t: +358 9 5860 580 *f:* +358 9 5860 5868
e: konservatorio@konservatorio.fi
w: www.konservatorio.fi

Course information Vocational (post secondary school) qualifications in music for students aiming to become musicians. Curriculum includes instrumental tuition, solfege, theory of music, orchestral/chamber music/choral studies, conducting.

Admissions information *Term dates* Mid Aug-end May. *Application deadline* 1-19 Mar. *Fees* None.

Facilities *Music facilities* Purpose-built facilities include 520-seat concert hall, chamber music hall, 85 classrooms. *Accommodation* Help finding accommodation not available.

SIBELIUS-AKATEMIA

PO Box 86, FIN-00251 Helsinki, Finland
t: +358 20 753 90; +358 20 753 9400 (international academic affairs) *f:* +358 20 753 9600 *e:* info@siba.fi; leena.veijonsuo@siba.fi
w: www.siba.fi

Contact Leena Veijonsuo, contact for international enquiries

Course information Degree programmes in church music, composition and theory, folk music, jazz, orchestral and choral conducting, music education, music technology, instrumental performance, vocal music; also degree in arts management. See website for full details.

Admissions information *Term dates* Sep-Dec (first semester); Jan-May (second semester) *Application requirements* Various requirements, depending on course; see website for full details. *Application deadline* Mar to be confirmed; see website. *Fees* No tuition fee; EUR 80 Student Union fee only. *No of students* 1500 students.

LAHTI

Lakeside city, though not especially picturesque, with a population of around 100,000.

MUSICAL LIFE

Highly respected Lahti Symphony Orchestra based at the relatively new 1250-seat Sibelius Hall; also performs for Lahti opera chamber orchestra drawn from the main orchestra also performs there, as do guest artists and occasional non-classical performers.

EUROPE

OTHER CULTURAL INFORMATION

Lahti Art and Poster museum has substantial collection of Finnish and international graphic art (for which country is renowned). One institution with musical connection is Finnish Military Music Museum; Ski Museum is a more unusual exhibition. City Theatre is modern designed building with wide range of shows and spectacles.

FESTIVALS AND EVENTS

Sibelius festival, organised by Lahti Symphony Orchestra, focuses on the composer. Major organ festival in August.

TOURIST INFORMATION

www.lahtiguide.fi, +358 20 7281 750

LAHDEN AMMATTIKORKEAKOULU (LAHTI UNIVERSITY OF APPLIED SCIENCES)

Faculty of Music, Svinhufvudinkatu 6 F-G, FIN-15110 Lahti, Finland
t: +358 3828 2996; +358 3828 2995 (international affairs) *f:* +358 3828 2998
e: music@lamk.fi *w:* www.lamk.fi
Contact Marjo Leppä, international co-ord.

Course information Professional higher education degree equivalent to a bachelors degree in music performance. Specialisation fields: orchestral instrument (includes principal instrument, orchestra, chamber music, repertoire and literature studies, analysis, orchestral repertoire); voice (voice, secondary instrument - piano, choir and ensemble, lied, basics of acting, repertory and literature studies, analysis); piano (principal study, chamber music/accompaniment, repertory and literature studies, analysis, lied).

Admissions information *Term dates* 31 Aug-31 May. *Application requirements* Entrance exam (audition, written theory/solfege/general knowledge test, interview and English language test). Appropriate school-leaving certificate (Finnish, International/European Baccalaureate, or national qualification) and required level of musical ability. Applicants without formal qualifications but with exceptional level of musical ability may be accepted. *Application deadline* Early Mar-early Apr. *Fees* Free tuition; students meet living expenses and cost of educational material. *Scholarships* None. *No of students* Approx 200 students in faculty *Language requirements* Good English language skills (written and spoken).

Facilities *Music facilities* New building built especially for music studies. 1 level of rehearsal rooms available for students any time of day. Faculty also has a small chamber music hall and rehearsal theatre. *Accommodation* Most used accommodation service is Oppilastalot, (www.oppilastalo.fi).

TURKU

Old port city (there are regular boats to Stockholm) in south west Finland, originally the capital until Helsinki took over in the 19th century. Home to Finland's oldest university, and still a major educational centre with around 35,000 students in higher education. Nominated European City of Culture for 2011 so visitors can expect a range of artistic activity then.

CLIMATE

Warmest month July (12-22°C), coldest month January (-8--2°C). Rainfall peaks in summer and autumn (around 70-75mm), but winters see frequent snowfall.

MUSICAL LIFE

Turku Philharmonic Orchestra is based at its own concert hall (there are performances from visiting groups too); it also gives concerts in Turku Castle and occasionally cathedral. Other city buildings also host regular concerts: Wäinö Aaltonen Museum (changing exhibitions) and the Sibelius museum (charts composer's life and work; there is also display of musical instruments); Brinkkala Mansion cultural centre has a regular concert series.

OTHER CULTURAL INFORMATION

As well as those mentioned, city has museums of history and archaeology, as well as modern art. Renovated castle puts on exhibitions alongside museum and restored rooms.

FESTIVALS AND EVENTS

Classical music festival in August. Various festival events (eg jazz, chamber music) in the archipelago surrounding the city.

TOURIST INFORMATION

www.turku.fi, +358 2 262 7444

TURUN AMMATTIKORKEAKOULU TAIDEAKATEMIA (ARTS ACADEMY AT TURKU UNIVERSITY OF APPLIED SCIENCES)

Linnankatu 54-60, FIN-20100 Turku, Finland
t: +358 2 263 350; +358 10 553 5225 (international relations) *f:* +358 2 2633 5200;

+358 1055 35 202 (international relations) e: antonella.storti@turkuamk.fi w: www.taideakatemia.turkuamk.fi
Course information Courses in instrumental, vocal, orchestral and chamber music, opera, lied, music theory and history.
Admissions information *Term dates* 1 Sep-18 Dec (autumn term); 4 Jan-31 May (spring term). *Application requirements* Upper secondary education with appropriate acceptable qualification. Also audition, including performance and music theory test. *Application deadline* 1 Apr. *Fees* None. *Scholarships* None. *No of students* 168 students, inc 8 from overseas.

MUSIC FESTIVAL

April Jazz Espoo Ahertajantie 6 B, FIN-02100 Espoo, Finland *t:* +358 9 455 0003 *f:* +358 9 465172 *w:* www.apriljazz.fi International jazz festival.
Avanti! Summer Sounds Tallberginkatu 1/146, FIN-00180 Helsinki, Finland *t:* +358 9 694 0091 *f:* +358 9694 2208 *e:* avanti@avantimusic.fi *w:* www.avantimusic.fi Orchestral and chamber music concerts, baroque and contemporary music.
Crusell Week Uudenkaupungin Kultuuritoimisto, Rauhankatu 10, FIN-23500 Uusikaupunki, Finland *t:* +358 2 8451 5302 *f:* +358 2 8451 5442 *e:* kulttuuritoimisto@uusikaupunki.fi *w:* www.crusell.fi Woodwind music festival.
Gergiev Festival Concert Hall Mikaeli, Sointukatu 1, FIN-50100 Mikkeli, Finland *t:* +358 15 162 076 *f:* +358 15 362 757 *e:* festival@mikkelinmusiikkijuhlat.fi *w:* www.mikkelinmusiikkijuhlat.fi Valery Gergiev and the Orchestra of the Mariinsky Theatre, plus guests.
Helsinki Festival Lasipalatsi, Mannerheimintie 22-24, FIN-00100 Helsinki, Finland *t:* +358 9 6126 5100 *f:* +358 9 6126 5161 *e:* info@helsinkifestival.fi *w:* www.helsinkifestival.fi Annual arts festival featuring classical, popular and world music, dance, theatre, visual arts, cinema and city events.
Hetta Music Event Virastotalo, FIN-99300 Enontekio, Finland *t:* +358 40 543 9876 *f:* +358 16 521 050 *e:* hetan.musiikkipaivat@enontekio.fi *w:* www.hetanmusiikkipaivat.fi Sacred, chamber and choral music.
Imatra Big Band Festival Heikinkatu 1, FIN-55100 Imatra, Finland *t:* +358 20 7479 405 *f:* +358 20 7479 401 *e:* vip@ibbf.fi *w:* www.ibbf.fi Jazz, blues, funk, world music, rock.
Kaustinen Folk Music Festival PO Box 24, FIN-69601 Kaustinen, Finland *t:* +358 207 2911 *f:* +358 207 291200 *e:* folk.art@kaustinen.fi *w:* www.kaustinen.net Annual folk music and dance festival. Folk, world, traditional, ethnic, folk-dance.
Klemetti Summer Festival Koulutie 5, FIN-35300 Orivesi, Finland *t:* +358 207 511 550 *f:* +358 207 511 512 *e:* klemettiopisto@kvs.fi *w:* www.klemettiopisto.fi Choral, symphonic, chamber music.
Korsholm Music Festival Frilundintie 2, FIN-65610 Mustasaari, Finland *t:* +358 6 322 2390 *f:* +358 6 322 2393 *e:* info@korsholmmusicfestival.fi *w:* www.korsholmmusicfestival.fi Chamber music with Nordic features.
Kuhmo Chamber Music Festival Torikatu 39, FIN-88900 Kuhmo, Finland *t:* +358 8 652 0936 *f:* +358 8 652 1961 *e:* kuhmo.festival@kuhmofestival.fi *w:* www.kuhmofestival.fi Annual. Chamber music, with over 150 visiting artists.
Lahti Organ Festival Aleksanterinkatu 16, FIN-15140 Lahti, Finland *t:* +358 3 877230 *f:* +358 3 877 2320 *e:* urkuviikko@lahtiorgan.fi *w:* www.lahtiorgan.fi
Lahti Sibelius Festival Sibeliustalo, Ankkurikatu 7, FIN-15140 Lahti, Finland *t:* +358 3 814 4460 *f:* +358 3 814 4451 *e:* sinfonialahti@lahti.fi *w:* www.sinfonialahti.fi Weekend of concerts centred around Sibelius.
Lieksa Brass Week Koski-Jaakonkatu 4, FIN-81700 Lieksa, Finland *t:* +358 13 6889 4147 *f:* +358 16 689 4915 *e:* nina.lackman@lieksa.fi *w:* www.lieksabrass.com Brass music festival, master courses. Lieksa International Trumpet Competition.
Musica nova Helsinki c/o The Helsinki Festival, Mannerheimintie 22-24, FIN-00100 Helsinki, Finland *t:* +358 9 6126 5100 *f:* +358 9 6126 5161 *e:* musicanova@musicanova.fi *w:* www.musicanova.fi Biennial international festival of contemporary music. Co-ordinated by Helsinki Festival.
Naantali Music Festival Henrikinkatu 1, PO Box 46, FIN-21101 Naantali, Finland *t:* +358 2 434 5363 *f:* +358 2 434 5425 *e:* info@naantalinmusiikkijuhlat.fi *w:* www.naantalimusic.com Chamber music, orchestras, recitals, masterclasses.
Our Festival PO Box 41, FIN-04401 Jarvenpaa, Finland *t:* +358 50 302 1669 *f:* +358 9 27 19 2835 *e:* info@ourfestival.fi *w:* www.ourfestival.fi Chamber music in the historical homes of renowned Finnish artists such as Jean Sibelius, Eero Järnefelt and Joonas Kokkonen. The violinist Pekka Kuusisto

has compiled a programme in which he will be joined by a host of elite musicians in an intimate and communicative atmosphere.

Pori Jazz Festival Pohjoisranta 11 D, FIN-28100 Pori, Finland *t:* +358 2 626 2200 *f:* +358 2 626 2225 *e:* festival@porijazz.fi *w:* www.porijazz.fi Annual. International jazz festival. Major open-air concerts in Kirjurinluoto concert park by the Kokemaki river, plus jam sessions in more intimate settings. Over 150 concerts, some free.

Riihimaki Summer Concerts Valtakatu 10, FIN-11130 Riihimaki, Finland *t:* +358 20 758 5040 *f:* +358 1 973 2626 *e:* riihimaen.kesakonsertit@riihimaki.fi *w:* www.riihimaenkesakonsertit.fi Recitals and chamber music.

Sata Hame soi International Accordion Festival PO Box 33, FIN-39501 Ikaalinen, Finland *t:* +358 3 440 0224 *f:* +358 3 4501 264 *e:* juhlat@satahamesoi.fi *w:* www.satahamesoi.fi Annual. Focus on traditional Finnish accordion music; programme features accordion and related instruments in various settings from concert halls to outdoor events. Also international light and classical music.

Savonlinna Opera Festival Olavinkatu 27, FIN-57130 Savonlinna, Finland *t:* +358 15 476750 *f:* +358 15 4767540 *e:* info@operafestival.fi *w:* www.operafestival.fi Annual. Opera, recitals, concerts.

Tampere Biennale Tullikamarinaukio aukio 2, FIN-33100 Tampere, Finland *t:* +358 50 405 5225 *f:* +358 3 223 0121 *e:* music@tampere.fi *w:* www.tampere.fi/biennale Biennial. 5-day contemporary classical music festival, mainly Finnish music.

Tampere Jazz Happening Tullikamarin aukio 2, FIN-33100 Tampere, Finland *t:* +358 50 530 8777 *f:* +358 3 223 0121 *e:* music@tampere.fi *w:* www.tampere.fi/jazz Festival of modern jazz, improvised music and related genres.

Tampere Vocal Music Festival Tullikamarin aukio 2, FIN-33100 Tampere, Finland *t:* +358 3 5656 6172 *f:* +358 3 223 0121 *e:* music@tampere.fi *w:* www.tampere.fi/vocal Biennial. Festival includes international chorus review, a contest for vocal ensembles; training for choir conductors and singers; concerts in choral and vocal ensemble music, vocal world music.

Turku Music Festival Sibeliuksenkatu 2, FIN-20100 Turku, Finland *t:* +358 2 262 0812 *f:* +358 2 262 0830 *e:* info@tmj.fi *w:* www.tmj.fi Annual. Orchestral, early, contemporary and chamber music.

EUROPE

REYKJAVIK

Main city in Iceland, characterised by its dramatic geographical setting, the result of many thousands of years of volcanic activity. Geology plays a major part in daily life, with most domestic heating exploiting geothermal activity; residents also take advantage of naturally heated water for outdoor swimming. And although not actually north of the Arctic Circle, the city is far enough north to experience substantial periods of darkness throughout winter. Today, the city's nightlife has wide reputation, or even notoriety; for a country of its size it has a vibrant cultural life.

CLIMATE

Cool, or cold, all year round although winters are relatively mild; warmest months July (8-13°C), coldest month January (-3-2°C). Wettest month October (85mm), driest month May (45mm).

MUSICAL LIFE

Iceland Symphony Orchestra is focus of classical music; currently gives concerts in the university cinema building (as well as numerous performances overseas), but a new hall, Tónlistarhus, is currently under construction. Many orchestra members also play for Icelandic Opera, a small company with its own building.

OTHER CULTURAL INFORMATION

Centre for Icelandic art is the main promoter of visual art, but a substantial number of independent galleries can be found across city. Theatre also prominent – National Theatre stages shows in a range of genres, from drama to musicals; City Theatre looks beyond presentation of plays, with concerts and discussions also on its programme.

FESTIVALS AND EVENTS

Reykjavik Arts Festival every other year in May; Dark Music Days (February), run by Society of Icelandic Composers, focuses on contemporary music; summer Festival of Sacred Arts includes music, but other art forms too. More sacred music, plus early music, at Skálholt cathedral in the Skálholt Summer Concerts festival (about 50 km to the east of Reykjavik). Jazz festival in autumn.

TOURIST INFORMATION

www.visitreykjavik.is, info@visitreykjavik.is, +354 590 1550

TONLISTARSKOLINN I REYKJAVIK (REYKJAVIK COLLEGE OF MUSIC)

Skipholit 33, IS-105 Reykjavik, Iceland
t: +353 553 0625 *f:* +353 553 9240
e: tono@tono.is *w:* www.tono.is

LISTAHASKOLI ISLANDS (ICELAND ACADEMY OF THE ARTS)

Solvholsgata 13, IS-101 Reykjavik, Iceland
t: +354 552 4000; +354 545 2205 (international co-ord) *f:* +354 562 3629
e: lhi@lhi.is; alma@lhi.is *w:* www.lhi.is
Contact Alma Ragnasdottir, international co-ordinator

Course information BMus degrees in instrumental/vocal performance (piano, strings/winds, voice, other); diploma in instrumental/vocal performance; BA degrees in musicology, music education, composition. Exchange students should contact international co-ordinator for further information. Course is divided equally between performance training, theory and other electives. *Composition* New media, film music, stage music, production.

Admissions information *Term dates* Late Aug-mid Dec (autumn semester); early Jan-early May (spring semester). *Application requirements* Secondary school exam (Icelandic 'studentsprof') or equivalent. Applicants who do not meet this general requirement must demonstrate maturity and knowledge which can be evaluated as equivalent to the missing education (detailed explanation to be enclosed with application form). For MA course, BMus or BA in music is required. *Application deadline* For exchange students: 15 Apr (for autumn semester/whole year); 15 Oct (for spring semester). See website for undergraduate deadlines. *Fees* Approx ISK 160 per semester (ISK 320 for whole year). *Scholarships* Via LLP Socrates or Nordplus for students within those organisations. *No of students* 82 students in dept of music, 4 from overseas. 460 students in total. *Language requirements* General language of instruction is Icelandic. International students are requested to have a reasonable level of English.

Facilities *Music facilities* Practice rooms, sound engineering and recording studios, chamber music hall.

Performance opportunities Opportunities in and out of the academy. Recitals are recorded and turned into podcasts. *Accommodation* No on-campus accommodation but assistance is offered to international students seeking rooms for rent at reasonable rates.

ICELAND

MUSIC FESTIVALS

Dark Music Days Society of Icelandic Composers, Lauf svegi 4, IS-101 Reykjavik, Iceland *t:* +354 5 524 972 *f:* +354 5 562 6273 *w:* www.listir.is Annual. Contemporary music.

Festival of Sacred Arts Hallgrimskirkja Skolavorduholt, IS-101 Reykjavik, Iceland *t:* +354 510 1000 *f:* +354 510 1010 *e:* kirkjan@kirkjan.is *w:* www.kirkjan.is Biennial festival focusing on the spiritual in the arts.

Reykjavik Arts Festival Laekjargata 3b, PO Box 88, IS-121 Reykjavik, Iceland *t:* +354 5 612 444 *f:* +354 5 622 350 *w:* www.artfest.is Multi-arts festival.

Skalholt Summer Concerts Laufasvegur 4, IS-101 Reykjavik, Iceland *t:* +354 866 4600 *e:* siha@ismennt.is *w:* www.sumartonleikar.is Annual. Baroque and contemporary sacred music.

BERGEN

City on the North Sea coast, encompassed by mountains; second largest in the country with a population of a quarter of a million. Its national importance dates back to medieval period when it was a key port as part of the Hanseatic League; now its historic harbourside is on Unesco world heritage list. Numerous wooden buildings are characteristic of the city (the city has suffered from fires throughout its history).

CLIMATE

Warmest month July (11-18°C), coldest month January (0-4°C). Rainfall is high: wettest month August (190mm), driest month May (106mm).

MUSICAL LIFE

City is home to one of world's oldest, and well-regarded, orchestras in the Bergen Philharmonic Orchestra (tours internationally as well). Grieghallen is home to the orchestra (the composer used to be its music director), but stages other music too, not least opera. USF Verftet a more visual performing arts venue, but music performed there too. BIT20 Ensemble is a small, contemporary music ensemble performing in the city and on tour. Grieg celebrated in a museum dedicated to him at Troldhaugen; museum also contains a small recital room, the Troldsalen.

OTHER CULTURAL INFORMATION

City is home to a large number of museums and attractions. Hanseatic Museum charts city's importance at the time; city's role during World War II explained at Theta Museum; others focus on local arts and crafts (eg Horda Museum), history of education (Bergen School Museum). Art galleries on so-called 'Art Gallery Street'.

FESTIVALS AND EVENTS

Bergen International Festival (May-June) covers classical music plus literature, dance, theatre, opera and visual arts, focusing on work from Nordic and Baltic countries. Jazz festival in May also.

TOURIST INFORMATION

www.visitbergen.com, info@visitbergen.com, +47 55 55 20 00

GRIEGAKADEMIET, INSTITUTT FOR MUSIKK

Lars Hillesgate 3, N-5015 Bergen, Norway
t: +47 55 58 69 50 *f:* +47 55 58 69 60 *e:* grieg@hffa.uib.no; bjorn.halvorsen@grieg.uib.no
w: www.grieg.uib.no
Contact Bjorn Halvorsen, enquiries.

Course information Bachelor programmes in performance, composition and pedagogy/music education; master's programmes in performance or composition, ethnomusicology, music therapy. Also offers 1-year international diploma in performance or composition (for international students). *Instrumental* Principal instrument (classical/jazz), second instrument, contemporary music, baroque studies, accompaniment, church music, *Vocal* Classical or jazz, second instrument, contemporary music, early music. *Conducting* Choral and orchestral conducting electives. *Historical performance* Available on all instruments and for voice; early music ensembles. *Orchestral* Chamber orch, placements with the Bergen Philharmonic Orcheststra. *Opera* Music/Drama. *Jazz/world* Jazz studies available for all instruments and voice. *Other* Music therapy, musicology.
Admissions information *Term dates* Mid Aug-end Jun. *Application requirements* Applicants assessed on musical and academic ability, inc written aural skills and music theory test; requirements vary, contact academy for further details. *Application deadline* 15 Dec for performance or composition courses; 1 Jun for ethnomusicology or music therapy courses. *Fees* No tuition fees. *No of students* Approx 160 *Language requirements* Norwegian language proficiency test required (exchange students, master's and international diploma students exempt)
Facilities *Performance opportunities* Bergen International Festival (placement scheme with the Bergen Philharmonic Orchestra) *Accommodation* International students may apply for housing at one of the Student Hostels. For more information and application details, contact the student welfare organisation (www.sib.no/hostels).

OSLO

Norwegian capital, towards the southern tip of the country and at the northern end of a long bay (the Oslofjord). Once known as Kristiania (Oslo only adopted definitively in early 20th century), city dates back to middle ages, but began developing more importance in early 19th century when Swedish ownership ended – the large Royal Palace dates from this time. Norway's main centre for higher education with many institutions covering various disciplines. Benefits from a location close to forests and hills, so ideal for outdoor activities.

CLIMATE

Warmest month July (12-22°C), coldest month January (-7--2°C). Wettest period between July

EUROPE

and October (80+mm), with substantial snow during winter.

MUSICAL LIFE

City has a new opera house for its national opera and ballet companies; has its own house orchestra too, which gives a few concerts in its own right. As well as stage performances, visiting soloists and orchestras come to perform. Several other orchestral groups based in Oslo: Oslo Philharmonic (based at Oslo Philharmonic Hall) the best known; Norwegian Radio Orchestra and Norwegian Chamber Orchestra play at university's concert hall.

OTHER CULTURAL INFORMATION

National Gallery is country's main art gallery, with a diverse range of artworks. Institutions devoted to Viking history (eg Viking Ship Museum) as well as other aspects of Norwegian culture (Norwegian Museum of Cultural History, Norwegian Folk Museum) and activity (Ski Museum). City's new House of Literature is a combination of bookshop, place for discussion, writers' workshops and accommodation for visiting writers.

FESTIVALS AND EVENTS

Well served for festivals. Apart from city's summer festival featuring a range of entertainment in main square and other venues, there is an international festival of church music in March; chamber music festival and jazz festival in August; contemporary music festival in Sep (the Ultima festiva); world music festival in October. Also biennial Queen Sonja Music Competition (August).

TOURIST INFORMATION

www.visitoslo.com, info@visitoslo.com, +47 815 30 555

BARRATT DUE MUSIKKINSTITUUT

Postboks 5344 Majorstuen, N-0304 Oslo, Norway
t: +47 22 06 86 86 *f:* +47 22 06 86 94
e: post@bdm.no *w:* www.barrattdue.no

Course information 4-year BA (240 credits) in music performance; final year students specialise in either performance or instrumental/voice tuition with practical teacher training. Masters course offered in co-operation of Norwegian Academy of Music; also some further education courses.

Admissions information *Application deadline* 15 Dec, BA and MA. Auditions early Mar for bachelors, mid Feb for masters.

NORGESMUSIKKHØLE (NORWEGIAN ACADEMY OF MUSIC)

PO Box 5190 Majorstua, NO-0302 Oslo, Norway
t: +47 23 36 70 00 *f:* +47 23 36 70 01
e: mh@nmh.no *w:* www.nmh.no
Contact Knut Myhre (international enquiries).

Course information 4-year undergrad courses in music performance, music education, church music, composition, individual programme. Postgrad courses: advanced studies for solo instrumentalists or chamber music ensembles, advanced studies in composition; masters degrees in performance, church music, music theory, conducting, music education, music therapy. More details on postgrad programmes available on the website.

Admissions information *Term dates* End Aug-end Jun. *Application requirements* A level qualification or equivalent, plus audition (see website for details of repertoire and other information). *Application deadline* 15 Dec. *Fees* None. *No of students* 475 students in total. *Language requirements* Classroom tuition in Norwegian; individual tuition may be in another language, mostly English.

Facilities *Music facilities* Approx 300 concerts organised each year. Applicants must show proficiency in Norwegian for admission. *Accommodation* No student housing facilities. For more information on accommodation, see www.sio.no

STAVANGER

Norwegian port city on south west coast; location means it is closely associated with the oil industry (previously had been a fishing town), but it retains a certain amount of charm, particularly in the Old Town. City used by visitors as a base for skiing, hiking and mountain sports.

CLIMATE

Warmest month August (11-18°C), coldest month January (-1-4°C). Rainfall levels generally high (100+mm August-December), and only really easing off in April and May.

MUSICAL LIFE

Stavanger Symfoniorkester at the Bjergsted Music Park and Konserthus; building for new 2-hall concert hall for 2011 is under way.

OTHER CULTURAL INFORMATION

Visiting exhibitions at the Rogaland Museum of Fine Arts, a combination of Norwegian and international artists. Its nomination as one of the European Cities of Culture in 2008 has left a legacy in the number of cultural initiatives

FESTIVALS AND EVENTS
Main classical music festival is the International Chamber Music Festival (August); there is also an annual jazz festival (May)

TOURIST INFORMATION
www.regionstavanger.com; info@regionstavanger.com, +47 51 85 92 00

UNIVERSITY OF STAVANGER
Dept of Music and Dance, Postbox 8002, N-4036 Stavanger, Norway
t: +47 51 83 40 00 *f:* +47 51 83 40 50
e: music-dance@uis.no *w:* www.uis.no/music; www.uis.no/dance
Contact Jens T Larsen, head of dept; Trim Holbek, head of office/international co-ord.
Course information Bachelor in music performance (classical or jazz), master in music performance (classical), extension courses in music performance; music production & recording.
Admissions information *Term dates* Mid Aug-mid Jun. *Application requirements* Entrance exam/audition; completed BA in music, plus entrance exam/audition for masters courses. Special entrance requirements for each programme. *Application deadline* 15 Dec (international students) *Fees* Approx EUR 87 per semester. *Scholarships* None. *No of students* 200 students in total, including 50 from overseas. *Language requirements* Norwegian required for bachelors programme; all others, Norwegian or English.
Facilities *Music facilities* Modern buildings with concert halls located in Bjergsted Music Park; good facilities for teaching and practice; recording studios. *Accommodation* Assistance available through university student welfare organisation.

TROMSØ
Small northern Norwegian city (around 60,000 people), based largely on an island just off the North Sea coast a substantial distance north of arctic circle (city linked to mainland by bridge). Natural surroundings are spectacular, and its northerly location means it is dark for most of the day during deepest winter months and light all day during summer. However, it also means that it is geographically isolated, with the nearest station 4 hours away; access possible by road, air or boat. Despite its size and location, the city has a vibrant nightlife.

CLIMATE
Warmest month July (8-16°C), coldest month January (-7--2°C).Rainfall highest September-January (100+mm).

MUSICAL LIFE
There is a professional orchestra, Tromsø Symphony Orchestra, though it is currently small in size, tending to focus on chamber music and small-scale orchestral work. Main cultural venue is the Kulturhuset, with music and a varied range of other performances.

OTHER CULTURAL INFORMATION
Main sights are city's 2 cathedrals, the old wooden Tromsø cathedral and the 1960s built Arctic cathedral. A handful of museums and galleries.

FESTIVALS AND EVENTS
Nordlysfestivalen (Northern Lights Festival – the city is perfectly placed for seeing the aurora borealis display), a January music festival featuring classical and folk performances from local and visiting artists. Annual film festival, also in January, attracts a large audience.

TOURIST INFORMATION
www.destinasjontromso.no, info@visittromso.no, +47 77 61 00 00

MUSIC CONSERVATORY OF TROMSØ UNIVERSITY COLLEGE
Krognessveien 33, N-9293 Tromso, Norway
t: +47 77 66 03 04 *f:* +47 77 61 88 99
e: kunst@hitos.no *w:* www.hitos.no

MUSIC FESTIVALS

Arts Festival of North Norway PO Box 294, N-9489 Harstad, Norway *t:* +47 77 041230 *f:* +47 77 067363 *e:* post@festspillnn.no *w:* www.festspillnn.no Concerts, theatre, dance, art exhibitions, literature and film, seminars, children's festival and youth festival.
Bergen International Festival PO Box 183 Sentrum, N-5804 Bergen, Norway *t:* +47 55 210630 *f:* +47 55 210640 *e:* info@fib.no *w:* www.fib.no Nordic impulses in music theatre, opera, dance, literature and visual art. Approximately 180 events in more than 14 venues in and around Bergen.

EUROPE

NORWAY

Forde Folk Music Festival PO Box 395, Fordehuset, Angedalsvn 5, N-6801 Forde, Norway *t:* +47 57 721940 *f:* +47 57 721941 *e:* info@fordefestival.no *w:* www.fordefestival.no Traditional and world music from all over the world. Concerts, workshops, exhibitions, children's events. Approx 80 events, 250 artists, 30,000 visits each year.

Ilios Festival for Contemporary Music NY Musikk, Box 244, N-9483 Harstad, Norway *t:* +47 913 94 673 *e:* post@ilios.no *w:* www.ilios.no

International Chamber Music Festival, Stavanger Sandviga 27, N-4007 Stavanger, Norway *t:* +47 51 846670 *f:* +47 51 846650 *e:* mail@icmf.no *w:* www.icmf.no Annual.

Lofoten Internasjonale Kammermusikkfest Vaaganveien 30, NO-8310 Kabelvag, Norway *f:* +47 760 74912 *e:* knut@lofotenfestival.com *w:* www.lofotenfestival.com Chamber music festival in concert hall and wooden churches on 4 of the Lofoten Islands

Nordlysfestivalen (Northern Lights Festival) Pb 966, N-9260 Tromso, Norway *t:* +47 77 68 90 70 *e:* post@nordlysfestivalen.no *w:* www.nordlysfestivalen.no Annual music festival.

Oslo Chamber Music Festival Grev Wedels Plass 2, N-0151 Oslo, Norway *t:* +47 23 100730 *f:* +47 23 100731 *e:* post@oslokammermusikkfestival.no *w:* www.oslokammermusikkfestival.no Annual.

Oslo International Church Music Festival Konens gate 4, N-0153 Oslo, Norway *t:* +47 22 41 81 13 *f:* +47 22 41 81 14 *e:* info@oicmf.no *w:* www.oslokirkemusikkfestival.no Annual festival bringing renowned choirs, orchestras and church musicians from Norway and abroad.

The Risor Festival of Chamber Music PO Box 304, N-4953 Risor, Norway *t:* +47 37 153250 *f:* +47 37 151440 *e:* info@kammermusikkfest.no *w:* www.kammermusikkfest.no Annual chamber music festival.

St Olav Festival of Trondheim PO Box 2045, N-7410 Trondheim, Norway *t:* +47 73 841450 *f:* +47 73 841451 *e:* info@olavsfestdagene.no *w:* www.olavsfestdagene.no Church services, concerts, lectures, guided tours, exhibitions, activites for children, chamber music courses and early music projects. Traditional market.

Ultima Oslo Contemporary Music Festival Kongensgate 4, N-0153 Oslo, Norway *t:* +47 22 429999 *f:* +47 22 424218 *e:* info@ultima.no *w:* www.ultima.no Annual. Contemporary music, including concerts and performances, sound-installations, multimedia concerts, films, educational arrangements and seminars.

Vestfold International Festival PO Box 500, N-3101 Tonsberg, Norway *t:* +47 33 308850 *f:* +47 33 308859 *e:* info@vestfoldfestspillene.no *w:* www.vestfoldfestspillene.no Classical music, early music, jazz, world music, dance, theatre.

EUROPE

GOTHENBURG (GÖTEBORG)

City on south west coast of Sweden. It has historical significance in trade with Asia, and its port is still busy today. Home to a number of higher education institutions, so there is a large student population in the city.

CLIMATE

Warmest month July (13-21°C), coldest month January (-3-1°C). Wettest period is autumn (around 80mm per month), driest period in spring with nearly half that amount.

MUSICAL LIFE

Two main venues, the opera house and concert hall. Opera house is home to opera and ballet, with diverse repertoire (includes music theatre), and has its own orchestra (who also perform concerts in the city and elsewhere). Göteborgs Symfoniker based at the concert hall, but venue has a broad programming policy, with chamber music, recitals, visiting orchestras, jazz and more.

OTHER CULTURAL INFORMATION

A number of museums, with a wide range of subjects covered: museums reflecting city's history as a trading port, such as East India house, and the Göteborg Maritime Centre; Museum of World Culture. Various science and industry-related places such as Volvo Museum, Radio Museum, Museum of Medical History, and Universeum science centre. Göteborg Art Hall focuses on contemporary art and visual culture

FESTIVALS AND EVENTS

Free entertainment events at the annual Göteborg Culture Festival. Major film festival in January-February, short jazz festival in August.

TOURIST INFORMATION

www.goteborg.com; turistinfo@goteborg.com, +46 31 61 25 00

GÖTEBORGS UNIVERSITET HOGSKOLAN FOR SCEN OCH MUSIC (ACADEMY OF MUSIC AND DRAMA, GOTHENBURG UNIVERSITY)

Box 210, SE-405 30 Göteborg, Sweden
t: +46 31 786 4020; +46 31 7864103 (international co-ordinator) *f:* +46 31 786 4030
e: Margareta.Hanning@hsm.gu.se *w:* www.hsm.gu.se
Contact Margareta Hanning, international co-ordinator.
Admissions information *Term dates* 1 Sep-20 Dec; 8 Jan-1 Jun. *Application deadline* 15 Jan; exchange students 1 Mar. *Fees* None

MALMÖ

City at southernmost tip of Sweden, linked to Denmark (Copenhagen) by the Øresund Bridge. Dates back to medieval times, and general layout of the city reflects this, although buildings are in the main from much later periods (especially 19th century onwards). Added attractions are the city's beaches; harbour area has also been recently redeveloped and is now a popular area for visitors and residents.

CLIMATE

Warmest months July and August (12-21°C), coldest month January (-3-2°C). Rainfall relatively moderate and consistent throughout the year (30-60mm).

MUSICAL LIFE

Opera house is base for Malmö Opera (although repertoire also includes musicals) and its orchestra; a separate orchestra is Malmö Symfoniorkester at city's 1200-seat Konserthuset. Receives visiting orchestras etc, but concert hall not just for classical music.

OTHER CULTURAL INFORMATION

Art Museum focuses on Nordic art. Many smaller exhibitions on various topic such as toys, sport, theatre, fishing.

FESTIVALS AND EVENTS

Malmö Festival (August) is city's main celebration featuring entertainment, culinary events etc.

TOURIST INFORMATION

www.malmo.se, malmo.turism@malmo.se, +46 40 34 12 00

MUSIKHOGSKOLAN I MALMÖ (MALMO ACADEMY OF MUSIC)

Box 8203, SE-200 41 Malmo, Sweden
t: +46 40 32 54 50 *f:* +46 40 32 54 60
e: joakim.nilsson@mhm.lu.se *w:* www.mhm.lu.se
Contact Joakim Nilsson, director of international affairs
Admissions information *Application deadline* 15 Apr.

ÖREBRO

Well-kept city in southern Sweden dating back to middle ages – a notable remnant of this time is the

EUROPE

castle, and the old town contains a number of characteristic 18th and 19th century wooden houses as well as some striking brick and stone buildings.

CLIMATE

Warmest months July and August (11-22°C), coldest months December and January (-4-0°C). Rainfall generally low, although the level tends to rise in summer.

MUSICAL LIFE

There is a 700-seat concert hall in the city, with performances from the up and coming Swedish Chamber Orchestra – has a wide repertoire, with contemporary music a key focus. The group tours widely outside the city as well as running its own subscriber and open concerts.

OTHER CULTURAL INFORMATION

Small collection of museums and galleries; at the heart of the city is an open-air museum demonstrating what life was like in the earlier days of its existence.

TOURIST INFORMATION

www.orebrokompaniet.se, info@orebrokompaniet.se, +46 19 21 21 21

ÖREBRO UNIVERSITET MUSIKHOGSKOLAN (ÖREBRO UNIVERSITY SCHOOL OF MUSIC)

Musikhogskolan vid Örebro, SE-701 82 Örebro, Sweden
t: +46 19 30 33 50; +46 19 30 30 00 (international office) *f:* +46 19 30 34 85
e: exchange@oru.se (international office)
w: www.oru.se

Course information A range of courses in music, music education, musicology, art and theatre education.

Admissions information *Application deadline* Mid Oct (for spring semester); early May (for autumn semester). *Language requirements* All undergraduate programmes taught in Swedish. Some masters programmes may be taught in English.

Facilities *Accommodation* Exchange students are guaranteed accommodation so long as the correct forms are received on time.

STOCKHOLM

Swedish capital, located on an archipelago on the east coast of the country. Developed in importance around 700 years ago as part of wealthy north European trading cartel the Hanseatic League. The old town retains medieval layout of narrow streets. Its geographical situation means water dominates, with numerous waterways between the islands; as well as trips to the many islands in the archipelago, there are also sea connections to Finland and Baltic countries.

CLIMATE

Warmest month July (13-22°C), coldest month January (-5--1°C). Wettest month July (70mm), driest month March (25mm), with snow during winter.

MUSICAL LIFE

Several concert venues. Berwaldhallen is home of Swedish Radio Symphony Orchestra and its associated choirs; Royal Stockholm Philharmonic Orchestra based at Stockholm Concert Hall, a 3-hall venue therefore able to host everything from solo recitals to symphony concerts. More popular music events at the modern-design arts centre Kulturhuset Stockholm. Variety of opera houses: Drottningholms Slottstheater a small renovated 18th century theatre at the Royal Palace; Folkoperan another intimate venue, in contrast to the neo-classical (actually late 19th century) Kungliga Operan building and its company.

OTHER CULTURAL INFORMATION

Waterfron Nationalmuseum is main art collection, featuring European masters and a substantial collection of Swedish art. Also a modern art museum (Moderna Museet). Many other galleries and museums besides. Several theatres such as art nouveau Royal Dramatic Theatre. Kulturhuset's programme encompasses all kinds of art (exhibitions, films, theatre, dance, literary events etc).

FESTIVALS AND EVENTS

Early Music Festival (early June) in the Old Town. Berwaldhallen hosts the annual Baltic Sea Festival focusing on classical music and performers from countries surrounding the Baltic; also events at Royal Palace and Konserthuset. Stockholms Kulturfestival (August) is a mix of events such as open air concerts, children's events, art and photography exhibitions, film shows etc.

TOURIST INFORMATION

www.stockholmtown.com, info@svb.stockholm.se, +46 8 508 28 500

KUNGL MUSIKHOGSKOLAN (ROYAL COLLEGE OF MUSIC)

Valhallavagen 105, Box 27711, SE-115 91

Stockholm, Sweden
t: +46 8 16 18 00; +46 8 16 32 00 (international co-operation) *f:* +46 8 664 14 24 *e:* info@kmh.se *w:* www.kmh.se
Contact Johan Falk, Anders Oman.
Course information Undergraduate programmes in performance, composition, conducting, music education, church music, piano tuner studies, music and media technology. Master's programmes in performance, composition, conducting, music education, music and media technology, intermedia, music therapy, vocal coaching. *Conducting* Orchestral and choral. *Composition* Western art music, jazz, electroacoustic music. *Other* Church music
Admissions information *Term dates* Late Aug-mid Dec; early Jan-mid Jun. *Application requirements* Official language is Swedish, except for Nordic master in folk music and Nordic master in jazz courses (offered in English only); for guest/exchange and postgraduate students, courses can be given in English at professor's discretion. Auditions held in person in Mar. *Application deadline* Jan (regular students); 15 Feb (Erasmus/guest students). *Fees* Small student union fee only. *Scholarships* No institutional scholarships available for overseas students. *No of students* 700. *Language requirements* Official language is Swedish, except for Nordic master in folk music and Nordic master in jazz (English only); for guest/exchange and postgrad students, courses can be given in English at professor's discretion.
Facilities *Music facilities* Concert halls, computer music studios, church organs, period instruments. *Accommodation* Exchange students are usually helped with accommodations

MUSIC FESTIVALS

Confidencen Ulriksdals Slottstheater, S-170 79 Solna, Sweden *t:* +46 8 85 70 16 *f:* +46 8 85 61 21 *e:* info@confidencen.se *w:* www.confidencen.se
Dalhalla Opera Festival *w:* www.dalhalla.se
Drottningholms Slottsteater Festival PO Box 15417, SE-10465 Stockholm, Sweden *t:* +46 8 556 93100 *f:* +46 8 556 93101 *e:* dst@dtm.se *w:* www.dtm.se Annual. 17th and 18th century opera and ballet, period productions.
Goteborg International Organ Academy Ebbe Lieberathsgatan 25, S-0412 65 Goteborg, Sweden *t:* +46 31 773 5211 *f:* +46 31 773 5200 *e:* organ.academy@hsm.gu.se *w:* www.organacademy.se Biennial. Includes concerts, workshops, seminars, lectures, discussions and services. Theme for 2009: Handel, Haydn.
Gotland Organ Festival Gotlands Orgelvecka, Visby Domkyrkoforsamling, V Kyrkog 5, S-621 56 Visby, Sweden *t:* +46 498 20 68 00 *f:* +46 468 20 68 12 *e:* thomas.fors@visbydf.se Organ, choral and harpsichord music.
International Music Week Geijerskolan, S-684 93 Ransater, Sweden *t:* +46 552 302 50 *f:* +46 552 304 48 *e:* info@geijerskolan.se *w:* www.geijerskolan.se Choirs, recorders, orchestras.
Läckö Slottsopera Box 2256, S-531 02 Lidkoping, Sweden *t:* +46 510 48 46 60 *f:* +46 510 48 46 60 *e:* info@lackoslott.se *w:* www.lackoslott.se
Nordic Music Days Council of Nordic Composers, Box 27327, S-102 54 Stockholm, Sweden *t:* +46 76 171 56 00 *e:* info@nordiccomposers.org; stina.lyles@nordiccomposers.org *w:* www.nordiccomposers.org; www.nordicmusicdays2010.org Collaborative festival of contemporary Nordic music, rotating between Denmark, Finland, Iceland, Norway and Sweden. 2010 festival in Copenhagen; 2011 in Iceland, 2010 in Sweden.
Opera på Skäret Skaret 111, SE-714 93 Kopparberg, Sweden *e:* info@operapaskaret.se *w:* www.operapaskaret.se
Osthammars Musikvecka (The Osthammar Music Festival) Box 66, S-74221 Osthammar, Sweden *t:* +46 173 86147 *f:* +46 173 17537 *e:* musikveckan@osthammar.se *w:* www.musikveckan.nu Popular music, choirs; jazz, folk and world music; classics and rock. Includes music workshops and family concerts.
Stockholm Early Music Festival Tangvagen 9, 1 tr, SE-126 38 Hagersten, Sweden *t:* +46 70 460 03 90 *e:* info@semf.se *w:* www.semf.se Baroque, renaissance and medieval music in Stockholm's Old Town.
Stockholm International Composer Festival Stockholm Concert Hall, PO Box 7083, S-10387 Stockholm, Sweden *t:* +46 8 786 0200 *f:* +46 8 5066 7720 *e:* info@konserthuset.se *w:* www.konserthuset.se
Vadstena Academy Opera Festival Bergsgatan 57, S-11231 Stockholm, Sweden *t:* +46 8 545 51 880 *f:* +46 8 545 51 887 *e:* info@vadstena-akademien.org *w:* www.vadstena-akademien.org Annual. Rare early operas, newly commissioned works and concerts at the castle and old theatre in historic setting of Vadstena's medieval town.

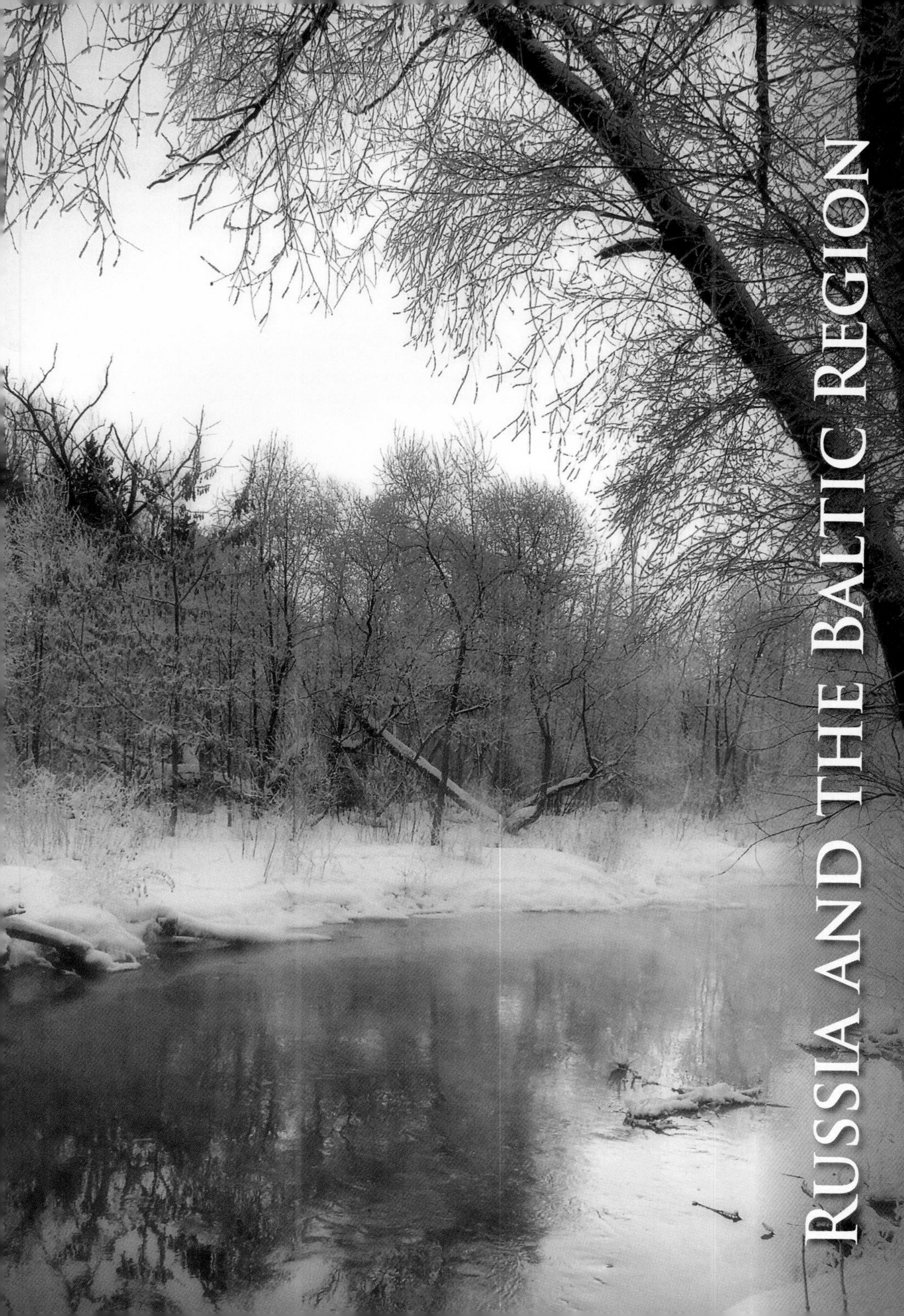
RUSSIA AND THE BALTIC REGION

Russia and the Baltic Region

Of all the places to study music, Russia probably has the most forbidding reputation. But if you have the ability, self-discipline, not to mention the thick skin, spending time at a Russian conservatoire will give you access to one of the most uncompromising music education traditions and put you in a long line among the great musicians who have passed through it. And as historical and cultural locations, Moscow and St Petersburg take some beating. The three Baltic states, though previously part of the USSR, offer something different, being to the average western eye relatively young countries (though this is, of course, far from the historical truth) which are keen to welcome visitors from overseas to observe and participate in their cultural life.

RUSSIA PAGE 193

The Russian system of higher music education does not easily fit with the 5-year bachelors-plus-masters scheme that is coming to the fore in Europe, with diploma courses (the undergraduate equivalent) lasting 5 years and postgrad programmes up to 3 further years. Other shorter courses are available, however – at St Petersburg, there are various 1-year non-degree programmes, particularly suitable for international students since these can be individually tailored and can start at any point in the academic year.

ESTONIA PAGE 196

The main music academy (which has university status) in Estonia is in the capital Tallinn, and students follow the Europe-wide system of bachelors and masters degrees, just as the rest of Estonia's higher education system does. Unlike the majority of Estonian higher education institutions, the academy authorities elected to make it a 4+1 system (ie 4-year bachelors followed by 1-year masters). It is estimated that 90% of students progress to masters level. Students arrive having spent time at extra-curricular primary and secondary music schools (there is also a music school providing specialist music education as part of a wider curriculum). Unusually, it is not necessary for students to attend the academy to gain professional qualification since this is also available through the regional music schools (those leaving are granted a professional diploma), though most do; singers entering the academy will have had the chance to attend 2 years of preparatory classes.

LATVIA PAGE 198

Advanced professional, musicological and music teacher training is provided by the sole institution set up for the purpose. The state-run, state-funded Latvian Academy of Music runs a 4-year bachelors programme followed by a 2-year masters in all areas; there is also the possibility to study for a doctorate (2-year course) in musicology, or possibly a specialist performance area such as piano accompaniment. Plans to increase the scope of doctoral studies are currently being investigated. Access to masters level courses are by possession of a professional bachelor's degree plus audition, exam and discussion, and the number of students progressing to this level is determined partly by budgetary considerations.

LITHUANIA PAGE 199

The Lithuanian Academy of Music and Theatre is the main music performance training institution, with teacher training provided in universities elsewhere, although the academy itself also has university status. As elsewhere in the Baltic states, the bachelors level degree is awarded after 4 years of successful study, after which students can progress to a 2-year masters. Doctorates are reserved for students of musicology, ethnomusicology and history; performers, however, can follow a 2-year course leading to the higher performing qualification. Funding comes from the state for half the student body, with the other half contributing a fee.

MOSCOW

Russian capital with an architecture all its own. As well as the famous St Basil's cathedral and the Kremlin building, visitors will find ornate buildings throughout the city, even in the underground system in which rococo ceilings and great chandeliers can be seen. At its heart is the famous Red Square (flanked by the Kremlin and St Basil's); Gorky Park another popular area for Muscovites to gather – there is skating on the lake in winter, among other social activities. As the centre of Russian political life it has a turbulent history, imposing itself forcefully on the world stage no matter what the regime, Russia having gone from imperial rule, by way of three quarters of a century of communism, to today's more liberal (though not uncontroversially so) society.

CLIMATE

Hottest month July (18-24°C), coldest month January (-11--5°C) – Russian winters being notoriously cold, with snow ever-present from November to March. Rainfall peaks in summer (around 90mm in July).

MUSICAL LIFE

Large number of major venues. Most famous is the Bolshoi Theatre, principally an opera house showcasing Russian opera and ballet but also stages concerts from its orchestra. More opera at the Galina Vishnevskaya centre and in the Hermitage museum gardens. A much newer building is Moscow International Performance Arts Centre with 2 concert halls (1753-seat Svetlanov Hall and 575-seat Chamber Hall; there is also a theatre for plays etc). Other notable venues include the chamber music hall at the Pavel Slobodkin centre; concert hall at the Pushkin museum; daily concerts in the 2 halls of the Moscow House of Composers. Many other venues besides. Conservatoire concert halls are also prestigious venues in life of the city; conservatoire Great Hall a regular venue for Russian National Orchestra, the best known in the city, along with Tchaikovsky Symphony Orchestra of Moscow. Moscow Chamber Orchestra and Chamber Orchestra Kremlin are 2 smaller groups.

OTHER CULTURAL ACTIVITIES

Moscow State Circus is world-renowned venue and troupe of performers. Wide range of museums and galleries: Pushkin Museum of Fine Arts a collection of paintings from various eras, plus other historic artefacts from around the world; Tretyakov Gallery displays the private collection of a patron of art; Museum of Contemporary Russian History focuses on events surrounding 1917 revolution, among other things. Dostoyevsky House Museum recreates domestic situation of the time, plus some ephemera from the writer's life; literary theme continued at the Tolstoy Museum.

FESTIVALS AND EVENTS

Various musical events – the Return Chamber Music Festival in early January takes its name from the fact that young musicians studying around Europe return to their families at Christmas. International film festival in June. Golden Mask festival focuses on stage work of all kinds, including opera, music theatre and operetta.

LOCAL PUBLICATIONS

The Moscow Times (www.themoscowtimes.com, daily) and Element (www.elementmoscow.ru, fortnightly) are both English-language publications about the city, the latter focusing more on entertainment, going out and cultural events.

TOURIST INFORMATION

www.moscow-city.ru; info@moscow-city.ru

MOSCOW PI TCHAIKOVSKY CONSERVATORY

Bolshaya Nikitskaya Street 13/6, 125009 Moscow, Russia
t: +7 495 629 20 60; +7 495 629 73 18 (dept for foreign students) *f:* +7 495 627 72 71 (dept for foreign students) *e:* international@mosconsv.ru; foreign@mosconsv.ru *w:* www.mosconsv.ru

Course information Undergrad preparatory course, including study of Russian; main undergrad course (exams in specialism, ear tests and harmony, Russian, piano). Postgrad courses available in organ; accompaniment; string, wind and brass instruments; opera and orchestral conducting, choral direction; chamber music; solo singing; composition.

Admissions information *Term dates* 15 Sep 2009-25 Jan 2010; 15 Feb-15 Jul 2010. *Application requirements* Entrance exams include Russian (written and oral) and specialism.

GNESINS' ACADEMY OF MUSIC

Povarskaya st 30/36, 121069 Moscow, Russia
e: mailbox@gnesin-academy.ru *w:* www.gnesin-academy.ru

Course information Private music college providing music education at 4 levels: elementary school, primary school, secondary school, academy. Awards bachelors, masters and professional degrees.

RUSSIA

ST PETERSBURG

Russian city on the river Neva near the Baltic coast near borders with Finland and Estonia. Its predominant architectural styles, in the centre of the city, are baroque and neo-classical. Known over the years variously as Petrograd and Leningrad until the fall of communism in 1991 when it was given back its historic name. Petrograd was at the heart of the 1905 uprising as well as the 1917 October Revolution when Lenin came to power. Suffered greatly during World War II thanks to the German siege of Leningrad that became a motivation behind Shostakovich's seventh symphony, whose Leningrad premiere (after performances in Moscow, London and New York) took place under extraordinarily defiant circumstances during the siege.

CLIMATE

Warmest month July (18-23°C), coldest months January and February (-6--3°C). Wettest months July and August (around 80mm), winter sees less rainfall but substantial snow cover from November to March.

MUSICAL LIFE

2 major performing companies perhaps best known under other names: Mariinsky Theatre (formerly the Kirov) a major opera and ballet company; the Leningrad Philharmonic Orchestra now the Saint Petersburg Philharmonic. Both now still major organisations, the theatre (and its orchestra, which does not restrict itself to opera performance) under Valery Gergiev, the orchestra under Yuri Temirkanov. St Petersburg Academic Symphony Orchestra another prominent orchestra in the city; more opera at the Mussorgsky Opera Theatre (another renamed establishment, formerly the Mikhailovsky and Maly Theatre); for lighter music theatre, the Musical Comedy Theatre programmes traditional operetta; Teatro Buffo for cabaret and children's comedy. Oktabrsky hall for rock and pop events.

OTHER CULTURAL ACTIVITIES

Home to the world famous Hermitage Museum and Winter Palace and its extensive collection of art from around Europe. Russian Museum focuses more on Russian art. Kunstkamera founded by Peter the Great is a history and archaeology museum.

FESTIVALS AND EVENTS

Winter Festival Arts Square is a classical music festival in December featuring groups based in the city plus visitors from elsewhere. Musical Olympus festival invites young competition winners from around the world to perform during second half of May. 'Stars of the White Nights' festival at the Mariinsky over the summer. Ballet festival also at the Mariinsky in March, also separate event 'Dance Open' in the same month. Early music festival in September.

TOURIST INFORMATION

www.st-petersburg.ru

THE RIMSKY-KORSAKOV ST PETERSBURG STATE CONSERVATOIRE

3 Teatralnaya Square, 190000 St Petersburg, Russia
t: +7 812 312 2129; +7 812 314 9693 (international student office) *f:* +7 812 571 6389; +7 812 571 8288 (international student office) *e:* foreigndep@conservatory.ru *w:* www.conservatory.ru
Contact Natalia Agababova, dean for international student affairs; Olga Makarova, admissions officer.
Course information 5 year Diploma course in music performance: piano, organ, orchestral instruments, folk instruments, vocal music, composition, conducting, musicology; also choreography. Postgrad (PhD) course in music performance. Non-degree special training course (1-10 months). 1 year preparatory course.
Admissions information *Term dates* 1 Sep-30 Jun. *Application requirements* Certificate of completed secondary education and suitable performance ability. Candidates must be age 18+. Knowledge of Russian at pre-intermediate level or above for students enrolling in 5 year Diploma course. *Application deadline* 1 Jul. *Fees* EUR 5500 pa (Diploma course); EUR 4000 (preparatory course); EUR 500 pm (special training course). *Scholarships* None. *No of students* 1300 national students and 250 from overseas.

MUSIC FESTIVALS

AD Sakharov International Art Festival The Nizhny Novgorod State Academic Philharmony, Rostropovich Kremlin, Build 2, 603082 Nizhny Novgorod, Russia *t:* +7 8312 391623 *f:* +7 8312 391608 *e:* otomina@philharmony.nnov.ru *w:* www.sakharov.innov.ru Biennial. Symphonic, chamber, choral music, theatre and art exhibitions.

Golden Mask *t:* +7 495 662 53 52 *f:* +7 495 629 92 42 *w:* www.goldenmask.ru Festival of staged performances including opera, music theatre

and operetta.

Musical Olympus International Festival Korablestroiteley st 14, 199226 St Petersburg, Russia *t:* +7 812 356 6104 *f:* +7 812 356 5042 *e:* mo@musicalolympus.ru *w:* www.musicalolympus.ru Parade of winners; recent winners of biggest and most prestigious competitions invited to perform in major St Petersburg venues.

Stars of the White Nights 1 Theatre Square, 190000 St Petersburg, Russia *t:* +7 812 326 4141 *f:* +7 812 314 1744 *e:* post@mariinsky.ru *w:* www.mariinsky.ru 3-month long summer festival featuring Mariinsky Theatre productions and orchestral works

St Petersburg British Music Festival, The *w:* www.britishmusicfest.co.uk

Serbia **Belgrade Music Festival - BEMUS** Terajize 41/1, 11000 Belgrade, Serbia *t:* +381 11 3241303 *f:* +381 11 324 0478 *e:* BEMUS@jugokoncert.rs *w:* www.jugokoncert.rs Annual.

EUROPE

ESTONIA

TALLINN

Capital of Estonia on the coast across the Gulf of Finland from Helsinki. It became independent of USSR in 1991 since when it has become a particularly popular destination for visitors. Based round a medieval old town (a Unesco world heritage site) which is well preserved today and features a number of prominent buildings from the period, including church, civic (eg the guild hall) and state buildings (eg the gothic town hall), narrow cobbled streets as well as a market square. Part of city walls with distinctive conical towers, still exist.

 CLIMATE

Warmest month July (12-21°C), coldest months January and February (-9--2°C). Rainfall is moderate throughout the year (wettest in August and September) but snow is predominant during winter months.

MUSICAL LIFE

Centres of musical life are Estonia Concert Hall (approx 900 seats) for classical music, with major concerts by Estonian National Symphony Orchestra (sometimes with Estonian Philharmonic Chamber Choir), and Estonia National Opera. Opera house includes a 'winter gardens' holding informal recitals of classical and lighter music. Regular events elsewhere, such as medieval town hall or Art Museum of Estonia; Linnahall for wider range of musical styles. Unusual outdoor venue, the Tallinn Song Stage, built in 1959 for mass national Song Festival, but holds other popular concerts too. City is an attractive destination for visiting amateur choirs, youth orchestras etc.

OTHER CULTURAL ACTIVITIES

Theatre and music museum displays antique instruments, music machines and curiosities; otherwise a large choice of galleries and exhibitions, particularly reflecting city's and country's history. Kumu is a brand new, award-winning art gallery focusing on both Estonian art and more general trends. Several theatres, as well as mainstream, there are puppet theatres, a Russian language theatre, revue and cabaret, dance etc.

FESTIVALS AND EVENTS

Numerous music events. International choir festival (April); organ festival and chamber music festival in August; also early music festival (January-February); annual contemporary music festival in October; short winter festival of concerts in December-January. Sacred music the focus of Credo festival of orthodox music (September). Several city fairs, markets and festivals.

 TOURIST INFORMATION

www.tourism.tallinn.ee, turismiinfo@tallinnlv.ee, +372 645 7777

EESTI MUUSIKA - JA TEATRIAKADEEMIA (ESTONIAN ACADEMY OF MUSIC AND THEATRE)

Rävala pst 16, EE-10143 Tallinn, Estonia
t: +372 6675 700; +372 6675 760 (international relations) *f:* +372 6675 800
e: ema@ema.edu.ee; *w:* www.ema.edu.ee
Contact Katrin Makarov, international relations co-ordinator.
Course information International bachelor's, master's and PhD study programmes, taught in English. Course specialisms: piano, organ, harpsichord, strings (inc harp and guitar), brass and woodwind (inc baroque flute and saxophone), percussion, voice, conducting, church music, music teacher studies, jazz studies, traditional music, composition, electronic music, musicology; accompaniment, chamber music, cultural management.
Admissions information *Application requirements* Entrance exam. *Application deadline* Mid-end Jun. *Fees* EU students can apply for state-funded courses and fee-based courses; non-EU students can only apply for fee-paying courses. See website for fees. *Scholarships* The Rector can reduce the tuition fee by 50% for students with a partial study load and for non-state-commissioned students in their additional year. *No of students* 690 students. *Language requirements* English.
Facilities *Music facilities* 60 classrooms plus 14 rehearsal rooms where classes can be held; chamber music hall seating up to 200; choir class with auditorium for 77 students; audition room with baroque organ; electronic music lab; recording studio; library with music listening and computer facilities. 95 pianos in total. *Performance opportunities* School performances. Symphony Orchestra of EAMT performs in Estonia and abroad. *Accommodation* Dormitories available.

VILJANDI

Town towards the south of Estonia. Historically it was part of the Hanseatic league indicating a certain importance in north European trade during the middle of the last millennium.

EUROPE

OTHER CULTURAL INFORMATION
Various small museums and galleries

FESTIVALS AND EVENTS
Early music festival runs for a week in July; a folk music festival runs in the same month.

TOURIST INFORMATION
www.viljandimaa.ee/turismiinfo

TARTU ULIKOOLI VILJANDI KULTUURIAKADEEMIA (UNIVERSITY OF TARTU VILJANDI CULTURE ACADEMY)
Posti 1, EE-71004 Viljandi, Estonia
t: +372 435 5254 (international relations)
f: +372 435 5231 *e:* kool@kultuur.edu.ee; margot@kultuur.edu.ee; piret.pumm@ut.ee; international@kultur.edu.ee *w:* www.kultuur.edu.ee (music school); www.ut.ee (main university site)
Contact Margot Must, head of international relations; Piret Pumm, international student co-ord.

Course information BA in jazz music, traditional music, school music; MA in music teaching. *Instrumental* Study avilable in: accordion, flute, bowed harp, kannel, guitar, piano, harpsichord, cklavichord, double bass, voice, diatonic accordion, percussion, organ, Jew's harp, saxophone, hornpipe, bagpipes, violin, whistles. *Orchestral* Students can play in the Viljandi Youth Symphony Orchestra *Choral* VCA choir *Jazz/world* Jazz course; weekly jazz club *Other* Traditional musicians club.

Admissions information *Term dates* Aug 30-Jan 30 (autumn term); Feb 2-Jun 26 (spring term). *Application requirements* Admission on the basis of results of state exams/final exams (international tests are converted to Estonian system) and entrance exam (solfeggio and test in applicant's specialism). Applicants must fill in an online application and send supporting documents. *Application deadline* 1 Jun (EU applicants); 15 Apr (non EU applicants). *Fees* EUR 985-1160 depending on course. *Scholarships* Limited number of scholarships available (see website for details) *No of students* 137 students in music dept, 1 or 2 from overseas. *Language requirements* The language of instruction is Estonian; students must complete the intensive language course before they commence their studies.

Facilities *Music facilities* Music house, completed in 2005, contains practice rooms, studio space and music tech facilities. *Accommodation* Two dormitories.

MUSIC FESTIVALS

Birgitta Festival Toompuiestee 20, EE-10149 Tallinn, Estonia *t:* +372 6699 940 *f:* +372 6699 947 *e:* fila@filharmoonia.ee *w:* www.birgitta.ee
Modern musical theatre in a medieval convent.

International Festival of New Music NYYD Eesti Kontsert, Estonia Avenue 4, EE-10148 Tallinn, Estonia *t:* +372 614 7700 *f:* +372 614 7709 *e:* neeme.punder@concert.ee *w:* www.concert.ee
Biennial.

The International Pianists Festival KLAVER Eesti Kontsert, Estonia Avenue 4, EE-10148 Tallinn, Estonia *t:* +372 614 7700 *f:* +372 614 7709 *e:* neeme.punder@concert.ee *w:* www.concert.ee
Biennial.

Viljandi Early Music Festival *w:* www.viljandima.ee/vanamusa

LATVIA

RIGA

City (country's capital) historically of fluctuating fortunes whose position on the Baltic coast and role as a trading port led to its rise in the 12th and 13th centuries; subsequently occupied by Germany and Russia between periods of independence, finally gaining independence from USSR in 1991. The historic old town displays a clear German influence; elsewhere there are a number of art nouveau creations (Alberta, Elizabetes and Strelnieku streets in particular).

CLIMATE

Warmest months July and August (12-21°C), coldest month January (-8--2). Snow is a fixture during winter, but rainfall relatively modest the rest of the year (August is wettest with around 85mm).

MUSICAL LIFE

Historic opera house, the Latvian National Opera, is a company performing a full season from autumn to early summer with its full-time orchestra and chorus; also a ballet company based in the building. Construction of new concert hall scheduled to begin soon. Orchestras include New Chamber Orchestra of Riga, which collaborates with Latvian National Theatre as well as putting on its own concerts; Sinfonietta Riga a small but ambitious orchestra performing a number of premieres each season. City's cathedral is home to what was once the world's largest organ.

OTHER CULTURAL ACTIVITIES

Literature, Theatre and Music Museum has aim of displaying and archiving those aspects of Latvian cultural life. Several historical institutions: Occupation Museum looks at country's history of invasion; other institutions focus on other aspects, either general history or more specific such as museum exploring role of Jews in country's history. Just outside city is a large 'museum reserve', with castle museums, 'folksong park' and sculpture garden. Art galleries.

FESTIVALS AND EVENTS

Opera Festival closes National Opera's season, reprising season's performances and bringing in guest companies and conductors. Choral music of sacred nature, both small and large-scale in various city locations (August-September), organised by country's state choir. Sound Forest festival features experimental music of various types. Every 3rd year, the multi-country Baltic Folklore Festival comes to Riga. Various non-music events: animation festival (April), book fair (February)

TOURIST INFORMATION

www.rigatourism.lv, tourinfo@riga.lv, +371 67037900

JÀZEPS VÏTOLS LATVIAN ACADEMY OF MUSIC

1 Krisjana Barona St, LV-1050 Riga, Latvia
t: +371 67228684; +371 67223522 (international relations) *f:* +371 67820271
e: maija.sipola@jvlma.lv (international relations); academy@jvlma.lv *w:* www.jvlma.lv
Contact Maija Sipola, vice rector for international relations

Course information Professional bachelor's and masters degree programmes in keyboard, string, woodwind, brass or percussion performance, conducting (choral and orchestral), vocal music; also bachelors in music teaching, musicology and ethnomusicology.

Admissions information *Term dates* Sep-Jun. *Application requirements* Entrance exams take place in Jul in music literature, solfeggio and music theory, plus interview and audition. *Application deadline* Jun. *Fees* Contact for details. *Scholarships* None. *No of students* Over 500. *Language requirements* Latvian

Facilities *Music facilities* Four halls within JVLMA (The Great Hall, The Organ hall, Chamber Hall and Stone Hall) *Accommodation* Limited places.

VILNIUS

Lithuanian capital is built up around a typical medieval old town, with narrow streets and numerous historic buildings, especially in the area around Cathedral Square (there are several other squares, Town Hall Square being the place for fairs and celebrations). Architecturally diverse – there are churches in various styles, gothic, renaissance, classic and baroque. Has a large student population of over 60,000 in higher education. It was the 2009 Capital of European Culture (with Linz in Austria).

CLIMATE

Warmest month July (12-22°C); winters very cold (-9--4 in January, and remaining below freezing for most of the time between late November and early March.

MUSICAL LIFE

2 main concert venues, National Philharmonic Hall and Palace of Congresses. Former has concerts from Lithuanian National Symphony Orchestra and the highly respected Lithuanian Chamber Orchestra; latter is home to the Lithanian State Symphony Orchestra. National opera and ballet companies share their own venue and have their own dedicated orchestra. City's numerous churches are regular concert venues.

OTHER CULTURAL ACTIVITIES

Contemporary Art Centre holds exhibitions, conferences and lectures (as well as music events). Various museums on different themes: Pushkin Museum on literature; Museum of Theatre, Music and Cinema (includes collections of mechanical instruments and recordings). Also art galleries and Lithuanian national museum.

FESTIVALS AND EVENTS

Banchetto Musicale has early music concerts in city's churches (September-October); 'Gaida' contemporary music festival in October; jazz festival in November. Modern dance festival in May; tango festival in June. St Christopher's Summer Festival features music in accessible areas around the city.

TOURIST INFORMATION

www.vilnius-tourism.lt, tic@vilnius.lt, +370 5 262 9660

LIETUVOS MUZIKOS IR TEATRO AKADEMIJA (LITHUANIAN ACADEMY OF MUSIC AND THEATRE)

Gedimino pr 42, LT-01110 Vilnius, Lithuania *t:* +370 5 2612691; +370 5 212 4967 (international relations) *f:* +370 5 2126982 *e:* rektoratas@lmta.lt (rectorate); roberta.cepulyte@lmta.lt (student exchange); rima.rimsaite@lmta.lt (international relations) *w:* www.lmta.lt

Contact Povilas Gylys, vice-rector of studies; Rima Rimsaite, international relations; Esta Urbonaviciene, academic affairs/admission, Roberta Cepulyte, international exchange programme.

Course information Music courses offered for international students: piano, organ, harpsichord, string instruments, wind and percussion instruments, accordion, conducting, vocal performance, jazz, composition. Study programmes in 3 cycles offered: art of music performance, composition, music pedagogy, musicology, ethnomusicology. BMus, MMus and doctorate all offered. *Conducting* Choral, orchestral and military bands. *Composition* Film music specialism offered at BMus level. *Chamber music* MMus in chamber music offered. Chamber music features in all courses. *Opera* Integrated opera studio programme in vocal studies course. *Jazz/world* Jazz course for all instruments inc jazz vocals. *Other* Sound design, arts management and piano accompaniment MMus course.

Admissions information *Term dates* 1 Sep-15 Jan (autumn semester); 1 Feb-15 Jun (spring semester). *Application requirements* 1 exam in area of principal study consisting of performance and interview. Contact admissions office for details of exam requirements or see website. *Application deadline* 25 Jun (national/EU applicants); 15 Jan (overseas applicants). *Fees* EU students pay same fees as national students (contact for details); LTL 18,900-34,000 (non EU students), depending on course. *Scholarships* None available for overseas students. *No of students* 1110 national students, plus 16 from overseas. *Language requirements* LIthuanian or English.

Facilities *Music facilities* 40 rooms with pianos for individual practice, library, recording library. *Performance opportunities* Concert opportunities, professional practice (inc participation in workshops, intensive educational and cultural projects). *Accommodation* Student dormitory; assistance in finding private accommodation is provided.

MUSIC FESTIVALS

Banchetto Musicale S Konarskio g 49, LT-03123 Vilnius, Lithuania *t:* +370 5 2333997 *e:* info@

bmfestival.lt *w:* www.bmfestival.lt Early music festival, including performances and masterclasses.

Contemporary Music Festival GAIDA Lithuanian Composers Union, Mickeviciaus 29, LT-08117 Vilnius, Lithuania *t:* +370 5 2123611 *f:* +370 5 2120939 *e:* gaida@lks.lt *w:* www.mic.lt Annual. Performances by leading new music ensembles, soloists, chamber and symphony orchestras; selection of programmes, including new works by international and Lithuanian composers. Pre-concerts talks, masterclasses, etc.

Jauna Muzika - New Music Festival Lithuanian Composers Union, Mickeviciaus 29, LT-08117 Vilnius, Lithuania *t:* +370 5 2721727 *f:* +370 5 2120939 *e:* jaunamuzika@lks.lt Annual. New contemporary music, mostly electroacoustic and electronic; various multimedia projects. Young composers from Lithuania and other countries as well as well-known authors.

Vilnius Festival Asmenos str 8, LT-01135 Vilnius, Lithuania *t:* +370 5 2127364 *e:* info@vilniusfestivals.lt *w:* www.vilniusfestivals.lt Classical music festival.

GREECE AND TURKEY

GREECE AND TURKEY

Although the two countries have been (often bitter) rivals, both have at various points been influential in the development of western civilisation – indeed, until independence in the mid 19th century, Greece was part of the Ottoman Empire, the precursor of modern-day Turkey (the current republic was established in 1923). Consequently, visitors with a keen interest in cultural history will find much to interest them.

Over its long history, the geographic location of what is now called Turkey, straddling the border between Europe and Asia, has meant it has absorbed aspects from east and west. Over the past century, it has developed especially strong links with Germany – the Ottoman Empire signed an alliance with Germany at the start of World War I; more recently, Turks migrated to Germany in large numbers during the 1960s helping the then West Germany overcome a labour shortage during its 'economic miracle' period of economic growth.

In Greece, the country more generally makes for an attractive place to stay, although cultural life and classical music is more restricted to the major cities. In more provincial and rural areas, however, there are several strong folk music traditions, some dating back hundreds of years. And of course, Greece was where many of our theoretical concepts – modes, acoustic properties and so on – were first articulated.

An interesting fact about Turkey's classical music education system is that it was devised and put in place by the German composer Paul Hindemith at the invitation of the Turkish government in 1935. His recommendations remained in place until reforms in 1982 which attached conservatoires to universities. But alongside western classical music, specifically Turkish classical music is well recognised; for those interested in the subject, the website www.turkishmusicportal.org has various articles and links.

GREECE PAGE 204

Conservatoires in Greece are, in the main, private institutions (the exception is the State Conservatory in Thessaloniki) so are not considered as having the same status as other higher education establishments – they are not obliged to participate in the quality assurance systems which universities are subject to, for instance, although the universities tend to concentrate on musicology and music education rather than professional training. As a result, the qualifications the conservatoires offer may not be considered elsewhere of equal standing to qualifications from other European institutions.

TURKEY PAGE 206

The conservatoires in Turkey offer a 2-cycle system (4 years + 2 years), with curricula that are at least 60% in common with each other and which are state approved.

ATHENS

Capital of Greece and one of the world's oldest cities, birthplace of many well-known philosophers and writers. Evidence of its importance as a classical city state is still present, with numerous examples of architecture of the time throughout the city; most obvious example is the acropolis, with the remains of the Parthenon temple, overlooking the city. The area at the foot of the hill is particularly distinctive; some areas have a more studenty feel, others are smarter.

CLIMATE

Hottest months July and August (20-34°C), coldest month January (-4-13°C). Rainfall low throughout the year, with December the wettest month (70mm), and summers extremely dry. This, together with the city's situation in a geographical basin, has meant Athens has suffered from poor air quality over the summer months.

MUSICAL LIFE

Main concert venue is the Megaron Moussikis; several performance spaces: main concert hall seats just under 2000, and Mitropoulos Hall (just under 500); opera/ballet theatre (Alexandra Trianti Hall). Chamber orchestra (Camerata-Friends of Music Orchestra) based there; various other orchestras include Athens State Orchestra and the Orchestra of Colours. National opera has its own orchestra.

OTHER CULTURAL INFORMATION

Very large number of sites of archaeological and historical interest with a newly opened acropolis museum. There is an exhibition with a musical theme at the Museum of Greek Traditional Instruments (over 1200 examples).

FESTIVALS AND EVENTS

Athens Festival has various theatre, music and other cultural events in venues throughout the city.

TOURIST INFORMATION

www.breathtakingathens.com

HELLENIC CONSERVATORY

53 Didotou str, GR-10681 Athens, Greece
t: +30 210 3818335 *f:* +30 210 3834485
e: eo@conservatory.gr *w:* www.conservatory.gr
Course information Taught courses in classical music (composition, theory, keyboard, wind instruments, strings, opera and vocal, percussion and guitar), Byzantine music, jazz, Greek music, popular music, music technology, music kinetics.

THESSALONIKI (SALONICA)

Main city and port in the province of Macedonia (not to be confused with the country, the Republic of Macedonia) in the northern part of Greece. Noted, among other architectural features, for its Byzantine churches, but despite its historical environment it is popular with young people (the city is home to the country's largest university) – there are a number of beaches close by and the city has a thriving nightlife.

CLIMATE

Hottest months July and August (18-31°C), coolest month January (1-9°C). Rainfall is uniformly low throughout the year, the city being slightly wetter in winter (around 50mm).

MUSICAL LIFE

Concert hall hosts concerts from Greek and international performers; also opera and ballet, and various jazz, world music and other performances. The city's main orchestra is the Thessaloniki State Symphony Orchestra.

OTHER CULTURAL INFORMATION

2 main contemporary art galleries: both the State Museum of Contemporary Art and Macedonian Museum of Modern Art have both permanent and temporary exhibitions; also other art galleries, plus a photography museum, which focuses to a substantial degree (but not exclusively) on Greek photographers. The city has a strong Jewish heritage, explored in the Jewish Museum.

FESTIVALS AND EVENTS

Dimitria festival an all-round arts event including classical music. Film festival in November, plus documentary festival in March.

TOURIST INFORMATION

www.thessalonikicity.gr

CONSERVATORY OF NORTHERN GREECE

16 Heronias Str, Zardinidis Villa, GR-546 55 Thessaloniki, Greece
t: +30 2310 422742 *e:* info@conservatoire.gr
w: www.conservatoire.gr
Course information Degree-level study in piano, strings, brass, percussion, theory, music education and electronic music; option of further study to gain a postgraduate diploma. Also children's music department and adult continuing education courses. Qualifications are usually validated by other national conservatoires or

institutions, such as the National Academy of Music, Sofia (Bulgaria) and the ABRSM.
Admissions information *No of students* Over 1000 students in total.

STATE CONSERVATORY OF THESSALONIKI
15 Fragon Str, GR-54625 Thessaloniki, Greece
t: +30 2310 510551 *f:* +30 2310 522158
e: odiokrat@yahoo.gr *w:* www.odiokrat.gr
Course information Courses in the following schools/departments: piano, harp, string instruments, guitar, woodwind, brass, percussion; monody, melodrama, Byzantine music; composition, wind orchestration, advanced theory. *Orchestral* Wind band, orchestra and youth orchestra. *Choral* Choir, Byzantine choir.
Facilities *Music facilities* 200-seat concert hall with 2 Steinway pianos, harpsichord. Library containing over 4000 books, scores, videos and sound recordings; musical instrument exhibition

MUSIC FESTIVALS

Hermopoulis Guitar Festival Byzantiou 88, GR-142 34 Kalogzeza, Greece *t:* +30 210 275 5466 *e:* festival@akroama.net *w:* www.guitarfestival.gr Concerts, guitar competition, master class, guitar ensemble

TURKEY

EUROPE

ANKARA

Capital of Turkey, located in the centre of the country, with a population approaching 4 million. Like much of the country, the city has a long and interesting history, ruled over the centuries by various regimes until modern Turkey was founded in 1923 (it was at this point the city became capital, taking over from Istanbul). This has left a varied architectural legacy today, with remains of ancient buildings dotted around the city and a concentration of traditional architecture in the walled citadel area; but much more modern buildings, particularly high-rise, are found everywhere. Apart from that there are a number of green spaces in the city. Ankara is the location for numerous universities.

CLIMATE

Hottest month August (12-28°C), coldest month January (-6-1°C). Wettest months April and May (50mm), driest in summer. Winters can be snowy.

MUSICAL LIFE

City is home to state opera and ballet companies, based mainly at Ankara Opera House although 2 other opera venues can be found there (Leyla Gencer Sahnesi and Operet Sahnesi). CSO Concert Hall and Bilkent Concert Hall are 2 main concert venues; latter is home to Bilkent Symphony Orchestra, the former to the Presidential Symphony Orchestra (CSO).

OTHER CULTURAL INFORMATION

Various museums and exhibitions, many focusing on country's history and art, such as the State Art and Sculpture Museum.

FESTIVALS AND EVENTS

International Ankara Music Festival runs every April covering wide range of music. International children's festival during the same month.

TOURIST INFORMATION

www.ankara.bel.tr

ANKARA DEVLET KONSERVATUVARI (ANKARA STATE CONSERVATORY)

Bahriye Ucok Caddesi 4, TR-06500 Ankara, Turkey
t: +90 312 212 62 10 11 12 13 *f:* +90 312 215 84 66 *e:* hudevkon@hacettepe.edu.tr
w: www.konser.hacettepe.edu.tr

BILKENT UNIVERSITY

Faculty of Music and Performing Arts, TR-06800 Bilkent Ankara, Turkey
t: +90 312 290 1777 (music dept); +90 312 290 2944 (international centre) *f:* +90 312 266 4787 *e:* intcent@bilkent.edu.tr (international centre); abasol@bilkent.edu.tr *w:* www.bilkent.edu.tr
Contact Berna Orge, International Centre co-ordinator; Aysegul Basol, exchange prog co-ord.
Course information Institute of music and performing arts offering undergraduate and postgraduate music programmes. *Orchestral* Bilkent Symphony Orchestra
Admissions information *Language requirements* Most courses are taught in English; Turkish language classes and courses are available.

ISTANBUL

Turkey's largest city, though not capital (though historically, as Byzantium and Constantinople, it had been), and one of populous in the world (around 12 million). Located at an important strategic point straddling the Bosphorus, the stretch of water linking Black Sea to Mediterranean; it is also the stretch of water separating Europe from Asia, meaning the city effectively located on 2 continents. Thanks to its location it has absorbed various architectural styles in its built environment, from ancient Rome to modern developments which sprung up as the city expanded (there is a concentration of high-rise buildings in the city's – and the country's – main financial district. Selected as one of European Capitals of Culture in 2010.

CLIMATE

Hottest months July and August (23-28°C), coolest month January (3-9°C). Wettest month December (over 100mm), driest in summer.

MUSICAL LIFE

City is home to Istanbul State Opera and Ballet and Istanbul State Symphony Orchestra (based at Caddebostan Cultural Centre); Cema Resit Rey hall is another major venue. Sanat Arts and Culture centre has concerts in a range of musical styles.

OTHER CULTURAL INFORMATION

Istanbul Modern is a contemporary art gallery with permanent and changing exhibitions. Institutions focusing on aspects of Turkish and associated culture and society include archaeology museum and museum of Islamic arts.

FESTIVALS AND EVENTS
Annual international music festival in summer (June); international film festival (April); jazz festival (July); biennial art festival (September-November, even years).

TOURIST INFORMATION
www.ibb.gov.tr

STATE CONSERVATORY AT 'MIMAR SINAN' FINE ARTS UNIVERSITY
Dolmabahce Caddesi, Akaretler Duragi,
TR-34357 Besiktas - Istanbul, Turkey
t: +90 2122616110 *f:* +90 2122610041
e: kons@msu.edu.tr; metin.ulku@hotmail.com
w: www.msgsu.edu.tr
Contact Metin Ulku
Course information Programmes in composition and conducting, piano, harp, guitar, strings, wind and percussion, musicology, ethnomusicology and folklore; also opera (part of performing arts dept). *Instrumental* Chamber music, sight reading, musical forms, instrument care, piano accompaniment, *Conducting* Harmony, counterpoint, composition, study of forms, orchestration, Turkish music, history and philosophy. *Contemporary* Contemporary Turkish music *Composition* Harmony, counterpoint, score reading, musical forms, auxiliary piano, orchestration, history of music, philosophy, Turkish language, fugue, modal music. *Orchestral* Orchestral conducting, orchestral repertoire sessions, wind orchestra. *Opera* Vocal technique, stage performances, history of opera, costume, musical diction in Turkish, Italian and German, acting and mime, repertoire classes, stage make-up. *Choral* Chorus for all students. *Jazz/world* Study of Turkish music and folklore, Asian languages, Ataturk and the history of revolution. *Other* Theory, aesthetics, instrument care and manufacture, Feldenkrais, improvisation.
Admissions information *Term dates* Oct-Dec (autumn semester); Feb-May (summer semester). *Application requirements* Differ for each programme and for level of entry. *Application deadline* Late Aug-early Sep. *Fees* YTL 700 (approx EUR 350). *Scholarships* None. *No of students* Approx 320; also approx 100 full time students at pre-college stage.

MUSIC FESTIVALS

Turkey **International Ankara Music Festival** SCA Music Foundation, Tunali Hilmi Cad 114/43, TR-06700 Ankara, Turkey *t:* +90 312 427 0855 *f:* +90 312 467 3159 *e:* sca@ankarafestival.com *w:* www.ankarafestival.com Annual. Classical music, baroque, early music, ballet, dance, jazz.

Turkey **International Istanbul Music Festival** Istanbul Foundation for Culture and Arts, Deniz Palas, Refik Saydam cad no 5, TR-34430 Sishane-Beyoglu, Istanbul, Turkey *t:* +90 212 334 07 74 *f:* +90 212 334 07 05 *e:* music.fest@iksv.org *w:* www.iksv.org Annual. Orchestra, chamber, recitals, opera, vocal, dance, traditional music.

Turkey **International Izmir Festival** Izmir Foundation for Culture, Arts and Education, Mithalpasa Caddesi no 138, Karatas, TR-35420 Izmir, Turkey *t:* +90 232 482 00 90 *f:* +90 232 482 01 66 *e:* izmirfestival@iksev.org *w:* www.iksev.org Annual. Classical, traditional and contemporary music, ballet, theatre and opera. Venues include the Great Theatre of Ephesus and the Library of Celsus.

UNITED STATES

UNITED STATES

Although it is one country, the USA offers a huge range of possibilities for the visiting student. It means, in a way, it is not enough simply to decide to go to the USA to study. Not only are there the obvious differences in courses and type of study, but each city, each state, each region has its own character. In the north east, the historic states of New England contrast with the highly urbanised New York city; in the south west, San Francisco is not the same as its neighbour Los Angeles; lovers of the outdoors can choose the mountainous Rocky Mountain states or the Pacific coast; some cities are famous for their homegrown traditions, others pride themselves on the great range of cultural backgrounds of the people living there.

As in Europe, professional music training in the USA is carried out in several types of educational establishment but which can broadly be defined as specialist music colleges or conservatoires based within universities with several faculties. The range of musical education taught depends on the institution: some place a strong emphasis on practical performance study, others include a substantial academic component, others still offer a number of joint degrees. In many cases, this weighting is reflected in the kind of qualification offered, with the bachelors-masters-doctorate stream providing practical courses in the liberal arts tradition on one hand; diplomas and licentiates rewarding more specialist practical study, but without the academic reputation that degree courses convey.

Course length is akin to the Bologna Process model, with a 4-year bachelors degree leading to the possibility of a 1or 2-year masters. This increasing harmonisation makes exchange between the continents increasingly attractive to students in either area. Unlike many places in Europe where doctorates tend to be awarded for study in the academic or pedagogical fields, it is possible to earn a doctorate for performance-based work. However, the existence of artist diplomas means that these more specialist practical courses may be more appropriate.

The other difference between the USA and most of Europe is the cost of tuition which usually reaches tens of thousands of dollars per year. There are, however, substantial scholarships and other awards – some governmental, some institutional, some from private sources – available to help with these costs. The extent of this aid does vary from institution to institution, however.

UNITED STATES

BALTIMORE

The principal city in Maryland and a major seaport on the east coast of the USA, a little upstream from the Chesapeake Bay estuary area (one of the country's key fishing areas; the city is known for its seafood as a result). Its history as a city dates back to the early 18th century and in common with many north eastern US locations played its part in the Revolution. The harbour area has seen much redevelopment recently, changing from a predominantly industrial zone to an area popular among visitors. City's buildings display variety of architectural styles reflecting mixed nature (historic industrial but redeveloped) of the place. The city is home to the historic Orioles baseball team.

 CLIMATE

Hottest month July (23-33°C), coldest January (-1-7°C). Precipitation fairly even throughout the year: driest February (79mm), wettest May (106mm).

MUSICAL LIFE

Baltimore Symphony Orchestra, under music director Marin Alsop, is based at Joseph Meyerhoff Symphony Hall (it also has a base elsewhere in Maryland), a 2400-seat hall that also puts on numerous concerts from visiting artists. A small-scale ensemble, the Baltimore Chamber Orchestra, puts on a small number of concerts each year; an international chamber concert series runs at Shriver Hall, Johns Hopkins University; contemporary classical music presented at the Contemporary Museum. The Lyric Opera House (modelled on the Concertgebouw in Amsterdam) was home to Baltimore Opera Company before the company closed in 2009; it now presents a varied programme of popular music, comedy etc as well as some classical concerts. Opera events in the city are easily traced using the www.baltimoreopera.com website; the Baltimore Sun newspaper (and website) renowned for its arts coverage.

OTHER CULTURAL INFORMATION

Museum dedicated to Edgar Allan Poe, a Baltimorean. City also birthplace of baseball legend Babe Ruth and there is museum about him too. Harbourside National Aquarium features various exhibits but also has a conservation mission – it is one of the world's most important marine life centres of its kind. Several exhibitions also reflect city's maritime and industrial heritage as well as art galleries such as Baltimore Museum of Art (changing and touring exhibitions) and the Walters Art Museum. Maryland's African American heritage explored at Reginald F Lewis Museum. Arts and culture generally in the city are supported by the Baltimore Office of Promotion and the Arts (www.bop.org).

FESTIVALS AND EVENTS

Artscape festival is a free festival of performing arts, crafts, and visual arts in July. An annual book festival runs in September.

LOCAL PUBLICATIONS

Baltimore Sun newspaper and website (www.baltimoresun.com); Visit Baltimore guide available from official tourist board; historic Baltimore Magazine (www.baltimoremagazine.net) for features general information on arts, shopping, food and drink, nightlife etc in the city.

TOURIST INFORMATION

Official tourist information at http://baltimore.org, +1 410 659 7300; www.baltimorecity.gov for general municipal information.

THE PEABODY INSTITUTE OF THE JOHNS HOPKINS UNIVERSITY

1 East Mount Vernon Place, Baltimore, MD 21202, USA
t: +1 410 234 4848 *e:* admissions@peabody.jhu.edu *w:* www.peabody.jhu.edu

Course information 3 undergrad programmes: music performance, music education, recording arts and sciences. Also postgraduate courses and artist's diploma. *Instrumental* All orchestral instruments; early music, keyboard, string, and wind instruments; guitar; organ and piano. *Vocal* Opportunities across the repertoire of vocal music, including song, oratorio, opera, vocal ensemble, symphonic works, and early music. *Conducting* Available at postgraduate level only. *Historical performance* Various early music ensembles including Peabody Renaissance Ensemble, Peabody Consort of Viols, and Baltimore Baroque Band. *Contemporary* Dedicated contemporary ensembles such as Peabody Camerata perform 20th and 21st century music, some written by students. *Composition* Weekly seminar in addition to private lessons. Numerous opportunities to hear one's work performed. *Orchestral* Instrumental students participate in at least one of the following large ensembles: symphony orchestra, concert orchestra or wind ensemble. *Chamber music* String and percussion majors complete four semesters of chamber music; woodwind and brass majors complete two semesters; piano majors fulfil specific accompanying and chamber music requirements.

AMERICAS

New Sandra Hittman Visiting Chamber Ensemble programme. *Opera* Two fully staged operas and a contemporary chamber opera annually. *Choral* Ensembles include Peabody-Hopkins Chorus and Peabody Singers. *Jazz/world* Jazz Orchestra, improvisation and multimedia ensemble, Latin Jazz Ensemble, and small groups. *Other* Computer music course (composition or performance); music education, in combination with instrumental or vocal performance or composition; recording arts and sciences; also BMus or dual degree program incorporating classes at the Johns Hopkins Whiting School of Engineering.
Admissions information *Term dates* 1 Sep-17 Dec 2010 (winter semester); 18 Jan-9 May 2011 (spring semester). *Application requirements* Applicants for all undergrad programmes must audition in a performance major (composition, computer music, early music instruments, guitar, jazz, keyboard instruments, orchestral instruments, voice). US applicants must present SAT or ACT scores. *Application deadline* 1 Dec. *Fees* $34,250 per year tuition (degree programmes); $28,700 tuition (artist diploma and graduate performance diploma programmes) *Scholarships* Various scholarships and forms of financial aid available *No of students* 682 students, 472 from US, 210 international (currently 2 from UK). *Language requirements* Each applicant whose native language is not English must submit a TOEFL score.
Facilities *Music facilities* 695-seat concert hall, 150-seat concert/rehearsal space with concert organ, 95-seat theatre; several recording studios, computer music studio. Collection of instruments, including early music instruments, available for students. Library with over 100,000 items, audio-visual centre. *Accommodation* Hall of residence spaces for 165 students; all 1st and 2nd year students required to stay on campus, unless excepted.

BLOOMINGTON

City in the state of Indiana in northern part of Midwest, not far from the state capital Indianapolis. Sizeable student population, largely due to the presence of Indiana University in the city. Predominant architectural feature is local limestone, reflecting the city's (and state's) industrial history as a source for the stone.

CLIMATE

Hottest month July (18-30°C), coldest January (-8-3°C). Precipitation: driest January (67.5mm), wettest May (130mm).

MUSICAL LIFE

The university is the major location for quality classical music, with 2010 seeing the Cleveland Orchestra beginning a residency, plus visiting artists and a large number of faculty and student concerts.

OTHER CULTURAL INFORMATION

As with music, the university is a focal point for arts with a number of public and college arts buildings on campus grouped around an area known as Fine Arts Square. Otherwise a key theatre group is the Bloomington Playwrights Project, performing contemporary works in both theatre and studio venues. The John Waldron Arts Center is home to the Bloomington Area Arts Council and promotes a range of artistic activity; the building includes small performance and exhibition spaces. Buskirk-Chumley Theater Local and community arts well supported, with Bloomington Arts and Entertainment District a community organisation promoting art and cultural activity reflecting the needs of the city.

FESTIVALS AND EVENTS

Early music festival in May; festival of world music in September.
All-round performing arts festival at Indiana University in February and summer music festival, June-August.

TOURIST INFORMATION

Official tourist information at www.visitbloomington.com, cvb@visitbloomington.com, +1 812 334 8900; http://bloomington.in.gov for general municipal information

INDIANA UNIVERSITY - JACOBS SCHOOL OF MUSIC

1201 E Third Street, Merrill Hall 101,
Bloomington, IN 47405-2200, USA
t: +1 812 855 7998 *f:* +1 812 856 6086
e: musicadm@indiana.edu
w: www.music.indiana.edu
Contact Rebecca Patrick Shipman, admissions co-ord
Course information Bachelor of music in composition, early music, jazz studies, performance (orch instruments, pno, sax, voice), also available as major with study in outside field; bachelor of music education; master of arts in musicology; master of music in composition, computer music composition, conducting, early music, jazz studies, music theory, organ & church music, performance; doctorate in

AMERICAS

music; artist diploma; performer diploma. Other courses available; see website for full details of all courses.
Admissions information *Term dates* Aug-May. *Application requirements* Audition and in some cases interview; recorded auditions may be acceptable. See website for details of requirements and audition dates. *Application deadline* 1 Dec; priority deadline for scholarship consideration is 1 Nov. Auditions Jan-Mar. *Fees* Full details of fees available on website. $65 non-refundable application fee. *Scholarships* All undergrad applicants automatically considered for merit-based financial aid. Merit-based awards also available for postgrad students, as well as small number of instructorships and assistantships. *No of students* 1600 students in total.
Facilities *Music facilities* Over 170 full-time faculty members. Facilities included recital halls, over 170 practice rooms, choral and instrumental rehearsal rooms, over 100 studios and offices; Musical Arts Center performance venue.

BOCA RATON

Relatively young city towards the southern tip of Florida in Palm Beach County with its principal period of development coming in the 1960s.

MUSICAL LIFE

The Boca Raton Symphonia is the home professional orchestra, promoting a handful of concerts in its annual season. High profile visiting artists come to perform at the Centre for the Arts at Mizner Park.

CLIMATE

Hottest month July (24-33°C) , coldest month January (14-25°C). Precipitation: driest month December (62mm), wettest June (186mm).

OTHER CULTURAL INFORMATION

As well as the Centre for the Arts, the city is home to the relatively new West Boca Performing Arts Theater, a venue predominantly for local and community performers. Numerous outdoor events at the Sunset Cove Amphitheater and two other outdoor spaces in the city.

FESTIVALS AND EVENTS

Festival of the Arts is held over a week in March.

LOCAL PUBLICATIONS

The Boca Raton Magazine (www.bocamag.com) for information about local and regional events and activities.

TOURIST INFORMATION

www.palmbeachfl.com; www.ci.boca-raton.fl.us

LYNN UNIVERSITY CONSERVATORY OF MUSIC

3601 N Military Trail, Boca Raton, FL 33431, USA
t: +1 561 237 9001 *f:* +1 561 237 9002 *e:* music@lynn.edu *w:* www.lynn.edu/music
Contact Dr Jon Robertson, dean; Marc Reese, asst dean
Course information BMus in performance and composition; MMus in performance, collaborative piano and composition; Professional Performance Certificate (non-degree graduate program).
Admissions information *Term dates* 31 Aug-7 May *Application requirements* Application form; live audition in Boca Raton or by submitting DVD. *Application deadline* 1 Feb. *Fees* Application fees $35-50. *Scholarships* Substantial merit-based aid available. *No of students* 43 national students, 48 international. *Language requirements* TOEFL required for all students with English as a second language seeking a degree (minimum score of 525+ for undergraduate, 550+ for postgraduate).
Facilities *Music facilities* Wold Performing Arts Centre, conservatory practice and rehearsal spaces and office building. *Accommodation* On-campus housing available.

BOSTON

Major city on the north east coast of USA in the area known as New England. One of the country's oldest urban developments, with a key role in both the founding of the modern America by English settlers in the 17th century and its eventual independence from Britain (hence events such as Boston Tea Party revolt). As a result, Boston is strongly associated with historic patriotism. Throughout the 19th century, significant numbers of Irish immigrants settled in the city, and today Boston is closely identified with Irish and Irish-Americans (hence Boston Celtics basketball team). A number of higher education institutions based in and around the city reinforce the city's tradition for intellectual and academic activity.

CLIMATE

Hottest month July (18-28°C), coldest month January

(-6-2°C). Precipitation: driest month July (71.1mm), wettest month November (112mm). Snowfall is common in the city from December to March.

MUSICAL LIFE

The Boston Symphony Orchestra is probably the most prominent performing organisation in the city, performing in the city and, every summer, at Tanglewood summer music academy; the Boston Pops, specialising in lighter classical music, is drawn from its members. The Boston Philharmonic is the other main large-scale group. Boston Ballet company has its own orchestra, and is highly regarded; there are 2 well-established opera companies, Boston Lyric Opera performs at Schubert Theatre (part of Citi Performing Arts Centre), and Opera Boston at the 1200-seat Cutler Theatre. The city is a notable centre for early music: Handel and Haydn Society originally a choral society (founded 1815) that has evolved to become chorus and orchestra performing music up to classical period; Boston Baroque a smaller group concentrating on that period.

OTHER CULTURAL INFORMATION

Strong for theatre; a 'theatre district' includes an opera house and City Performing Arts Centre (not just opera and ballet, but plays, lectures etc). The Institute of Contemporary Art on the riverfront has art exhibitions, films, discussions, readings and other activities – it includes a theatre staging drama, music and multi-media performances; the Museum of Fine Arts and Isabella Stewart Gardner Musuem hold permanent collections of mostly older works. Various institutions with exhibitions about city's heritage such as Commonwealth Museum, the Paul Revere House celebrating him and his role in American Revolution, or properties looked after by Historic New England; also wider interest, such as Museum of Afro-American History or Museum of Science.

FESTIVALS AND EVENTS

Hosts an annual early music festival which also encompasses a trade show. Boston Arts Festival based around the city's harbour showcases both visual and performing arts Also annual celtic music festival in Jan. Civic events include Patriot's Day celebrations (20 Apr) and traditional reading of Declaration of Independence (4 Jul).

LOCAL PUBLICATIONS

The Boston Globe is the major newspaper (www.bostom.com/bostonglobe); Boston Magazine (www.bostonmagazine.com) features editorial about the city, plus consumer information and listings; The Improper Bostonian (www.improper.com) another magazine covering events and activities in the city, as is the Boston Phoenix (http://thephoenix.com/boston).

TOURIST INFORMATION

www.bostonusa.com, info@bostonusa.com, +1 617 536 4100

BERKLEE COLLEGE OF MUSIC

1140 Boylston St, Boston, MA 02215, USA
t: +1 617 266 1400 *e:* admissions@berklee.edu; registrar@berklee.edu *w:* www.berklee.edu

Admissions information *Term dates* Autumn semester Sep-Dec; Spring semester Jan-May. *Application requirements* Live audition and interview in the US or internationally in Europe (including dates in UK and Ireland), North and South America, Asia, Africa and Australasia. Audition dates depend on country; see website for details. *Application deadline* Early action deadline: mid Dec; final deadline mid-Jan. *Fees* $150 non-refundable application fee; $500 tuition deposit; $14,600 tuition (degree programme), $12,590 tuition (diploma programme). Fees per semester. *Scholarships* All students considered for scholarships as part of audition/interview process. Berklee International Grant available for overseas students.

Facilities *Music facilities* Berklee Performance Center (seats 1212) for student and professional performances; 4 recital halls in various locations (capacity ranges from 80-180); 3 electronic piano rooms (40 keyboards in each); 50 ensemble rooms; film scoring lab; 8 music synthesis labs (over 250 types of synthesizer); 300 private practice rooms, including special units for percussionists and pianists; recording studios including 12 professional production facilities. Also library and media centre. *Accommodation* 800 places in halls of residence; off-campus student service has a bulletin board for information about other housing.

THE BOSTON CONSERVATORY

8 The Fenway, Boston, MA 02215, USA
t: +1 617 536 6340 *f:* +1 617 912 9101 *e:* admissions@bostonconservatory.edu *w:* www.bostonconservatory.edu

Course information Bachelors and masters degrees, graduate performance diploma, artist diploma. 25 curricula offered in several depts: piano, strings, voice and opera, woodwind, brass, harp and guitar, percussion/marimba, composition, choral conducting, orchestral conducting and music education. Also musical theatre/theatre arts dept. Website gives full details of bachelors and masters course content.

Admissions information *Term dates* Early Sep-early Dec (fall semester); mid Jan-end Apr (spring semester). *Application deadline* Oct 15 (for spring term); Dec 1 (for Sep intake) *Fees* $31,900 (full time bachelors); $29,900-30,100 (full time masters). See website for full details of other fees. *Scholarships* All applicants considered for scholarships on basis of merit. See website for details of grants and financial aid available. *No of students* Total of 350 students in music division.

Facilities *Performance opportunities* Orchestra, solo opportunities, ensembles, chamber music, choirs, new music, fully staged productions, opera scenes.

NEW ENGLAND CONSERVATORY

290 Huntington Ave, Boston, MA 02115-5018, USA
t: +1 617 585 1100 *f:* +1 617 585 1115
w: www.necmusic.edu

Course information Undergrad diploma, bachelor of music, double degree programmes, master of music, graduate diploma, doctor of musical arts, artist diploma; also professional string quartet and piano trio training programmes. Training in orchestal instruments; also jazz, improvisation, voice, early music, composition, theoretical and intercultural studies programmes, music education and entrepreneurial courses.

Admissions information *Term dates* Sep-Dec (1st semester); Jan-May (2nd semester) *Application deadline* 1 Dec for priority admission to fall semester and for financial aid applications. Once admitted students have until 15 Apr to accept offer. *Fees* $32,900 undergrad tuition per year (bachelors, diploma, master of music, doctor of musical arts); $30,000 graduate diploma. *Scholarships* Some; see website for details. *Language requirements* TOEFL required for non-native English speakers (61 iBT, 500 paper-based); some exemptions may be granted.

Facilities *Music facilities* Spaulding and Firestone Libraries house more than 150,000 scores, books and resources. *Performance opportunities* Opportunities to perform as a soloist and as a member of large and small ensembles. Off-campus performing opportunities through NEC's Community Performances & Partnerships Program (fellowships and one-off service concerts) and through the Music Referral Service (paid gigs). *Accommodation* Hall of residence with double rooms and small number of single rooms. All undergrads live in hall of residence in first year unless living with parents, aged 21 or over, or married.

BOULDER

City in the western US state Colorado at the eastern edge of the Rocky Mountains. Its location means there are numerous opportunities for outdoor activity (rock climbing, cycling etc), but the city also attracts many to its higher education and research institutions, one of which, Naropa, is a Buddhist institution combining western scholarship and eastern contemplative traditions. The number of scientific research institutions are reflected in the city's major industries which include microtechnology, engineering and pharmaceuticals.

CLIMATE

Hottest month July (13-31°C), coldest month January (-7-8°C). Precipitation: generally dry throughout the year driest month January (18mm), wettest month May (77mm). Climate is affected to a large extent by geography – altitude means nights can be cold, even in summer; location in the lee of the Rockies and in the path of the local warm chinook winds mean winters are typically mild and dry.

MUSICAL LIFE

One of the world's premier chamber groups, the Takács Quartet, is based at University of Colorado at Boulder. For orchestral music, the Boulder Philharmonic is the main group, performing at Macky Auditorium on university campus; Boulder Chamber Orchestra is a newer, smaller group presenting an annual season of half a dozen or so programmes. The nearby Chautauqua landmark (a cultural and educational retreat, remnant – one of only a small number – of a nationwide non-denominational religious/self-improvement movement which began in New York at the end of the 19th century) includes an auditorium programming a range of music during the summer.

OTHER CULTURAL INFORMATION

Boulder Museum of Contemporary Art has a changing programme of exhibitions; many smaller galleries and workshops besides. Theatre and dance performance, plus exhibitions, at Dairy Center for the Arts; other theatres on university campus. The Boulder Theatre presents various entertainments.

FESTIVALS AND EVENTS
Colorado Music Festival runs for 6 weeks every summer. The annual MahlerFest in May features recitals, discussions etc and culminates in a performance of a Mahler symphony. Another composer featured in festival is Bach at the Boulder Bach Festival (various dates throughout the year). Main non-music events are Boulder International Film Festival (Feb) and summer Shakespeare Festival in open-air Mary Rippon Theater at Colorado University.

LOCAL PUBLICATIONS
Main newspaper is the Daily Camera (www.dailycamera.com); there is also the Boulder Weekly.

TOURIST INFORMATION
www.bouldercoloradousa.com; visitor@bouldercvb.com; +1 303 442 2911

UNIVERSITY OF COLORADO AT BOULDER - COLLEGE OF MUSIC
301 UCB, Boulder, CO 80309-0301, USA
t: +1 303 492 6352 *e:* ugradmusic@colorado.edu; gradmusic@colorado.edu *w:* www.colorado.edu

Course information Bachelors and masters degrees in music and music education; doctor of musical arts; also post-masters professional certificates in opera and solo vocal performance, string quartet performance (for pre-established groups), woodwind performance. Certificates in jazz studies and music technology. *Historical performance* Early music ensemble *Orchestral* Symphony orchestra, wind band, marching band, concert band. *Choral* Female and male voice choirs, collegiate chorale, university choir, university singers. *Jazz/world* Jazz bands and combos.

Admissions information *Application requirements* Application by application form, letter of recommendation and audition (some other supplemental material required for postgraduate applications). *Application deadline* 15 Jan (pre-screening for some instruments by Dec 1; check website for details). *Scholarships* Wide range of scholarships at undergrad and postgrad level; also assistantships etc. Postgrad applicants automatically considered for scholarships, assistantships and other financial aid.

Facilities *Music facilities* Practice rooms, computer laboratories, faculty studios, orchestral libraries, production studio and ensemble music rehearsal areas. Entrerpreneurship Center for Music gives career advice and courses in making the most of music marketplace (business and communication skills etc).

CHICAGO
Major city in Illinois, in the north of the USA, with a population approaching 3 million and one of the world's busiest airports. It is located on the shores of Lake Michigan (at some 58,000 square kilometres in area it is more like the sea) with the waterfront a major feature in its character. The city developed rapidly in the late 19th century, partly thanks to a city-wide fire in 1871, leading to first US experiments in skyscrapers; today Chicago's skyline is renowned because of the large numbers of high-rise buildings, the Sears Tower being, at one point, the world's tallest building. The city has had a major input into history of jazz, with many African American musicians arriving from southern states in early part of 20th century, a favourite period of the film industry which has been much attracted by the more colourful aspects of the Prohibition era. It is also an important city for sports fans, with two baseball teams (the Cubs and the White Sox) and an American football team (Chicago Bears) that all have great historical significance, plus a world-renowned basketball team (Chicago Bulls).

CLIMATE
Its nickname 'the windy city' is due to its lakeside location. Hottest month July (18-29°C), coldest month Jan (-1-9°C). Wettest part of the year is spring-summer, with substantial snowfall common in winter.

MUSICAL LIFE
Symphony Center is the main venue for classical music with regular performances from Chicago Symphony Orchestra; it is also a regular venue (though the group plays in a variety of locations in the city) for Chicago Sinfonietta which explicitly aims to be as culturally diverse as possible in its make-up and artistic activity. Cube Ensemble is Chicago-based new music group. Chicago Opera Theater promises a fresh approach to opera at its base, the Harris Theater for Music and Dance; there is music theatre at Light Opera Works. Chicago Chamber Musicians promotes wide range of chamber music events from a variety of city-based artists and guests. Outside of classical music, city has a very strong tradition of jazz and blues music that remains today.

UNITED STATES

OTHER CULTURAL INFORMATION

Chicago Cultural center, once a library, now a municipal arts venue with performances and exhibitions across a range of disciplines. Chicago is known for its tradition of theatre, in particular social and political theatre (Steppenwolf company is perhaps the best known) and improvised theatre. Three museums devoted to natural sciences are found at Museum Campus Chicago; nearby is the Art Institute of Chicago with its wide-ranging collection of fine and decorative arts, notably Impressionist and Post-Impressionist painting (it houses a companion painting to Seurat's famous Bathers at Asnières, itself kept at London's National Gallery). There are various galleries and museums besides devoted to a range of subjects including contemporary art, African American history, and Polish and Polish American culture.

Festivals and events Grant Park Music Festival has around 30 free outdoor concerts around Millennium Park, many by the festival's own orchestra and chorus.

LOCAL PUBLICATIONS

The two major newspapers are the Chicago Tribune and the Chicago Sun-Times (the latter being home to the influential film critic, Roger Ebert). Chicago Magazine (www.chicagomag.com) for city-related information and activities.

TOURIST INFORMATION

www.choosechicago.com, +1 312 567 8500

CHICAGO COLLEGE OF PERFORMING ARTS - THE MUSIC CONSERVATORY

430 S Michigan Ave, Chicago, IL 60605, USA
t: +1 312 341 6735 *e:* music@roosevelt.edu; applyru@roosevelt.edu *w:* http://ccpa.roosevelt.edu

Course information Bachelor of music in composition, jazz studies, music education or performance; 5-year double major in music education and performance; master of music in composition, performance, orchestral studies (woodwind, brass, percussion only); professional diploma in orchestra studies (woodwind, brass, percussion only) or opera; performance diploma.

Admissions information *Application requirements* Audition, music theory diagnostic exam. See website for audition requirements for each discipline. *Application deadline* 15 Jan (fall entry); 1 Dec (spring entry; at discretion of admissions office). *Fees* $75 application fee ($100 if postmarked after 15 Jan). $200 deposit; tuition fees for performing arts: $1167 per hr, $28,000pa (undergrad); $1556 per hr, $28,000pa. (postgrad)

Facilities *Music facilities* Performing Arts Library, soundproof practice studios, 195-seat recital hall, concert facilities, orchestra rehearsal room, electro-acoustic facilities, technology lab, piano lab with digital pianos. Concerts in Roosevelt University's 3700-seat Auditorium Theatre, 1400-seat Harris Theater (off-campus). *Accommodation* Student accommodation available.

CAMBRIDGE

Part of greater Boston area, across the Charles River from Boston itself and close to many historic American Revolutionary locations such as Concord and Lexington. Home of Harvard University and Massachusetts Institute of Technology, and the relaxed academic atmosphere spills over into the town itself, which boasts a vibrant, youthful attitude.

CLIMATE

Hottest month July (18-28°C), coldest December (-6-2C). Precipitation: rainfall steady throughout the year, from 77mm in July to around 100mm in November.

MUSICAL LIFE

Radius Ensemble is a small group with an eclectic programme; otherwise the conservatoire and other educational establishments are the focus for classical music in the town. Proximity to Boston means a varied musical diet is available.

OTHER CULTURAL INFORMATION

Varied theatres and entertainment venues: eg American Repertory Theatre for varied programme including classics and new work; Central Square Theater houses 2 professional companies; Cambridge Multicultural Arts Center stages a range of interdisciplinary performance events and exhibitions. Large number of galleries: Carpenter Center for the Visual Arts (at Harvard) a large example, but other smaller establishments with interesting range of exhibitions.

TOURIST INFORMATION

www.cambridge-usa.org; info@cambridge-usa.org; tel: +1 617 441 2884

LONGY SCHOOL OF MUSIC

1 Follen St, Cambridge, MA 02138, USA

t: +1 617 876 0956 *f:* +1 617 876 9326
e: admission@longy.edu; music@longy.edu
w: www.longy.edu
Contact Alex Powell, dir of admissions & student services.
Course information Master of music degree, graduate performance diploma, artist diploma, Dalcroze certificate & licence, undergrad diploma, bachelor of music degree (from Emerson College).
Admissions information *Term dates* Sep-mid May. *Application requirements* Application form and audition (live or recorded). Application includes personal statement along with letters of recommendation, resumé, TOEFL score (for non-English-speaking international applicants) and financial information. *Application deadline* 1 Dec for priority scholarships consideration; late applications also accepted. *Fees* $100 application fee. $28,000 for full time bachelors or masters course. *Scholarships* Generous merit scholarships based on audition and file review *No of students* Approx 200 students, 35% of whom are from more than 20 overseas countries. *Language requirements* TOEFL examination.
Facilities *Music facilities* Edward Pickman Concert Hall, Wolfinsohn Recital Room, numerous teaching studios, classrooms and practice rooms in 2 historic buildings in Cambridge MA. Bakalar music library contains resources and scores. *Performance opportunities* Year-long concert series in which students participate. *Accommodation* Hall of residence space near campus; school also operates a housing network to help students find apartments and roommates.

CLEVELAND

City in Ohio on the shores of Lake Erie. Developed as an industrial city, but suffered a decline after immediate post-war prosperity; recently has benefitted from various redevelopment projects. Many of the educational establishments, including music school, situated just outside the city in an area called University Circle.

CLIMATE

Hottest month July (17-28°C), coldest month January (-7-1°C). Summers are typically humid, with most rain falling in July, while December-March sees significant snowfall.

MUSICAL LIFE

Cleveland Orchestra traditionally one of the figurehead US orchestras, with concerts at Severance Hall (in University Circle area). Opera Cleveland performs a short season at the State Theatre. Rock and Roll Hall of Fame located in the city. Pops orchestra performs at Severance Hall, as well as holiday series at Playhouse Square. Oberlin Conservatory in nearby city of Oberlin has many concerts too.

OTHER CULTURAL INFORMATION

Theatre district (including opera theatre) based round Playhouse Square Center with its diverse range of entertainment and performance in several venues. For art, Cleveland Museum of Art a prominent gallery with wide range of exhibits; Museum of Contemporary Art Cleveland has variety of changing exhibitions. Several dance companies (eg Ohio Dance Theatre, Dance Cleveland)

FESTIVALS AND EVENTS

Blossom Festival features Cleveland Orchestra in summer outdoor concerts at a purpose-built venue outside the city in a national park location. Biennial international piano competition (odd years). Great Lakes Theater Festival in fact a regular theatre season (Sep-May).

LOCAL PUBLICATIONS

Cleveland Magazine (www.clevelandmagazine.com) for general leisure and entertainment information; Cleveland Scene promises an alternative weekly news, arts and entertainment perspective.

TOURIST INFORMATION

www.positivelycleveland.com, visinfo@positivelycleveland.com, +1 216 875 6600

CLEVELAND INSTITUTE OF MUSIC

11021 East Boulevard, Cleveland, OH 44106, country
t: +1 216 791 5000 *e:* admission@cim.edu
w: www.cim.edu
Contact William Fay, dir of admission
Course information Bachelor of music, master of music, doctor of musical arts offered; non-degrees include artist certificate (undergrad), artist diploma or professional studies diploma (postgrad). Distance learning programmes available through high-speed videoconferencing.
Admissions information *Application requirements* Audition held in Cleveland; DVD recorded applications may be accepted for some disciplines. Apply online at www.unifiedapps.org *Application deadline* 1 Dec (autumn application); 1 Oct (spring

AMERICAS

application) *Fees* $100 application fee; rises after 1 Dec. *Scholarships* Application for financial aid and scholarships is part of general application process. *No of students* 450 conservatory students. *Language requirements* TOEFL test for non-native English speakers.
Facilities *Music facilities* CIM recently expanded, adding two new buildings to its main facility. 540-seat Kulas Hall, recital hall, library with 52,000 scores and music books, also 23,000 AV materials. Teaching studios and practice rooms in main building and annex equipped with Steinway pianos. Technology learning centre, facilities for audio recording and distance learning. Opera theatre studio, music shop. *Accommodation* Hall of residence with dormitories for 100 students.

COLUMBUS

Capital of Ohio in American Midwest. Being the location of Ohio State University, the city has a substantial number of students (around 100,000) at higher education level. Generally relaxed and friendly, the city is praised for its gay scene, the Short North area being a particular focus.

CLIMATE

Hottest month July (18-29°C), coldest month January (-7-2°C). Summer is the rainy season (July is the wettest month); winters are drier, but snow is not uncommon in the winter, especially January-February.

MUSICAL LIFE

City has an active musical life. Main orchestra is Columbus Symphony at the Ohio Theater (over 2700 seats); ProMusica Chamber Orchestra a much smaller group performing at various venues in the city. Ohio Theatre is also venue for city's opera company Opera Columbus. Capital Theater (900+ seats) has a range of music performance, particularly world and folk, jazz, musicals etc. Various classical music promoters such as Chamber Music Columbus.

OTHER CULTURAL INFORMATION

As well as a Jack Nicklaus Museum, Ohio State University is location for the Wexner Center for the Arts, an institution promoting live performance (including some music), films and exhibitions, with a focus on contemporary work. Elsewhere, Columbus Museum of Art has its own collection and hosts special exhibitions. Several theatre venues run by Columbus Association for the Performing Arts. King Arts Complex focuses on African American performance, visual art and cultural awareness.

FESTIVALS AND EVENTS

Columbus Arts Festival in Jun primarily craft and art fair, but music and other performance also involved. Opera Columbus runs an annual international singing competition (Mar). Various cultural and community events throughout the year.

LOCAL PUBLICATIONS

The Other Paper (www.theotherpaper.com) offers news, features, reviews and information about arts and entertainment; similar publications are Columbus Monthly (www.columbusmonthly.com) and Columbus City Scene (www.columbuscityscene.org). The main newspaper is the Columbus Dispatch (www.dispatch.com).

TOURIST INFORMATION

www.ExperienceColumbus.com; VisitorInfo@ExperienceColumbus.com; tel: +1 614 221 6623

CAPITAL UNIVERSITY CONSERVATORY OF MUSIC

1 College and Main, Columbus, OH 43209-2394, USA
t: +1 614 236 6101 *e:* visit@capital.edu
w: www.capital.edu
Contact Heather Massey, conservatory admission counselor
Course information BMus courses in performance, music educaiton, jazz, composition, keyboard pedagogy, piano, church music, organ, music industry, music media, music merchandising, music technology, vocal performance (with emphasis on opera and musical theatre); BA in music; also available as a minor subject. MMus in music education (can choose emphasis from options including Kodály, jazz pedagogy and instrumental). *Instrumental* Wind symphony orchestra, chamber winds, Capital University/Bexley community orchestra, brass choir, trombone choir, clarinet choir, concert percussion ensemble, horn choir, trumpet choir, flute choir, guitar ensemble. *Chamber music* Piano in chamber music/accompanying course; piano ensemble. *Opera* Opera/musical theatre ensembles *Choral* Chapel choir, choral union, womens chorus, chordsmen. *Jazz/world* Big band, fusion band, jazz percussion ensemble jazz guitar ensemble, jazz combos, vocal jazz ensemble. *Other* MIDI Band
Admissions information *Fees* $27,680 for undergrad students. *Scholarships* Nearly all students receive

AMERICAS

some form of financial aid, either through scholarships awarded on merit or financial assistance loans and grants.
Facilities *Music facilities* 950-seat auditorium with 3-manual organ; 180-seat recital hall; 30 practice rooms, various sizes; electronic/recording studio; music technology space; range of acoustic and electronic instruments; *Accommodation* 6 halls of residence.

DENTON

City in the north east of Texas.
Climate Hottest months July and August (22-34°C), coldest month January (0-12°C). Rainfall highest in spring and autumn and relatively uniform the remainder of the year (roughly 65-85mm per month).

FESTIVALS AND EVENTS

Denton Arts & Jazz Festival (April) focuses primarily on jazz and is a major event in the art form's calendar.

TOURIST INFORMATION

www.discoverdenton.com

UNIVERSITY OF NORTH TEXAS

College of Music, 1155 Union Circle #311367, Denton, TX 76203-5017, USA
t: +1 940 565 2791 *f:* +1 940 565 2002 *e:* music.information@unt.edu *w:* www.music.unt.edu
Course information BMus, MMmus and DMus in performance (strings inc guitar and harp, woodwind, brass, percussion, piano, harpsichord, organ and voice) and composition; MMus, DMus in conducting (orchestral, choral, opera or wind specialism); BMus, MMus and PhD in music education, music history and musicology or music theory; BA and MA in music; Grad certificate in performance (strings inc guitar and harp, woodwind, brass, percussion, piano, harpsichord, organ, voice, jazz and early music); also specialised study in opera, early music performance, music and medicine, ethnomusicology and world music.
Admissions information *Term dates* Aug 26-Dec 17, 2010 (autumn term); Jan 18-May 5, 2011 (spring term) *Application requirements* Varies by degree. See www.music.unt.edu *Application deadline* See website. *Fees* Varies according to instrument and course. *Scholarships* Scholarships are determined during auditions. On-campus audition dates for 2010-2011 are January 29, February 4 (Graduate piano, percussion, voice, strings), February 5, February 26. *No of students* 1600 music school students in total. *Language requirements* Varies according to degree.
Facilities *Music facilities* Six-building music school complex with rehearsal space, recital and concert halls, classrooms and computer labs. In addition, there is an intermedia theater, the Winspear Performance Hall and the Lyric Theater. The concert hall will reopen after a complete renovation in August 2010. *Performance opportunities* Over 1000 performances per year.

DENVER

Capital of Colorado, originally a mining town in the second half of the 19th century; underwent significant development during 1970-80s due to oil boom. Known as the Mile High City due to its height above sea level, although not actually situated in mountainous region – the Rockies are some 25km to the west of the city – being located on the High Plains region of the US prairie area. A centre of the US brewing industry (with a beer festival in September).

CLIMATE

Hottest month is July (14-31°C), coldest month is January (-9-6°C). Winters characterised by prolonged snow (from October to April); rainfall generally low, May and July being the wettest months on average.

MUSICAL LIFE

Opera Colorado puts on a short season of standard opera at the Ellie Caulkins Opera House. Colorado Symphony Orchestra performs at Boettcher Concert Hall, unusual in being designed in the round. Both venues are part of Denver Performing Arts Complex (DPAC). Open air concerts at the spectacular Red Rocks Amphitheatre

OTHER CULTURAL INFORMATION

Various theatre spaces at DPAC; Denver Center for the Performing Arts is a tenant organisation at DPAC, focusing on plays and musicals, plus cabaret and student performances. Denver Art Museum has a large collection of native American art and has recently added a striking modern-style building designed by Daniel Liebeskind.

FESTIVALS AND EVENTS

Central City Opera is a festival running Jun-Aug in Central City, a town a short distance to west of Denver; 3 or 4 productions each year. Jazz Festival in Mar.

AMERICAS

LOCAL PUBLICATIONS
Denver events covered and promoted by Westword (www.westword.com); Denver Magazine (www.denvermagazine)a glossier publication. The city is one of a small number of US cities to receive the satirical magazine The Onion for free.

TOURIST INFORMATION
www.denver.org, VisitorInfo@visitdenver.com, +1 303 892 1505

UNIVERSITY OF DENVER - LAMONT SCHOOL OF MUSIC
2344 E Iliff Ave, Denver, CO 80208, USA
t: +1 303 871 6400 *f:* +1 303 871 3118
w: www.du.edu/lamont/
Course information BA in music; BMus in performance, composition, jazz studies or commercial music; MMus (composition, conducting, performance or pedagogy focus); MA in musicology, MA in music theory. Minor studies: artist's diploma certificate; Suzuki teaching certificate.
Admissions information *Application requirements* Application and audition. Some disciplines require a pre-screening tape to be sent (jazz and commercial music). *Application deadline* 1 Nov for early applicants; 15 Jan for regular decision applicants. *Fees* $50 non-refundable application fee ($60 for postgrad applicants). *Language requirements* Non-native international applicants must submit TOEFL scores with application.
Facilities *Music facilities* Robert and Judi Newman Center for the Performing Arts houses concert hall/opera theatre and flexible performance space. School also has teaching, rehearsal and practice studios, music library with computer lab, recording studio, small performance spaces, individual practice rooms; rehearsal spaces include vocal arts room, instrumental room, jazz room and virtual practice rooms (with computer-generated reverberation effects to mimic acoustics of different types of performance space). All-Steinway school.

EUGENE
City in Pacific coastal state of Oregon, known for its scenic location and prevalence of outdoor activities (the city is close to a number of ski resorts) but also its artistic atmosphere – as well as the existence of traditional performing arts, the city has a reputation for alternative art and lifestyles, perhaps in part due to the presence of the University of Oregon in the city.

CLIMATE
The presence of the ocean leaves temperatures mild all year round; warmest months July and August (11-28°C), coldest month January (1-8°C). Precipitation fluctuates throughout the year, with low rainfall in summer and wetter winters.

MUSICAL LIFE
Eugene Symphony based at Hult Center for the Performing Arts; it is also home to opera and ballet companies. Oregon Mozart Players is a chamber orchestra based in the city The Shedd Institute includes a classical concert series among its variety of performing arts events.

OTHER CULTURAL INFORMATION
Hult Center has a 500-seat theatre as well as the concert hall, plus an art gallery. A range of theatre companies, galleries etc dot the city – the Maude Kerns Art Center promotes visual arts through exhibitions, classes and events.

FESTIVALS AND EVENTS
Oregon Bach Festival (June-July) based at University of Oregon, focuses on music and musical influence of Bach. Oregon Festival of American Music annual event in August taking in a variety of American idioms such as jazz, folk and art music. Summer series of outdoor concerts in the city's parks.

LOCAL PUBLICATIONS
The Register-Guard (www.registerguard.com) is a family-owned daily; the Oregon Daily Emerald (www.dailyemerald.com) another daily, published at the University of Oregon although operating independently of it. The main weekly, with substantial arts and entertainment coverage, is Eugene Weekly (www.eugeneweekly.com)

TOURIST INFORMATION
www.eugene-or.gov

UNIVERSITY OF OREGON SCHOOL OF MUSIC AND DANCE
1225 University of Oregon, Eugene, OR 97403-1225, USA
t: +1 541 346 3761 *f:* +1 541 346 0723
e: audition@uorgeon.edu
w: http://music.uoregon.edu
Course information Undergraduate: BA or BSc in music ; BMus in performance, composition, music education or jazz studies; BA option in music theory, history and literature; BSc option in music technology. Postgraduate: MA in musicology or music theory;

MMus in composition, music education, performance, conducting, intermedia technology, piano pedagogy or jazz studies; PhD in composition, performance, music education or music theory; DMA in composition or performance; also dance.
Admissions information *Application requirements* See website for details. *Application deadline* Jan 5 for postgraduate applications; Jan 15 for undergraduates. *Fees* See website. *Scholarships* Scholarship fund totalling nearly $300,000 per year. *No of students* 400 music majors, approx 10% from overseas. *Language requirements* See website for details.
Facilities *Music facilities* 540-seat concert hall, electro-acoustic music studios, piano lab with digital keyboards, computer lab with Mac workstations. *Performance opportunities* Approximately 30 student ensembles. *Accommodation* A variety of student accommodation available both on and off campus: dorms, quads, and apartments.

GAINESVILLE

City in northern Florida, most notable as home to one of the country's largest universities (over 50,000 students), the University of Florida. Prior to the founding of the university in the early 20th century, the city thrived as an agricultural centre specialising in citrus fruits; there are some architectural remnants of the period, although the city's appearance is dominated by later developments.

CLIMATE

The city has a subtropical climate with heavy rain and high temperatures throughout the year. Hottest months July and August (22-33°C), coolest January (7-19°C).

MUSICAL LIFE

Classical performances (among others) at the university's Curtis M Phillips Center for the Performing Arts.

OTHER CULTURAL INFORMATION

The Harn Museum of Art has a permanent collection and puts on regular temporary exhibitions. The museum is based on the university campus in an area known as the Cultural Plaza. Various theatres, the largest being the Hippodrome State Theatre and the Curtis M Phillips Center; the Acrosstown Repertory Theatre has strong links to the wider community. Various small events at the city's Civic Media Centre, a library and archive as well as a community space.

FESTIVALS AND EVENTS

Spring Arts Festival in April and university-staged Downtown Festival and Art Show in the autumn.

LOCAL PUBLICATIONS

The daily newspaper The Gainesville Sun and Gainesville Magazine are run by the same organisation and between the provide news and arts coverage.

TOURIST INFORMATION

www.visitgainesville.com; tel: +1 352 374 5260

UNIVERSITY OF FLORIDA - SCHOOL OF MUSIC

101 Fine Arts Building A, PO Box 115800, Gainesville, FL-32611-5800, USA
t: +1 352 392 0223 *f:* +1 352 392 0461
e: music@arts.ufl.edu *w:* www.arts.ufl.edu
Admissions information *Application requirements* Bachelors and masters in choral conducting, composition/theory, music education, instrumental conducting, musicology/ethnomusicology, brass, keyboard, percussion, string, woodwind, voice, sacred music.
Facilities *Music facilities* University Auditorium concert hall (900 seats) with large organ. 3-storey building housing practice rooms, teaching studios, classrooms, ensemble rehearsal rooms, electronic music lab, music library; university also has a 61-bell carillon.

HOUSTON

City on the coast of the Gulf of Mexico in Texas. Success over the years in several industries makes it a relatively wealthy place with knock-on effects for well-supported arts provision; added to the various academic institutions such as the University of Houston and Rice University, this gives the city an international appeal and a diverse population. The city has a distinctive skyline and has a unique urban feature, a tunnel system – a 10km network linking various buildings; tunnels are air conditioned so are a means of escaping Houston's long periods of hot weather. City is famous as the location for NASA's Mission Control.

CLIMATE

Subtropical climate with warm to hot weather all year round; hottest month July (24-34°C), coolest January (7-17°C). Rainfall totals are steady throughout the year from 76mm in February to 174mm in June. The city is vulnerable to tornados

AMERICAS

and its location on the Gulf of Mexico puts it in the path of hurricanes moving up from the Caribbean.

MUSICAL LIFE

Houston Grand Opera at Wortham Theater Center has its own orchestra; Houston Ballet another full-time professional company based at the theatre, performing in each of its 2 spaces. Houston Symphony Orchestra (with associated chorus) based at Jones Hall for the Performing Arts with a substantial series (many concerts repeated 2 or 3 times). Other visiting artists and ensembles perform there also. Hobby Center for Performing Arts is home to a professional string orchestra called Maggini. The Houston Friends of Music society arranges chamber music concerts at the Shepherd School of Music.

OTHER CULTURAL INFORMATION

Hobby Center for the Perfoming Arts with its 2 halls, is a venue for local performers as well as visiting artists. It is part of the theatre district along with Wortham Theater and Alley Theater (2 spaces, 800+ seater and 310 seater), the latter being the main repertory theatre in the city. As well as theatre district, city has a museum district including an extensive fine arts museum and a contemporary arts museum. Nearby is Rothko Chapel, a modern contemplation space containing a number of works by Mark Rothko; the building was the inspiration for Morton Feldman's piece of the same name for viola and choir. Arts in the city are supported by Houston Arts Alliance, a grant-awarding organisation whose aim is to increase the profile of the city in the country's cultural mind.

FESTIVALS AND EVENTS

Various short events, particularly folk and world music and events celebrating different national cultures represented in the city.

LOCAL PUBLICATIONS

The Houston Chronicle (www.chron.com) is the city's major newspaper.

TOURIST INFORMATION

www.visithoustontexas.com, +1 713 437 5200

THE SHEPHERD SCHOOL OF MUSIC

MS 532, Rice University, PO Box 1892, Houston, TX 77251-1892, USA
t: +1 713 348 4854 *e:* music@rice.edu *w:* www.music.rice.edu

Contact Susan Kersey Sachnik (undergrad admissions); Phyllis Smith (postgrad admissions)
Course information Music students accepted according to needs of school's ensembles, so specific numbers of voice types and orchestral instruments. Undergrad performance majors required to study at least 4 semesters of chamber music. Undergraduate and postgraduate courses in the following departments: brass, composition and theory, conducting, musicology, opera studies, organ, percussion and harp, piano, strings, woodwind and voice. *Instrumental* Campanile orchestra, percussion ensemble, symphony orchestra *Historical performance* Shepherd Collegium Musicum ensemble performs early music. *Contemporary* Electronic music studio. *Chamber music* String quartet in residence, chamber music provision for all students. *Opera* Shepherd School opera *Choral* Several school choirs and chorales.
Admissions information *Application requirements* Most applicants must audition in person, and it is responsibility of applicant to arrange audition time and date. *Application deadline* 2 Jan. *Scholarships* Merit awards available, renewable annually upon review. No financial need-based aid available for international students. *No of students* Approx 120 each undergrad and masters students and 50+ doctoral students at Shepherd School.
Facilities *Music facilities* Alice Pratt Brown Hall includes 1000-seat auditorium, 250-seat recital hall, organ recital room, opera studio, 65 practice rooms, 7 classrooms, rehearsal/ensemble spaces, 54 teaching studios. *Accommodation* All 1st years at Rice University encouraged to live on campus; halls of residence arranged into 9 colleges of approx 230 residential places.

LOS ANGELES

With a population of nearly 4 million, the west coast city is country's second largest, despite the precarious geological location (on the San Andreas Fault) making it vulnerable to earthquakes. Perhaps ironically in view of this, the city is one of the USA's most diverse in terms of modern architectural styles. Most famous, arguably, for its central role in the film industry, an industry which has in the past attracted large numbers of classical composers to the city, particularly European émigrés and exiles, Stravinsky, Schoenberg, Korngold being three of the best known. Another consequence of the predominance of the film industry – and its associated glamour, allure and inevitable darker side – there is that the city has become familiar through its appearance in countless films, especially films noirs of the 40s-50s and more recent blockbusters. Its importance in American cultural life extends beyond film to include the entertainment industry more generally, although the city is, naturally, home to many other industries and commercial enterprises besides.

CLIMATE

The city has a southern-European style climate; hottest month August (18-25°C), coolest are December and January (9-19°C). Rainfall is low throughout the year: wettest month February (64mm), while June-August sees very almost none. This lack of rain, together with the area's physical geography and car use, is one of the reasons for the city's notorious smog in the summer months.

MUSICAL LIFE

The unusually shaped Walt Disney Concert Hall (designed by Frank Gehry) is home to Los Angeles Philharmonic and its associated chorus. Orchestra formerly based at 3200-seat Dorothy Chandler Pavilion where LA Opera is resident; there are numerous other concerts there from recitals to orchestral. Both venues part of Performing Arts Center of Los Angeles. Performance spaces can be found at universities – eg UCLA which has a 4-hall arts complex with 2 concert halls (one large, one medium-sized). Hollywood Bowl is probably the world's best-known outdoor venue; it has its own orchestra for light classical type music, and has performances from LA Phil during year, especially during summer. The city is a centre for the music recording industry, so it attracts many musicians from fields of pop, rock, rap etc, but also provides opportunities for many classically trained musicians too.

OTHER CULTURAL INFORMATION

Performing Arts Center includes theatrical venues as well as opera and music (Ahmanson Theatre, and the recently renovated Mark Taper Forum). Skirball Cultural Centre provides a mix of modern art forms, including film, readings, plays, exhibitions (as well as music). LA is home to many well-known paintings, especially modern art – galleries include the LA County Museum of Art and Getty Center; the Hammer Museum has both a permanent collection and regular changing exhibitions of contemporary art. The entertainment industry attracts visitors too, whether to the big studios such as Universal, Disneyland theme park or locations associated with film industry. The city's NoHo (North Hollywood) area has a particular concentration of cultural activity with numerous theatres, the NoHo Arts Center and Lankershim Arts Center.

FESTIVALS AND EVENTS

As one would expect with a city the size of LA, events abound, whether these focus on ethnic and national cultures and cuisines, different art forms, LA's traditional expertise in film and TV, special interests, community arts, children's and family events etc. One of the USA's major literary festival, the Los Angeles Times Festival of Books takes place at UCLA.

LOCAL PUBLICATIONS

Los Angeles Times is in reality more than a city daily, having instead a national – even international – reach.

TOURIST INFORMATION

www.discoverlosangeles.com

THE COLBURN SCHOOL

200 South Grand Ave, Los Angeles, CA 90012, USA
t: +1 213 621 4534 *f:* +1 213 625 0371
e: admissions@colburnschool.edu
w: www.colburnschool.edu
Contact Kathleen Tesar, assoc dean for admissions.

Course information Bachelor of music, performance diploma, artist diploma, professional studies certificate. Studies in instrumental performance; opportunities for chamber music and orchestral music making.

Admissions information *Term dates* Late Aug-May. *Application requirements* Prescreening recording, live audition for selected applicants. *Application deadline* Jan 15 *Fees* $110 application fee; $500 enrolment fee (once accepted). *Scholarships* All students receive full tuition, room and board scholarships. *No of students* c 35% of students are from overseas. *Language requirements* Strong English skills (TOEFL score of 500+).

Facilities *Music facilities* 415-seat concert hall, 200-seat hall, 85-seat hall; 45 practice rooms with 24 hr access, teaching studios. School is located across the street from Walt Disney Concert Hall, home of LA Philharmonic, and near home of LA Opera. *Performance opportunities* 6 orchestral performances per year, recitals, chamber music performances, etc. *Accommodation* All students housed in school residence hall on campus.

USC THORNTON SCHOOL OF MUSIC

Los Angeles, CA-90089-0851, USA
t: +1 213 740 6935 *f:* +1 213 740 3217
e: uscmusic@usc.edu
w: www.usc.edu/schools/music
Contact P J Woolston, dir of admissions.

Course information Academic programmes in several areas: choral music, classical guitar, composition, early music performance, jazz studies, keyboard studies, keyboard collaborative arts, music education, musicology, music industry, organ studies, popular music, scoring for film and TV, strings, studio/jazz guitar, vocal arts & opera, winds & percussion. Other minor credit programmes offereed. BM degrees are 4 years, MM degrees are 2 years; graduate certificate 2 years.

Admissions information *Application requirements* Application by audition; some courses require pre-screening. Entrance exam for postgraduate and transfer applicants. *Application deadline* Applications to be received by 1 Dec. *No of students* 1072 students in total, 627 of whom undergrad. Students come from approx 40 countries.

Facilities *Music facilities* Main performance venues: Bovard Auditorium (1220 seats), 3 recital halls (1 with 280, 2 with 90 seats); also proscenium theatre (590 seats). Various rehearsal spaces. Music library with over 90,000 items.

MADISON

Capital city of northern US midwest state of Wisconsin; combines plentiful green space and lakeside location (the main centre is located on a finger of land protruding between lakes Mendota and Monona) with attractive urban environment and proximity to outdoor activities outside the city. Known for its generally liberal outlook, perhaps due to the importance of the University of Wisconsin-Madison (and its 40,000+ students) in the city.

CLIMATE

Generally moderate, though winters are cold with substantial snow December-March: hottest month July (16-28°C), coldest month January (-13--3°C).

MUSICAL LIFE

Madison Symphony Orchestra performs its concert series at 2200+ seater Overture Hall; it also provides accompaniment for Madison Opera's 2 or 3-opera season (there is also a one-day opera in the park event) and Madison Ballet. Wisconsin Chamber Orchestra performs concert series throughout year, plus a short summer outdoor season. Chamber music recitals take place from autumn to spring at the university's Chazen Museum of Art and performances are occasionally scheduled to accompany its exhibitions.

OTHER CULTURAL INFORMATION

The Chazen gallery has its own collection of American and European art and hosts temporary exhibitions on various themes. As well as the orchestra, the Overture Center houses various theatre spaces and Madison Museum of Contemporary Art.

FESTIVALS AND EVENTS

City hosts a number of music festivals covering rock and pop, jazz, world and folk/traditional music. Annual pair of visual art festivals: Art Fair On The Square and Art Fair Off The Square

LOCAL PUBLICATIONS

Alternative newspaper, covering Madison events and entertainment, is the weekly Isthmus (www.thedailypage.com) The city (or rather the university) was the birthplace of satirical magazine The Onion.

TOURIST INFORMATION

www.visitmadison.com, info@visitmadison.com, +1 608 255 2537

UNIVERSITY OF WISCONSIN-MADISON - SCHOOL OF MUSIC

3561 Humanities, 455 North Park Street,
Madison, WI 53706-1483, USA
t: +1 608 263 1900 *f:* +1 608 262 8876
e: music@music.wisc.edu *w:* www.music.wisc.edu

Course information Variety of BMus, BA and BSc degrees, and MMus, MA, DMus and PhD postgraduate courses in collaborative piano and piano pedagogy, conducting, jazz, composition, music education, music performance, musicology and ethnomusicology, music theory; courses are available as part of double major; also artists certificates and professional development courses.

Admissions information *Application requirements* Online application. Audition is 10-15 minute performance in chosen specialism, plus theory and piano tests. *Application deadline* 1 Dec. Auditions in Jan and Feb. *Fees* Around $23,000pa for international students. *Scholarships* Applicants who audition in person are eligible to apply for scholarships. Scholarships are tenable upon certain

conditions (participation in performing organisations, satisfactory level of achievement and progress). Some teaching assistant posts may be available for eligible postgraduate students.
Facilities *Music facilities* 9 classrooms; 3 large rehearsal rooms for choral, band and orchestra rehearsals; 111 practice rooms, some suitable for small ensembles; 3 concert halls (700-seat main hall, 170-seat recital hall, 160-seat organ recital hall). Ensembles in residence include Pro Arte String Quartet, Wingra Wind Quintet and Wisconsin Brass Quintet. *Performance opportunities* Various student ensembles; bands, orchestras, choirs, chamber music and opera group.

NASHVILLE

Capital city of Tennessee. Known as 'music city'; another nickname ('Athens of the South') relates to the large number of higher education institutions in the city (Vanderbilt University and Tennesse State University are the major ones) – it also boasts a full-sized reconstruction of the Parthenon. The history of the city is bound up with the Civil War (it joined the Confederate side) from which it emerged to become an important centre for trade in the latter part of the 19th century.

CLIMATE

Hottest month July (21-32°C), coolest month January (-2-8° C). Its subtropical climate is also evinced by a steady rate of rainfall throughout the year, ranging from 73mm in October to around 130mm in May.

MUSICAL LIFE

Schermerhorm Symphony Center the relatively recently completed home of the Nashville Symphony, the orchestra performing around 100 concerts a year there. City's musical heritage lies more with country music (city is location for Country Music Hall of Fame) and rock and roll. Tennessee Performing Arts Centre, previous home for the orchestra, now concentrates on opera (Nashville Opera Association runs small number of productions each year), musicals, rock etc, with occasional classical events. Perhaps best known for Grand Ole Opry radio broadcast, unique in having its own dedicated venue (Grand Ole Opry House).

OTHER CULTURAL INFORMATION

City's art museum based at the reproduction of the Greek Parthenon in Centennial Park. State Museum explores Tennessee's history, not least its involvement in Civil War. Frist Center for the Visual Arts is a converted municipal building which puts on exhibitions on various subjects

FESTIVALS AND EVENTS

Annual book festival and major film festival. CMA Music Festival in June features country music.

LOCAL PUBLICATIONS

The Tennessean (www.tennessean.com) is the main daily newspaper and The Nashville Scene (www.nashivillescene.com) its alternative weekly counterpart.

TOURIST INFORMATION

www.visitmusiccity.com, Nashcvb@visitmusiccity.com, +1 800 657 6910

BLAIR SCHOOL OF MUSIC - VANDERBILT UNIVERSITY

2400 Blakemore Ave, Nashville, TN 37212-3499, USA
t: +1 615 322 7651 *f:* +1 615 343 0324
e: Blair-web@vanderbilt.edu; dwayne.p.sagen@vanderbilt.edu (audition enquiries) *w:* www.vanderbilt.edu/blair
Admissions information *Application requirements* Audition in person; set pieces. Auditions take place at various national venues; see website for details.
Facilities *Music facilities* Over 60 teaching studios; over 50 practice rooms; 3 electronic labs; 3 interactive practice rooms; 286-seat recital hall; performing arts centre with 618-seat hall (inc pit, scene shop and dock, dressing rooms), choral rehearsal hall, instrumental rehearsal hall, audio recording studio; music library with over 40,000 volumes and scores, 5500 CDs, 14,500 LPs.

NEW HAVEN

Small harbour city in north eastern state of Connecticut closely linked with Yale University and with a history dating back to Native American villages prior to the arrival of colonisers in the mid 17th C. Its age reflected in the range of architectural examples

CLIMATE

Hottest month July (16-28°C), coldest month January (-8-2°C); low winter temperatures often accompanied by snow. Rainfall relatively high throughout the year, with monthly averages dropping below 100mm in February only.

MUSICAL LIFE
New Haven Symphony Orchestra is one of the country's oldest, performing at Yale's Woolsey Hall or Shubert Theatre (for its pops series). School of Music a focus for much of the area's classical music.

OTHER CULTURAL INFORMATION
University is location for several museums, including a collection of historic musical instruments and a gallery concentrating on British art; it also houses its own repertory theatre. Other venues include the Shubert Theatre and the Long Wharf Theatre for drama productions

FESTIVALS AND EVENTS
Chamber music festival and jazz festival is summer; there is also a series of free concerts in July.

LOCAL PUBLICATIONS
The New Haven Advocate (www.newhavenadvocate.com) offers a more alternative view on the city's goings on. The New Haven Register is its daily broadsheet.

TOURIST INFORMATION
www.newhavencvb.org, +1 800 332 7829

YALE SCHOOL OF MUSIC
PO Box 208246, New Haven, CT 06520-8246, USA
t: +1 203 432 4155 (admissions) *f:* +1 203 432 7448 *e:* gradmusic.admissions@yale.edu *w:* http://music.yale.edu
Course information Graduate professional school within Yale University. Certificate in performance; BA/MM programme for performance or composition; MM (2-year postgrad); master of musical arts (3-year predoctoral programme); DMA.
Admissions information *Term dates* 31 Aug 2010-6 May 2011 *Application requirements* All applicants must submit prescreening recordings and 3 letters of recommendation. *Application deadline* 1 Dec. *Fees* $100 application fee. *Scholarships* Full tuition award and fellowship made to all students, except those receiving awards from other agencies. *Language requirements* TOEFL 86 IBT / 567 PBT
Facilities *Music facilities* Woolsey Hall (seats 2695), includes pipe organ; Sprague Memorial Hall building, for chamber music and recitals (seats 680), also houses recording studio, music technology centre, multimedia room, practice rooms; music faculty studios. All-Steinway school.

NEW YORK
The largest city in the USA (population of over 8 million), though not the capital (in fact, it is not even capital of the state with which it shares its name). Its history as a gateway for immigrants from around the world means many diverse cultures are now well established there, something reflected in the pan-global nature of New York cuisine. Has a diverse architecture, ranging from skyscrapers for which it is famous to 'brownstone' terraces and townhouses, stretching across its five boroughs. Perhaps one of the world's best known cities, its landmarks and locations familiar to many through their appearance in countless films.

CLIMATE
The city is generally warmer and more humid than the surrounding state. Hottest month July (21-29°C), coldest month January (-3-3°C). Rainfall ranges between 79mm in Feburary up to 120mm in May with no season notably dry; snow makes an appearance in the winter months.

MUSICAL LIFE
One of foremost musical cities in the world, with New York Philharmonic one of the foremost orchestras, performing concerts at its home in the Lincoln Center, Avery Fisher Hall, as well as Carnegie Hall (actually main stage, recital hall and medium sized hall, so a venue for performers of all kinds, and not just classical) and on tour. Other main orchestra is the Met Orchestra, the accompanists for Metropolitan Opera, the major city opera house. American Symphony Orchestra presents fewer concerts, but still a large group. Prestigious chamber orchestras include Orpheus Chamber Orchestra, notable for performing without conductor or fixed section principals; Orchestra of St Luke's a versatile group of up to 55 musicians, but often performing in different sized groups; Jupiter Symphony Chamber Players has a season of about 40 concerts in the city. Much opera besides the Met, eg New York City Opera, performing in various venues across city. Jazz at Lincoln Center the country's most prominent jazz promoter and has its own orchestra; the centre is a major music venue with several performance spaces.

OTHER CULTURAL INFORMATION
Performing arts of all kinds are plentiful, from experimental to mainstream. Theatre district on Broadway with more experimental or intimate performances 'off-Broadway'. Some of world's greatest art galleries and museums, particularly on

'museum mile': Metropolitan Museum of Art and Guggenheim Museum with its distinctive spiral are best known there; MoMA (Museum of Modern Art) another popular destination.

FESTIVALS AND EVENTS

As well as its year-round events, Lincoln Center promotes various festivals such as the Mostly Mozart Festival (July-August). Music and other events in Central Park during summer months. Music Theatre festival in autumn.

LOCAL PUBLICATIONS

The city is home to numerous world-famous publications. The New York Times (www.nytimes.com) and Wall Street Journal (http://online.wsj.com) are two daily broadsheets with international reputations. The Village Voice (www.villagevoice.com) is a freesheet with a broad coverage although it is no longer the alternative voice it was in its heyday. The New Yorker (www.newyorker.com) is another venerable arts, culture and lifestyle magazine.

TOURIST INFORMATION

www.nycgo.com, visitorinfo@nycgo.com, +1 212 484 1200

AARON COPLAND SCHOOL OF MUSIC

Room 203, Queens College CUNY, 65-30 Kissena Blvd, Flushing, NY 11367, USA
t: +1 718 997 3800 *f:* +1 718 997 3849
w: http://qcpages.qc.cuny.edu/music

Admissions information *Application requirements* Audition and qualifying exam (including listening exam). *Application deadline* 31 Jan.

Facilities *Music facilities* Concert hall with organ, theatrical lighting, professional quality audio and visual equipment; 487-seat recital hall; music library with 50,000 books and scores, 12,000 recordings, 65,000 items of performance music; media centre; 169-seat choral room/recital hall; orchestral rehearsal room; 40 practice rooms; recording studio overlooking concert hall, orchestral and choral rooms; 3 electronic music studios (computer studio, synthesizer room, editing studio).

THE JUILLIARD SCHOOL

60 Lincoln Center Plaza, New York, NY 10023-6588, USA
t: +1 212 799 5000 *e:* admissions@juilliard.edu
w: www.juilliard.edu

Course information 4-year bachelor of music degree or 3-year diploma available in classical disciplines or jazz; 2-year artist diploma in opera studies; artist diploma in string quartet studies for pre-formed quartets; master of music available in orchestral instruments, composition, conducting, collaborative piano, early music, voice and jazz.

Admissions information *Application requirements* In-person audition for all applicants; overseas students may supply recording with application for pre-screening. *Application deadline* 1 Nov (opera studies course); 1 Dec for other music disciplines. *Fees* Tuition $30,500; non-refundable application fee (amount varies according to course) and miscellaneous admin fees also payable. *Scholarships* Financial aid (Juilliard scholarships, loans and work-study aid) available for international applicants. All doctor of musical arts students receive full-tuition scholarships. *Language requirements* TOEFL required for all non-native English speakers, regardless of citizenship; score to be submitted by 15 Feb.

Facilities *Music facilities* Most floors in halls of residence have 2 practice rooms with pianos; 84 practice rooms in addition; rehearsal rooms, classrooms and 35 private teaching studios; more than 200 pianos; Alice Tully Hall for concerts, 1000-seat theatre, 200-seat drama theatre, 278-seat recital hall; 2 smaller recital/masterclass halls. Library with approx 68,000 scores and 20,000 books plus LPs, CDS, tapes and videos; orchestral library with complete collection of standard repertoire; media centre with 32 listening stations. *Accommodation* All first-time college students required to live in hall of residence; housing not guaranteed for complete period of study.

MANHATTAN SCHOOL OF MUSIC

120 Claremont Avenue, New York, NY 10027, USA
t: +1 212 749 2802 *e:* administration@msmnyc.edu; admission@msmnyc.edu *w:* www.msmnyc.edu

Course information Majors in classical or jazz; orchestral performance programme at postgrad level. Pinchas Zukerman Performance Program for exceptionally gifted violinists and violists. Special programmes available outside curriculum.

Admissions information *Application requirements* Application via www.unifiedapps.org only. Certain instruments require prescreening by CD; also audition and online essay. *Application deadline* 1 Dec. *Fees* $100 non-refundable application fee. *Scholarships* Manhattan School of Music Scholarships and President's Awards available to international students; awarded in varying amounts to highly qualified students on basis of audition and financial need. *Language requirements* TOEFL for non-native English speakers; min score depends on level of degree programme (some exceptions may be granted).

Facilities *Music facilities* 846 auditorium, 281-seat recital hall, 35-seat performance space, 58 practice rooms; 2 spaces for student recitals, lectures etc. 2 new performance spaces (recital hall and flexible space). *Performance opportunities* More than 400 scheduled performances each academic year. Master classes given by notable professionals. *Accommodation* New residence hall with 19 floors and 380 rooms, practice rooms and security.

OBERLIN

Small city (population is around 9000) in Ohio in the north of USA near Lake Erie; nearest major city is Cleveland. Oberlin University the main focus for events and other activities.

 **CLIMATE**

Hottest month July (16-28°C), coldest month January (-9-0°C). Wettest months in the summer with around 100mm in June, down to 50mm in February).

ⓘ TOURIST INFORMATION

www.cityofoberlin.com

OBERLIN COLLEGE - CONSERVATORY OF MUSIC

39 W College St, Oberlin, OH 44074-1588, USA

t: +1 440 775 8413 *f:* +1 440 775 6972

e: conservatory.admissions@oberlin.edu *w:* www.oberlin.edu/con

Course information Bachelor of music; performance diploma; double degree programme; bachelor of arts; combined bachelor's/master's programme in opera, conducting, historical performance; masters programme in historical performance; masters in music teaching; artist diploma.

Admissions information *Term dates* Aug-Dec (autumn semester); Jan-Feb (winter term); Feb-May (spring semester). *Application requirements* Auditions on campus, at regional audition sites and in Asia; candidates living more than 600 miles from campus and 200 miles from regional centre may submit recording. Under 15% of international applicants accepted each year. *Application deadline* Dec 1 *Fees* $38,012 tuition; $268 other required fees. *Scholarships* Over 80% of international students receive financial aid (scholarships or loans); average aid package is approx 75% of cost of attendance. *No of students* 615 students in total. *Language requirements* Applicants whose first language is not English should submit the results of the Test of English as a Foreign Language (TOEFL). To be eligible to enroll in the bachelor of music degree program, applicants must receive a TOEFL score of 80 on the internet-based test or a score of 550 on the paper-based test. Students who receive a lower score may enroll in the Performance Diploma Program and transfer to the Bachelor of Music degree program if they retake the test and receive a score of 550 or better within one year of admission to the Conservatory. Applicants may substitute the IELTS results for TOEFL. The minimum IELTS score expected for bachelor of music study is 6.5.

Facilities *Music facilities* 5 concert halls (including 696-seat auditorium with organ, 144-seat Kulas Hall); 150 practice rooms; 40 studios; 10 classrooms; 200 Steinway grand pianos; 14 practice organs; over 1500 musical instruments for student use. Library has over 121,000 books and scores, 47,000 sound recordings, 43 listening stations. Over 500 concerts promoted staged per year. *Performance opportunities* Performances by vocal and instrumental, solo and ensemble, students, faculty, and professionals. All styles, genres and periods of music represented. *Accommodation* Various halls of residence and other housing options on campus.

PHILADELPHIA

Located on Atlantic coast in north east USA, 'Philly' was a major 19th century industrial city having also played a key role in America's successful fight for independence (it is the city where the Liberty Bell, symbolic of American independence, is kept). A centre for higher education with over 120,000 students at institutions (covering many disciplines) in the city. The city gave its name to a style of soul music (the Philadelphia sound or Philadelphia soul) in 1970s.

 **CLIMATE**

As in a number of other cities in the east, the weather is characterised by hot humid summers and cold winters. Hottest month July (21-30°C), coldest month January (-4-4°C). Wettest month is also July (112mm).

The Philadelphia Orchestra is one of the principal

US symphony orchestras, with a long tradition. Based at modern Kimmel Center for the Performing Arts, with its 2 concert halls (2500-seater and 650-seater) and 4-manual organ; building also home to the Chamber Orchestra of Philadephia. Chamber music concerts promoted at Kimmel Center and elsewhere by Philadelphia Chamber Music Society. Annenberg Center for the Performing Arts has a more eclectic selection of modern music styles. Opera comes from Opera Company of Philadelphia, with a varied season at Academy of Music.

OTHER CULTURAL INFORMATION
Pennsylvania Academy of the Fine Arts holds important collections of American arts. Museum of Art has various changing exhibitions as well as its own varied collection; Rodin Museum, owned by the Musuem of Art, is dedicated to the French sculptor and has the largest collection of his work outside France. The African American Museum has collection of African American art and objects, the oldest of its kind. Walnut Street Theatre has been in constant use since 1809, making it the oldest in the country and one of the oldest in the English-speaking world. Various other theatres and cultural centres (the Merriam and Wilma theatres, for example, and the Kimmel Center) in an area known as the Avenue of the Arts

FESTIVALS AND EVENTS
Classical music festivals include a summer season of outdoor concerts by the Philadelphia Orchestra at Mann Center for the Performing Arts; Bach Festival of Philadelphia runs over several months. Philadelphia Live Arts Festival has an all-round programme of arts events, plus an associated fringe festival. Annual folk festival in August.

LOCAL PUBLICATIONS
The Philadelphia Inquirer (www.philly.com) is one of the country's oldest daily papers. Philadelphia Magazine (www.phillymag.com) covers lifestyle matters.

TOURIST INFORMATION
www.independencevisitorcenter.com, inforequest@independencevisitorcenter.com, +1 800 537 7676

THE CURTIS INSTITUTE OF MUSIC
1726 Locust St, Philadelphia, PA 19103-6187, USA
t: +1 215 893 5262 *f:* +1 215 893 9065
e: admissions@curtis.edu *w:* www.curtis.edu

Course information Diploma or bachelor of music degree; master of music or professional studies certificate open to vocal students.
Admissions information *Term dates* Sep-May. *Application requirements* Auditions in Feb-Mar. Places are awarded solely on artistic merit. *Application deadline* 11 Dec. *Fees* $150 application fee; $350 if postmarked after deadline. *Scholarships* All-scholarship policy to undergrad and postgrad students, regardless of financial situation (worth $33,500 and $46,000 per year respectively). *No of students* Over 160 students in total. *Language requirements* Min level of English required (written TOEFL 550).
Facilities *Music facilities* 240-seat concert hall for recitals and faculty concerts, organ lessons, masterclasses etc. Opera studio black box theatre, seating 125. Resource centre has over 57,000 scores and books; orchestra library has over 1000 sets of parts. Instrument loans available, especially keyboard instruments for specialist students and conductors. *Accommodation* 13 2-bed apartments available, with priority to new students.

ROCHESTER
Mid-sized city in the north of New York State on the south edge of Lake Ontario, known for offering a high quality of life. Close to wine-growing region, and various wine-related attractions can be found in or near the city.

CLIMATE
Cold, snow-filled winters give way to warm summers, with summer and autumn providing the wettest period. Hottest month July (16-27°C), coldest month January (-8--1°C)

MUSICAL LIFE
Conservatoire is main focus for city's classical music – Rochester Philharmonic performs substantial concert series there.

OTHER CULTURAL INFORMATION
Rochester Contemporary Art Center has exhibitions and contemporary performing arts events. Geva Theatre Center has 2 stages and put on wide variety of work, including premiers and comedy. The Strong National Museum of Play is a slightly unusual institution, being an interactive museum devoted to play and playtime activities. An area of the city known as the Neighborhood of the Arts has a strong cultural/artistic flavour and includes a number of institutions such as the George Eastman House, a

photography museum and archive taking its name from the founder of Kodak (the company was set up in Rochester and its HQ remains there today).

FESTIVALS AND EVENTS
Jazz festival in June includes free outdoor concerts. Deaf Rochester in Film Festival (March) – the city has a large deaf community.

LOCAL PUBLICATIONS
Freetime (www.freetime.com) magazine covers entertainment and arts options

TOURIST INFORMATION
www.visitrochester.com, info@visitrochester.com, +1 585 279 8300

EASTMAN SCHOOL OF MUSIC
26 Gibbs Street, Rochester, NY 14604, USA
t: +1 585 274 1000; +1 585 274 1060 (admissions) *e:* admissions@esm.rochester.edu
w: www.esm.rochester.edu
Course information As well as undergraduate degrees and postgraduate courses, various specialist diplomas and certificates available: performer's certificate, artist's certificate, arts leadership certificate, certificate in college/ community teaching, world music certificate, ethnomusicology.
Admissions information *Term dates* Sep-May *Application requirements* Audition at Eastman, at US regional centre, by recording, or by audition in Asia (Japan, South Korea, Taiwan, Singapore, Hong Kong, Thailand, China); some majors and degree programmes require applicants to submit recording for prescreening). Overseas students must send 3 letters of recommendation and samples of written work. *Application deadline* 1 Dec. *Fees* $37,870 undergrad tuition fee (2009 figure); graduate fees vary but are in the region of $1,100 per credit hour. $100 application fee plus other mandatory charges.. *No of students* Approx 25% of students from overseas. *Language requirements* Min proficiency in English required.
Facilities *Music facilities* Eastman Theatre for large ensembles, Kilbourn Hall for recitals; 2 smaller venues, black box theatre for small opera, organ recital hall.

SALT LAKE CITY
Capital city of state of Utah, founded in mid 19th century by religious figure Brigham Young, a leader in the Mormon (Latter Day Saint) movement; the church is still very visible today. Its proximity to the mountains has made the city a centre for outdoor activities, notably skiing – it has hosted the Winter Olympics, for example.

CLIMATE
Hottest month July (17-33°C), coldest month January (-7-2°C), although both summer and winter are long. Relatively little rainfall throughout the year although this is made up for by heavy snow from November to April – the first flakes fall as early as September, only subsiding in May.

MUSICAL LIFE
Utah Symphony Orchestra is based at the purpose-built Abravanel Hall – it programmes a substantial annual season and attracts international calibre soloists. It shares the hall with with Utah Opera.

OTHER CULTURAL INFORMATION
Main receiving theatre is the Capital Theater; there are also several drama companies based in the city. There is also arts provision on the University of Utah campus.

FESTIVALS AND EVENTS
Devotees of the Utah Symphony Orchestra and Festival can join them during the summer at the nearby Deer Valley Festival. The Utah Arts Festival takes place annually in the city and covers both visual and performing arts. The world renowned Sundance Film Festival happens in nearby Park City.

LOCAL PUBLICATIONS
Salt Lake City Weekly (www.cityweekly.net) is the city's main alternative newspaper; there are two mainstream broadsheets, The Salt Lake Tribune (www.sltrib.com_ and Deseret Morning News (www.deseretnews.com).

TOURIST INFORMATION
www.visitsaltlake.com, +1 801 534 4900

UNIVERSITY OF UTAH - SCHOOL OF MUSIC
204 David P Gardner Hall, 1375 E Presidents Circle, Salt Lake City, UT 84112-0030, USA
t: +1 801 581 6762 *f:* +1 801 581 5683
w: www.music.utah.edu
Course information BA, BMus, MA, MMus, DMus, PhD. Undergaduate and postgraduate programmes in instrumental performance or education, vocal performance or education, conducting, composition or jazz. *Conducting* Instrumental or choral *Opera* Opera workshop and productions
Admissions information *Application requirements*

Acceptance to the University of Utah; successful audition for the music school. *Application deadline* 15 Feb (national); 15 Jan (international) *Scholarships* Undergraduate scholarships and graduate assistantships available. *No of students* 450 students in total. *Language requirements* TOEFL score of 500 minimum for international students.
Facilities *Music facilities* 2 concert halls, recital hall, chamber music room, music library.

SAN FRANCISCO

City on a peninsula jutting on the Pacific coast of the USA that developed in the late 19th century during the gold rush when population numbers exploded. It recovered quickly from a catastrophic earthquake in 1906, establishing a strong footing as a financial centre allowing construction of projects such as the Golden Gate Bridge in the aftermath of the great depression that hit other cities in the USA. It has many distinctive features (steep hills, cable cars and tramways, Victorian architecture) and is particularly noted for its seafood cuisine. Politically liberal in outlook, the city was central in 60s alternative culture and a pioneer in fighting for gay rights.

CLIMATE

Moderate climate with mild but very dry summers and similarly temperate, though wetter, winters (rainfall is highest in December and January). Warmest month September (13-21°C), coolest January (7-13°C)

MUSICAL LIFE

The major arts venue is War Memorial and Performing Arts Center: it holds San Francisco Opera and Ballet (over 3000 seats); San Francisco Symphony in the neighbouring Louise M Davies Symphony Hall, its sweeping elegant interior seating over 2700; Herbst Theater, with over 900 seats is a large venue for recitals and chamber music. The San Francisco Chamber Orchestra gives numerous concerts in SF and nearby Californian cities. Other orchestras include the San Francisco Composers Chamber Orchestra, made up of composer-performers and concentrating on new music, as do San Francisco Contemporary Music Players; Kronos Quartet based in San Francisco, enhancing the city's contemporary credentials. Concert promoting organisations include San Francisco Performances which puts on events (especially chamber music and recitals) in many of city's main venues; Old First Concerts brings wide range of classical music to church that gives the series its name. Some contemporary music at Yerba Buena Center for the Arts.

OTHER CULTURAL INFORMATION

Dance, particularly folk/ethnic-originating, at World Arts West centre and Yerba Buena Center. Unusual building of the San Francisco Musuem of Modern Art has works by numerous major 20th century artists; de Young Museum, also a striking modern design, is another important gallery. Prominence of gay communities in the city reflected in cultural activities from Pride March to organisations and societies, and theatre and performance events.

FESTIVALS AND EVENTS

Mozart festival in July, various locations. A range of performance at International Arts Festival in May. Various events celebrating city's multi-cultural make-up, eg Chinese moon festival in early autumn (the city has a Chinatown and the Chinese have been notable part of city's demographics from the days of the goldrush).

TOURIST INFORMATION

www.onlyinsanfrancisco.com, tourismsales@sfcvb.org, +1 415 391 2000

SAN FRANCISCO CONSERVATORY OF MUSIC

50 Oak St, San Francisco, CA 94102-6011, USA
t: +1 415 503 6231 *f:* +1 415 503 6299
e: admit@sfcm.edu; mcocco@sfcm.edu
w: www.sfcm.edu
Contact Melissa Cocco-Mitten, dir of admission.
Course information Performance-related instruction, theory, musicianship, history etc.
Admissions information *Term dates* Aug-May. *Application requirements* By audition only. *Application deadline* 1 Dec. *Fees* $100 application fee. *Scholarships* 94% of students currently on scholarship; average award is half-tuition. *No of students* 28% of students are from overseas. *Language requirements* TOEFL IBT: 61.
Facilities *Music facilities* £80 million building in the civic centre area of San Francisco, a short distance from SF Symphony, Ballet and Opera.

TALLAHASSEE

Capital city of state of Florida, located at the very north of the state, home to Florida State University and Florida A & M University, among other higher education establishments.

AMERICAS

Climate Hottest months July and August (23-33°C); coolest January (4-18°C), with substantial rainfall throughout the year (although it drops off slightly in later autumn).

MUSICAL LIFE

Tallahassee Symphony Orchestra is the city's main orchestra, although its annual run of concerts is short; in addition there is a concert series of chamber music recitals (the Artist Series)

OTHER CULTURAL INFORMATION

Both universities are home to art galleries. Elsewhere in the city there are a handful of theatres (the Monticello Opera House a noteworthy historical building featuring a range of entertainment, for example). The Council of Culture and Arts exists in the city to promote artistic activity of varying kinds from professional to community standard.

TOURIST INFORMATION

http://talgov.com

FLORIDA STATE UNIVERSITY - COLLEGE OF MUSIC

122 N Copeland St, Tallahassee, FL 32306-1180, USA
t: +1 850 644 6102 (music admissions) *f:* +1 850 644 2033 *e:* musicadmissions@fsu.edu
w: www.music.fsu.edu

Course information Bachelors in music (general, commercial music, jazz, sacred music), composition, music education, music in performance, music therapy, music theory. Master of music (music theory, music therapy, musicology); also master of music in composition, music education, opera production, music in performance. Doctorate in music composition, music in performance, music education, musicology, music therapy. Arts administration courses and graduate diplomas and certificates.
Admissions information *Application deadline* 4 Aug-1 Dec; later applications accepted if space available. *Scholarships* Scholarships available for US citizens or residents. *No of students* 750 undergrad students, 400 postgrad; includes students from approx 20 countries. *Language requirements* Min level of English required (TOEFL 550 or higher).

WINCHESTER

Small, historic city in the state of Virginia in eastern USA dating back, as a settlement at least, to early 18th century, and a characteristic old town area remains today. The area was heavily involved in fighting during the American Civil War, and was home to George Washington at one time

CLIMATE

Hottest month July (18-29°C), coldest month January (-6-4°C). Rainfall is at a relatively constant level throughout the year, peaking in May (92mm) and reaching a low in February (54mm).

MUSICAL LIFE

The Winchester Orchestra has a small annual season of classical favourites

OTHER CULTURAL INFORMATION

The Shenandoah Arts Council promotes various culture events including exhibitions, performances and literary activities.

FESTIVALS AND EVENTS

The main festival event is the Shenandoah Valley Apple Blossom Festival (April-May), an umbrella event featuring various performances and entertainment and attracting sizeable numbers of visitors,

TOURIST INFORMATION

www.visitwinchesterva.com, info@visiwinchesterva.com, +1 540 542 1326

SHENANDOAH CONSERVATORY

Shenandoah University, 1460 University, Winchester, VA 22601, USA
t: +1 540 665 4581 (admissions) *w:* www.su.edu/conservatory

Course information 64 degree programme choices in several areas: arts management, arts studies, church music, collaborative piano, composition, dance, ethnomusicology, jazz studies, music education, music performance, music production and recording technology, music therapy, theatre and music theatre.
Admissions information *Application requirements* Applications must include letter of recommendation.
Facilities *Music facilities* Facilities include teaching and performing venues, dance space, recording studio, piano lab, individual practice facilities, small and large rehearsal rooms, MIDI lab, media centre, music education/therapy lab, voice lab. *Performance opportunities* Five vocal ensembles and various instrumental ensembles - jazz and classical.

AMERICAS

MUSIC FESTIVALS

American Festival of Microtonal Music 318 East 70th St, Suite 5FW, New York, NY-10021, USA *t:* +1 212 517 3550 *e:* afmmjr@aol.com *w:* www.afmm.org

American International Choral Festival - St Louis, The INTERKULTUR, Am Weingarten 3, D-35415 Pohlheim, Germany *t:* +49 6403 9565 25 *f:* +49 6403 9565 29 *e:* mail@interkultur.com *w:* www.interkultur.com Choir competition with versatile festival character. Concerts plus workshops for conductors and singers.

American Landmark Festivals Federal Hall National Memorial, 26 Wall St, New York, NY 10005, USA *t:* +1 212 866 2086 *f:* +1 212 864 1665 *e:* contact@americanlandmarkfestival.org *w:* www.americanlandmarkfestivals.org Cultural and performing arts events in landmark venues. Solo and chmbr mus, opera and operetta, poetry reading, historic film with live music and commentary.

Aspen Music School and Festival 2 Music School Rd, Aspen, CO 81611, USA *t:* +1 970 925 3254 *f:* +1 970 925 8077 *e:* festival@aspenmusic.org *w:* www.aspenmusicfestival.com Annual. Orchestra, chamber music, opera.

Bach Festival of Philadelphia Peregrine Arts Inc, Crane Arts Building Suite 412, 1400 North American St, Philadelphia, PA 19122, USA *w:* www.bach-fest.org

Bang on a Can Summer Music Festival 80 Hanson Place #701, Brooklyn, New York, NY 11217, USA *t:* +1 718 852 7755 *e:* info@bangonacan.org *w:* www.bangonacan.org Residency for composers, performers and conductors of contemporary music at one of the foremost US contemporary art museums. Faculty includes Bang on a Can founders Michael Gordon, David Lang and Julia Wolfe.

Bard Music Festival The Richard B Fisher Center for the Performing Arts, PO Box 5000, Annandale-on-Hudson, NY 12504-5000, USA *e:* bmf@bard.edu *w:* http://fishercenter.bard.edu

Bloomington Early Music Festival Early Music Associates Inc, PO Box 734, Bloomington, IN 47402, USA *t:* +1 812 331 1263, also fax *w:* www.blemf.org Concerts, opera, talks, education events. Exceptional musicians from around the world. Performance on period instruments.

Blossom Festival The Cleveland Orchestra, Severance Hall, 11001 Euclid Ave, Cleveland, OH 44106-1796, USA *t:* +1 216 231 7300 *e:* info@clevelandorchestra.com *w:* www.clevelandorchestra.com Weekend concerts by the Cleveland Orchestra at large outdoor venue in national park outside Cleveland.

Boston Early Music Festival 161 First Street, Suite 202, Cambridge, MA 02142-1207, USA *t:* +1 617 661 1812 *f:* +1 617 661 1816 *e:* bemf@bemf.org *w:* www.bemf.org Biennial. Around-the-clock performances of mediaeval, renaissance and baroque music, public discussions, nearly 100 fringe concerts, performance masterclasses, dance workshops, the world-famous trade show of instrument makers and exhibitors from all over the world, Family Day programs, and more.

Boulder Bach Festival PO Box 1896, Boulder, CO 80306 *t:* +1 303 776 9666 *e:* info@boulderbachfestival.org *w:* www.boulderbachfestival.org Local professional orchestra, volunteer chorus and nationally known soloists.

Bowdoin International Music Festival Bowdoin College, 6300 College Station, Brunswick, ME 04011-8463, USA *t:* +1 207 373 1400 *f:* +1 207 373 1441 *e:* info@bowdoinfestival.org *w:* www.bowdoinfestival.org

Central City Opera Festival 400 S Colorado Blvd, Suite 530, Denver, CO 80246, USA *t:* +1 303 292 6500 *f:* +1 303 292 4958 *e:* admin@centralcityopera.org *w:* www.centralcityopera.org Annual. 3 productions in the Central City Opera House, in the Rocky Mountains.

Chautauqua Institution PO Box 28, Chautauqua, NY 14722, USA *t:* +1 716 357 6217; +1 716 357 6200 (information) *f:* +1 716 357 9014 *e:* mmerkley@ciweb.org *w:* www.ciweb.org

Colorado MahlerFest PO Box 1314, Boulder, CO 80306-1314, USA *t:* +1 303 447 0513 *e:* info@mahlerfest.org *w:* www.mahlerfest.org Festival dedicated to life and times of Mahler and culminates in a performance of one of his symphonies.

Colorado Music Festival 900 Baseline Rd, Cottage 100, Boulder, CO 80302, USA *t:* +1 303 449 1397 *w:* www.coloradomusicfest.org Annual 6 week summer festival at Chautauqua Auditorium, Boulder. Well known classical music repertoire, world music and works by modern composers.

Daytona Beach International Festival PO Box 1310, Daytona Beach, FL 32115-1310, USA *t:* +1 386 257 7790 *f:* +1 386 238 1663 *w:* www.fif-lso.org Biennial. Classical, jazz, dance, chamber, masterclasses. 60 performances, plus free public events. Featuring the London Symphony Orchestra.

Festival Miami University of Miami, 1320 South

Dixie Hwy, Suite 731, Coral Gables, FL 33146, USA *t:* +1 305 284 4940 *f:* +1 305 284 3901 *e:* festivalmiami.music@miami.edu *w:* www.festivalmiami.com Annual. Orchestral, choral, chamber music, jazz, musical theatre, solo artists.

Gilmore International Keyboard Festival 359 Kalamazoo Mall, Suite 101, Kalamazoo, MI-49007, USA *t:* +1 269 342 1166 *e:* gilmore@thegilmore.org *w:* www.GilmoreKeyboardFestival.org Biennial festival celebrating keyboard music.Concerts, recitals, lectures, chamber music, master classes and film.

Glimmerglass Opera Festival Box 191, Cooperstown, NY 13326, USA *t:* +1 607 547 5700 *f:* +1 607 547 6030 *w:* www.glimmerglass.org Operas, recitals, symposia.

Grand Teton Music Festival 40125 W Lake Creek Drive 1, Wilston, WY 83014, USA *t:* +1 307 733 3050 *f:* +1 307 739 9043 *e:* gtmf@gtmf.org *w:* www.gtmf.org Annual. The nation's finest classical musicians in orchestras and chamber music concerts.

Grant Park Music Festival 205 East Randolph Drive, Chicago, IL 60601 *t:* +1 312 742 7638 *e:* info@grantparkmusicfestival.com *w:* www.grantparkmusicfestival.com Festival with free outdoor concerts around Millennium Park, many by the festival's own orchestra and chorus.

International Choral Festival PO Box 8203, Missoula, MT 59807, USA *t:* +1 406 721 7985 *e:* info@choralfestival.org *w:* www.choralfestival.com

The International Festival at Round Top PO Drawer 89, Round Top, TX 78954-0089, USA *t:* +1 979 249 3129 *f:* +1 979 249 3100 *e:* info@festivalhill.org *w:* www.festivalhill.org Classical, orchestral, chamber, solo.Young artists studying and performing with faculty, all studying on full scholarship.

Marlboro Music School and Festival 1616 Walnut St, Suite1600, Philadelphia, PA 19103 *t:* +1 215 569 4690 *f:* +1 215 569 9497 *e:* info@marlboromusic.org *w:* www.marlboromusic.org Festival in Vermont with performances from young musicians and established artists who have worked together exploring a variety of chamber music.

The MasterWorks Festival PO Box 700, Winona Lake, IN 46590, USA *t:* +1 574 267 5973 *f:* +1 574 267 8315 *e:* MWFadminstrator@christianperformingart.org *w:* www.masterworksfestival.org Classical performing arts camp for dedicated individuals aged 14-26 in a Christian setting. Orchestra and chamber music; intensive study, private lessons, masterclasses, rehearsals, recitals; concerto competition; classical guitar, piano, dance, opera and theatre; bible studies.

Midsummer Mozart Festival 760 Market St # 749, San Francisco, CA 94102, USA *t:* +1 415 627 9141 *f:* +1 415 627 9142 *e:* amadeus@midsummermozart.org *w:* www.midsummermozart.org Concerts featuring renowned soloists and local performers.

Mostly Mozart Festival Lincoln Center for the Performing Arts, 70 Lincoln Center Plaza, 9th Floor, New York, NY 10023, USA *t:* +1 212 875 5456 *e:* customerservice@lincolncenter.org *w:* www.lincolncenter.org Festival celebrating Mozart and contemporaries.

Music@Menlo Chamber Music Festival and Institute 50 Valparaiso Ave, Atherton, CA 94027, USA *t:* +1 650 330 2030 *e:* info@musicatmenlo.org *w:* www.musicatmenlo.org Internationally acclaimed chamber music festival in the San Francisco Bay area. Founded by David Finckel and Wu Han, features unique immersive programming, roster of world-class artists, and a chamber music institute for emerging and pre-professional musicians.

Music in the Mountains 1063 Main Avenue, Durango, CO 81301, USA *t:* +1 970 385 6820 *f:* +1 970 382 0982 *e:* info@musicinthemountains.com *w:* www.musicinthemountains.com Festival in Durango and Pagosa Springs, Colorado.

Newport Music Festival PO Box 3300, Newport, RI 02840, USA *t:* +1 401 846 1133 *f:* +1 401 849 1857 *e:* staff@newportmusic.org *w:* www.newportmusic.org Classical chamber music in the Gilded Age Newport mansions, with America debut recitals of international artists. Composer Series features select chamber music of a major composer. 67 concerts featuring music from the romantic era.

Norfolk Chamber Music Festival Woolsey Hall, 500 College St, Ste 301, New Haven, CT 06520 *t:* +1 860 542 3000 *e:* norfolk@yale.edu *w:* www.norfolkmusic.org Summer chamber music festival and the Yale Summer School of Music with a concert series by leading musicians, plus chamber music study and student recitals, in the Litchfield Hills of NW Connecticut. O

Ojai Music Festival 201 South Signal St, Ojai CA 93023, USA *e:* info@ojaifestival.org *w:* www.ojaifestival.org

Opera Theatre of St Louis PO Box 191910, 210 Hazel Ave, St Louis, MO 63119-7910, USA *t:* +1 314 961 0171 *f:* +1 314 961 7463 *e:* info@opera-stl.org *w:* www.opera-stl.org

Oregon Bach Festival 1257 University of Oregon, Eugene, OR 97403-1257, USA *t:* +1 800 457 1486 *f:* +1 541 346 5669 *e:* gevano@uoregon.edu *w:* www.oregonbachfestival.com Choral-orchestral concerts focusing on the music and influence of JS Bach. Also chamber music, conducting masterclass, family events, educational programme.

Oregon Festival of American Music PO Box 1497, Eugene, OR 97440-1497, USA *t:* +1 541 687 6526 *e:* info@ofam.net *w:* www.theshedd.org Festival of a variety of American music; different theme each year.

Other Minds Festival 333 Valencia St, Suite 303, San Francisco, CA 94103-3552, USA *t:* +1 415 934 8134 *f:* +1 415 934 8136 *e:* otherminds@otherminds.org *w:* www.otherminds.org Experimental and avant-garde contemporary music plus panel discussions.

Portland International Piano Festival 222 NW Davis St, Suite 405, Portland, OR 97209 *t:* +1 503 228 1388 *f:* +1 503 228 1407 *e:* info@portlandpiano.org *w:* www.portlandpiano.org

Princeton Festival PO Box 2063, Princeton, NJ 08543 *t:* +1 609 537 0071 *w:* www.princetonfestival.org

Sarasota Music Festival 709 North Tamiami Trail, Sarasota, FL 34236, USA *t:* +1 941 952 9634 *f:* +1 941 953 3059 *w:* www.sarasotamusicfestival.org Masterclasses and performances of a wide variety of chamber music.

Spoleto Festival USA PO Box 157, 14 George St, Charleston, SC 29402-0157 *t:* +1 843 722 2764 *f:* +1 843 723 6383 *e:* info@spoletousa.org *w:* www.spoletousa.org

Tanglewood 297 West St, Lenox *e:* bhorgan@bso.org *w:* www.tanglewood.org

CANADA

CANADA

Canada's major cities are some of the best reputed for quality of life – the country is often seen as the ideal place for visitors who wish to experience the scale of North America but not through the eyes of its neighbour to the south. Even though the cliché of the country is of the chilly north (certainly true during winter!), the cities by the Great Lakes are on the same line of latitude as the Mediterranean Sea in Europe.

As for music, classical music is a firmly established part of Canadian cultural life with well-supported performing organisations across the country. The Canadian Music Centre (www.musiccentre.ca), which has offices in six centres, is a useful source of information for those with an interested in the contemporary side of classical music – its website has event listings plus information on Canadian composers and their music. But the country's musical culture extends much further, with music of both European and north American origin part of its national traditions.

In many respects, the situation for music students in Canada is similar to that in the US – training comes through specialist institutions and universities with practical music faculties; honours degrees at bachelors level come after 4 years' study, for instance (although masters degrees can take up to 2 years to complete); students will be expected to pay sizeable tuition fees (although in general not as much as in the US), but again with the possibility of significant financial support.

One difference that interested students will have to note is that Canada has two official languages, with French the official language in the north eastern province of Québec (which includes Montréal), English elsewhere. Non-native speakers of those languages will be expected to pass a language test or be able to demonstrate sufficient proficiency. That said, McGill University in Montréal is an anglophone institution. So, as with everything, students are advised to make full enquiries as to entrance requirements; but as North American college websites are very well maintained, and most include comprehensive information for international students, keeping well informed should pose no problems for the prospective visiting student.

CALGARY

City towards the west of Canada near the Rocky mountains; it became prosperous during the postwar period due to oil industry, but also a regional centre for winter sports. One of Canada's larger cities, with a population of over 1 million and a reputation for a high quality of life.

CLIMATE

Hottest month July (11-25°C), coldest month January (-24--13). Wettest month June (66mm), and relatively dry during winter. In general, weather is highly changeable.

MUSICAL LIFE

Calgary Opera and Alberta Ballet companies based at Southern Alberta Jubilee Auditorium. Calgary Philharmonic Orchestra, whose home for concerts is the concert hall at the Epcor Centre, is also opera and ballet orchestra. Cantos Music Foundation promotes musical activity through various projects; also has performance spaces and a collection of historic musical instruments (old and modern). City has a thriving country music scene.

OTHER CULTURAL INFORMATION

Other art forms at Epcor – each of its 3 theatre spaces is home to a theatre company: conventional theatre with Theatre Calgary; Alberta Theatre Company has many commissions and strong focus on Canadian work; One Yellow Rabbit more experimental work. Several art galleries, including Art Gallery of Calgary (4 exhibition cycles per year); the New Gallery and Truck gallery both artist-run organisations promoting contemporary work; Artevo Gallery also has performance space as well as art collection.

FESTIVALS AND EVENTS

Honens Piano Competition a major international event every 3 years. Just outside the city is Banff, the arts and cultural centre location for a major annual summer arts festival, summer school and various other cultural events (including triennial string quartet competition). Calgary Kiwanis Music Festival (early March) gives a high profile opportunity for local amateur musicians. Various jazz and blues, folk and traditional music festivals, including a Caribbean festival. Non-music events include film festival, spoken word festival, comedy festival.

LOCAL PUBLICATIONS

Avenue magazine (www.avenuecalgary.com) has news, views and information about the city. FFWD (www.ffwdweekly.com) is similar but with a more alternative perspective.

TOURIST INFORMATION

www.tourismcalgary.com, viquih@tourismcalgary.com, +1 403 263 8510.

QUÉBEC (QUEBEC CITY)

City in north east Canada, capital of the province of the same name, overlooking (with some spectacular views) the St Lawrence River; its first language is French. One of the oldest settled cities in the country, and much of its architecture is north European in flavour. Saint-Roch district has been recently redeveloped and is noted for its relaxed atmosphere; the Grande Allée is a good area for nightlife.

CLIMATE

Hottest month July (17-26°C), coldest month January (-13--5°C). Snow is usual and abundant in winter; rain most common in summer (around 90mm in August).

MUSICAL LIFE

Orchestra Symphonique de Québec is the principal orchestra (it has an associated choir), performing in city at the Grand Théâtre de Québec; the theatre's 2 halls (one has 1875 seats, one approx 500) stage various other music events including some opera. Les Violons du Roy is a well-known string ensemble performing music from baroque to present day music, associated with choir La Chapelle de Québec; main venue in city is Palais Montcalm (main hall has 1100+ seats). Traditional/folk music strongly influenced by French traditions.

OTHER CULTURAL INFORMATION

Musée National des Beaux-Arts has a collection spanning several centuries of art; also hosts touring and special exhibitions. Of particular interest to area is Musée de l'Amérique Française (the oldest museum in Canada) with various collections of artefacts, botanical samples, books etc, plus exhibitions examining development of French culture on the continent. L'Institut Canadien de Québec predominantly promoter of French Canadian literature but also has visual and performing arts activities. Contemporary dance at La Rotonde from various small local and international companies.

AMERICAS

FESTIVALS AND EVENTS
Summer festival has various kinds of performance, with music covering various styles, principally non-classical; includes outdoor and indoor performances.

TOURIST INFORMATION
www.quebecregion.com, +1 418 641 6654

CONSERVATOIRE DE MUSIQUE DE QUÉBEC
270 rue Saint-Amable, Québec, Québec G1R 5G1, Canada
t: +1 418 643 2190 *f:* +1 418 644 9658
e: CMQ@conservatoire.gouv.qc.ca *w:* www.conservatoire.gouv.qc.ca
Course information Courses in orchestral instrument study, voice, piano, conducting, organ, theory and composition. Training spans five levels, from foundation level to postgraduate. The conservatoire in Québec is the central hub of a network of nine higher education institutions that span the Québec region. Different institutions have different specialist areas, so do check website for full details, but almost all are available at the main Québec City site. Final-level postgraduate courses are only available at Montréal and Québec.
Admissions information *Term dates* End Aug-mid May *Application requirements* Audition in May. *Application deadline* 1 Mar. *Fees* $375.53 per academic unit for non-residents (no maximum fee). *Language requirements* All courses given in French.
Facilities *Music facilities* Library

MONTRÉAL
Largest city in the province of Québec, located on confluence of St Lawrence and Ottawa rivers. Its importance in 19th and early 20th century, along with its previous incarnation as a port city, have left a historic architectural legacy which, combined with new building more recently means the city's built environment is diverse – the Old Montreal area around the old port has a characteristic atmosphere, but other districts have their own character too. An significant feature of Montréal is the RÉSO, an underground network of tunnels (over 30km), shopping areas, living areas, transport links etc. Above ground the city has a large amount of green space, especially around the Mount Royal (from where the city gets its name); as this might suggest, the official language is French.

CLIMATE
Hottest month July (15-28°C), coldest month January (-14--6°). Rainfall highest in summer (around 90mm), although levels are fairly constant throughout the year; snow is frequent during winter.

MUSICAL LIFE
Place des Arts arts complex is home to 3 orchestras: Orchestre Symphonique de Montréal and Orchestre Métropolitain du Grand Montréal are the largest city orchestras; I Musici de Montréal a small chamber group also performing at other venues such as Salle Pollack at McGill University and Salle Claude Champagne at Université de Montréal (both venues with substantial musical programmes). Opéra de Montréal and city's ballet company also at Place des Arts (both OSM and OMGM provide orchestral accompaniment, depending on the show). Contemporary music promoted by Société de Musique Contemporaine de Québec (SMCQ) through its regular concert series.

OTHER CULTURAL INFORMATION
Musée d'Art Contemporain de Montréal has permanent collection of over 7000 pieces; also visiting and special exhibitions. Thriving contemporary dance scene; city is home base for Cirque du Soleil. Centre Pierre Péladeau includes 2 rehearsal rooms as well as auditorium (Salle Pierre-Mercure); Segal Centre for the Performing Arts includes 2 theatre spaces and cinema, plus company dedicated to Yiddish theatre.

FESTIVALS AND EVENTS
Annual chamber music festival in May, with performances in various venues across the city. New music festival run by SMCQ in late winter. International music competition annually in May (disciplines change from year to year). Just for Laughs festival is the world's largest comedy festival; also international jazz festival.

TOURIST INFORMATION
www.tourisme-montreal.org, info@tourisme-gouv.qc.ca, +1 514 873 2015

SCHULICH SCHOOL OF MUSIC - MCGILL UNIVERSITY
Strathcona Music Building, 555 Sherbrooke St West, Montreal, QC H3A 1E3, Canada
t: +1 514 398 4546 *f:* +1 514 398 8873
e: conservatory.music@mcgill.ca
w: www.mcgill.ca/music
Course information BMus available in composition, music education, music history, music theory, performance (keyboard, voice, orchestral),

performance (church music), early music performances, jazz. Also diploma programmes: licentiate for instrumentalists/singers wishing to focus on performance rather than theory; artist diploma for students of advanced level who already have bachelor or licentiate. MA, MMus, DMus and PhD available in various areas. Students studying orchestral instrument included in orchestral training programme.

Admissions information *Application requirements* 15-20 min audition in Feb. Applications must include statement of intent explaining reasons for applying to the school. Audition tapes must be received by 15 Feb. *Application deadline* 15 Jan, for entry and scholarships. *Fees* CAN $85 application fee, CAN $60 audition fee, both non-refundable; for postgrad, fee is CAN $100. *Scholarships* Various scholarships available: approx 40 Schulich Scholarships of CAN $5000-10,000; entrance scholarships; limited number of string scholarships (CAN $10,000);

UNIVERSITÉ DE MONTRÉAL - FACULTÉ DE MUSIQUE

PO Box 6128, 200 Ave Vincent-d'Indy, Montréal QC, H2V 2T2, Canada
t: +1 514 343 6427 *f:* +1 514 343 5727
e: musique@umontreal.ca *w:* www.umontreal.ca

Course information Courses in singing, orchestral instruments, jazz, musicology, early music, electroacoustic music, composition; other minor studies. MA, MMus, DMus and PhD also taught. *Composition* Instrumental and computer assisted composition; composition for films and video games. *Other* Music criticism and analysis

Admissions information *Term dates* See www.futursetudiants.umontreal.ca for details. *Application requirements* Applicants for performance or composition course required to have technical ability and knowledge of repertoire, theory and solfege. Examples of tests available on website. *Application deadline* 1 Feb or 1 Mar, depending on course. *Fees* International students: CAN $500.53 per credit (undergrad); CAN $6296.55 (full time masters). *Scholarships* No university scholarships for international students; some government awards for students from developing countries or for those with high academic scores. *No of students* Over 800 students. *Language requirements* Language of instruction and administration is French.

Facilities *Music facilities* Details available on website. *Performance opportunities* Over 600 concerts per year at the University of Montréal. *Accommodation* Dorms and apartments for rent near the campus.

TORONTO

City in province of Ontario on the shores of Lake Ontario. Although the city began growing in importance at the start of the 19th century (and there are older areas), the predominant architectural styles are more modern; CN Tower a distinctive feature which was world's tallest structure for many years. Population is approx 2.5 million, with a very diverse multicultural profile.

CLIMATE

Hottest month July (17-27°C), coldest month January (-8--1°C). In keeping with its continental climate, rainfall peaks in summer (71mm in July); snow is common in winter, sometimes up until early spring.

MUSICAL LIFE

The city is a major centre for performing arts in Canada. Toronto Symphony Orchestra based at distinctively designed purpose-built hall (Roy Thompson Hall); Toronto Philharmonia is smaller group based at Toronto Centre for the Arts (George Weston Recital Hall; non-professional Orchestra Toronto also resident at the centre). New music, especially Canadian, from chamber-sized Esprit Orchestra. Canadian Opera Company is the country's largest; it has its own orchestra and venue at Four Seasons Centre, shared with National Ballet of Canada. Chamber music promotions from Music Toronto at St Lawrence Centre for the Arts; centre has other resident music groups, Opera in Concert, Operetta Theatre and brass band (as well as Esprit Orchestra). City has its own early music centre, reflecting the large amount of period music in the city; centre promotes concerts, runs workshops and raises awareness of early music. Sony Centre has a varied programme of entertainment events.

OTHER CULTURAL INFORMATION

Various theatres: Princess of Wales Theatre purpose-built for musicals. Elgin and Winter Gardens complex unusual in being a double-decker theatre (has 2 rooms, one above the other); has range of shows. Young Centre for the Performing Arts has a resident company (Soulpepper) but is visited by many others as well.

FESTIVALS AND EVENTS

Main arts event is LuminaTO (June), with various art forms and styles across the city. Summer Music Festival focuses more on classical (July-August), including opera. Prestigious comedy festival; jazz festival (June-July); various ethnic cultural events.

LOCAL PUBLICATIONS
Toronto Life (www.torontolife.com) covers events, going out and features about the city. NOW Magazine (www.nowtoronto.com) offers a more alternative perspective.

TOURIST INFORMATION
www.seetorontonow.com, toronto@torcvb.com, +1 416 203 2500

THE ROYAL CONSERVATORY - THE GLENN GOULD SCHOOL
273 Bloor Street West, Toronto ON, M5S 1W2, Canada
t: +1 416 408 2824 *f:* +1 416 406 3096
e: glenngouldschool@rcmusic.ca
w: www.rcmusic.ca

Course information School is part of The Royal Conservatory, a larger community-based music education organisation. Course programmes: performance diploma program (PDP) has practical focus; bachelor of music degree in performance allows PDP students to obtain accredited degree; artist diploma programmes in solo, piano, orchestral instruments. Also young artists performance academy.

Admissions information *Term dates* Sep-Dec (winter semester); Jan-May (spring semester). *Fees* Application fee: $100; 2009 tuition fees $10,500-13,205 (inclusive of reduction from donors and government subsidies). *Scholarships* All students eligible for some financial aid; government and donors offset up to 75% of tuition fees; also full tuition awards, scholarships (renewable depending on progress and performance), assistantships, bursaries for those in financial need. All awards subject to conditions. *No of students* 130 students in total.

Facilities *Music facilities* Based at TELUS Centre; facilities include 1140-seat concert hall, smaller hall, multipurpose rehearsal hall, chamber/recital room, 77 practice studios, 20 classrooms, music tech lab, library. *Performance opportunities* Royal Conservatory Orchestra, chamber music, opera workshop, new music ensemble, competitions, engagements, vocal showcase, masterclasses and community projects. *Accommodation* No on-campus housing facilities; website gives details of accommodation organisations.

VANCOUVER
Canada's main port, on the Pacific west coast of British Columbia and the country's third largest city (over 2.5 million inhabitants) – Vancouver can refer to the city and the island just off its coast, though it's primarily the former. Relatively young as a city, coming to the fore at the end of the 19th century, with forestry and port-related services being its main industries. Partly because it is a port, the city has welcomed immigrants from various countries, but particularly Asia. Noted for its parks and gardens – Stanley Park is a major recreational area with substantial forest coverage; the nearby mountains add a sense of natural beauty to its seafront urban environment (particularly when the skyline is viewed from the sea). In general, Vancouver is widely praised for its quality of life

CLIMATE
Warmest months July and August (17-22°C), coldest months December and January (-1-3°C). Rainfall is highest during winter, with 150mm or more each month from Novermber to January.

MUSICAL LIFE
City's main orchestra is Vancouver Symphony Orchestra, although Vancouver Opera also has its own professional group for its 4 annual productions. City Opera of Vancouver a company producing chamber opera. Early Music Vancouver promotes appreciation of early music through educational events, performance opportunities, sponsorship etc. Active world music scene with various intercultural collaborations and folk groups/events.

OTHER CULTURAL INFORMATION
Vancouver Playhouse and Arts Club Theatre for standard theatrical performance; the latter has a particular emphasis on Canadian writing. The main gallery is the Vancouver Art Gallery, and the Museum of Vancouver has numerous historical artefacts on display; it also stages temporary exhibitions.

FESTIVALS AND EVENTS
PuSh International Performing Arts Festival (January-February) has all-round programme of live performance, including music, dance, theatre. Vancouver Early Music Festival in July-August has concerts, workshops and lecture/presentations. International folk and jazz festivals. Shakespeare festival overlooking the main bay (May-September); alternative theatre events at Vancouver Fringe. The city's ethnic make-up also reflected in events – Chinese New Year, for example.

LOCAL PUBLICATIONS
Vancouver Sun (www.vancouversun.com) is the main

daily paper. Georgia Straight (www.straight.com, named after the Georgia Strait, the stretch of water on which the city is located) is a free weekly paper with listings, leisure activies, reviews. Vancouver Magazine (www.vanmag.com) provides information and guidance on goings-on in the city.

TOURIST INFORMATION
www.vancouvertourist.com

UNIVERSITY OF BRITISH COLUMBIA SCHOOL OF MUSIC
Music Building, 6361 Memorial Rd, Vancouver BC, V6T 1Z2, Canada
t: +1 604 822 3113 *f:* +1 604 822 4884
e: musicoff@interchange.ubc.ca
w: www.music.ubc.ca
Course information 4-year BMus, MMus, MA, DMA, PhD qualifications available.
Admissions information *Application requirements* For BMus, candidates must audition and meet minimum academic requirements for entry into university. Auditions in Jan/Feb or Apr; audition in person preferred, but recordings acceptable in some circumstances. *Fees* International students: CAN $20,623 (undergraduate); additional fees apply. *Scholarships* Various awards and financial aid available. *Language requirements* Minimum level of English required; see website for details of conditions.
Facilities *Music facilities* 600-seat Old Auditorium, ideal for opera performance (restoration due to be completed early 2010), 1200-seat Chan Shun Hall and Centre for the Performing Arts; recital hall, recording facilities. Instrument collection, practice rooms and music library. *Accommodation* Some housing on campus. See http://housing.uba.ca for details.

MUSIC FESTIVALS

Banff Summer Arts Festival The Banff Centre, PO Box 1020, Banff AB, T1L 1H5, Canada *t:* +1 403 762 6100 *f:* +1 403 762 6444 *e:* arts_info@banffcentre.ca *w:* www.banffcentre.ca Annual festival of concerts, performances, exhibitions, art walks, readings, lectures etc.

Canada's National Arts Centre Summer Music Institute National Arts Centre, Music Dept, 53 Elgin St, Ottawa Ontario K1P 5W1, Canada *t:* +1 613 947 7000 ext 568 *f:* +1 613 943 1400 *e:* charris@nac-cna.ca *w:* www.nac.cna.ca/smi Young Artists Program: Pinchas Zukerman and an exceptional faculty provide private instruction and chamber music coaching for over 65 highly talented students. All perform in chamber ensemble concerts. Senior and pre-college levels. Conductors Program: intense workshops with dedicated professional ensemble directed by Kenneth Kiesler. Conductors conduct NAC orchestra in final concert. Composers Programme: opportunity to workshop new music with dedicated chamber musicians directed by NAC Award composer Gary Kulesha.

The Elora Festival - A Celebration in Song PO Box 370, Elora, Ontario N0B 1S0, Canada *t:* +1 519 846 0331 *f:* +1 519 846 5947 *e:* info@elorafestival.com *w:* www.elorafestival.com Primarily classical choral music; also chamber music and contemporary series.

Festival de Musique de Chambre de Montréal 5560 Sherbrooke St W, Montreal QC, H4A 1W3, Canada *t:* +1 514 489 7444 *f:* +1 514 481 6270 *e:* festivalmontreal@videotron.org *w:* www.festivalmontreal.org Performances in historic sites by renowned artists and rising stars.

Festival International de Lanaudiere 1500 Base-de-Roc Boulevard, Joliette PQ J6E 3Z1, Canada *t:* +1 450 759 7636; +1 800 561 4343 (tickets during festival) *f:* +1 450 759 3082 *w:* www.lanaudiere.org Largest classical music festival in Canada located 30 minutes from the eastern tip of the island of Montreal. Concerts in covered 2000-seat amphitheatre in forest surroundings.

Festival International de Musique Actuelle de Victoriaville CP 460, Victoriavile PQ G6P 6T3, Canada *t:* +1 819 752 7912 *f:* +1 819 758 4370 *e:* info@fimav.qc.ca *w:* www.fimav.qc.ca New music festival, jazz, improvised rock, contemporary and electroacoustic music.

Festival Orford 3165 Chemin du Parc, Orford, Quebec J1X 7A2, Canada *t:* +1 819 843 9871 *f:* +1 819 843 7274 *e:* centre@arts-orford.org *w:* www.arts-orford.org Chamber and symphonic music, opera, sacred music with musicians of international repute.

Montreal/New Music International Festival Societe de Musique Contemporaine de Québec, Centre Pierre-Peladeau, 300 blvd de Maisonneuve Eest, Montreal QC, H2X 3X6, Canada *t:* +1 514 843 9305 *e:* smcq@smcq.qc.ca *w:* www.smcq.qc.ca

Niagara International Music Festival c/o Arts Bureau for the Continents, 2121 Carling Ave, Suite 202A, Ottawa, ON K2G 1H2, Canada *t:* +1 613 234 3360 *f:* +1 613 236 2636 *e:* abc@abc.ca *w:* www.abc.ca Annual choral, band and orchestral festival for groups of all ages hosted in the Niagara

Falls area of Ontario.

Ottawa International Music Festival Arts Bureau for the Continents, 350 Sparks St, Suite #207a, Ottawa, Ontario K1R 7S8, Canada *t:* +1 613 234 3360 *f:* +1 613 236 2636 *e:* abc@abc.ca *w:* www.abc.ca For world choirs, bands and orchestras.

PuSh International Performing Arts Festivals 300-640 West Broadway, Vancouver, BC V57 1G4, Canada *t:* +1 604 605 8284 *f:* +1 604 874 7874 *e:* info@pushfestival.ca *w:* http://pushfestival.ca Live performing arts: theatre, dance, music and interdisciplinary performance.

Summer Music from the Comox Valley PO Box 3056, Courtenay BC V9N 5NS, Canada *t:* +1 250 338 7463 *f:* +1 250 703 2251 *e:* info@cymc.ca *w:* www.cymc.ca International youth music camp and festival. Jazz, chamber music, orchestra, concert band, opera, musical theatre. Student and faculty performances in venues on Vancouver Island.

Toronto International Choral Festival Arts Bureau for the Continents, 350 Sparks St, Suite #207a, Ottawa, Ontario K1R 7S8, Canada *t:* +1 613 234 3360 *f:* +1 613 236 2636 *e:* abc@abc.ca *w:* www.abc.ca For world choirs.

Toronto Summer Music 720 Bathhurst St, Suite 501, Toronto, ON M5S 2R4, Canada *t:* +1 647 430 5699 *w:* www.tsmaf.ca Canadian and international musicians in concerts, opera, workshops, lectures.

Unisong Festival, Ottawa Arts Bureau for the Continents, 350 Sparks St, Suite #207a, Ottawa, Ontario K1R 7S8, Canada *t:* +1 613 234 3360 *f:* +1 613 236 2636 *e:* abc@abc.ca *w:* www.abc.ca For Canadian choirs singing en masse on Canada Day.

Vancouver Early Music Festival 1254 West 7th Avenue, Vancouver BC V6H 1B6, Canada *t:* +1 604 732 1610 *f:* +1 604 732 1602 *e:* workshops@earlymusic.bc.ca *w:* www.earlymusic.bc.ca Series of summer courses and early music concerts.

WSO International New Music Festival 1020-555 Main St, Suite 101, Winnipeg, Manitoba R3B 1C3, Canada *t:* +1 204 949 3950 *f:* +1 204 956 4271 *e:* wso@wso.mb.ca *w:* www.wso.mb.ca WSO welcomes guest composers and artists from round the world to present a broad range of musical styles.

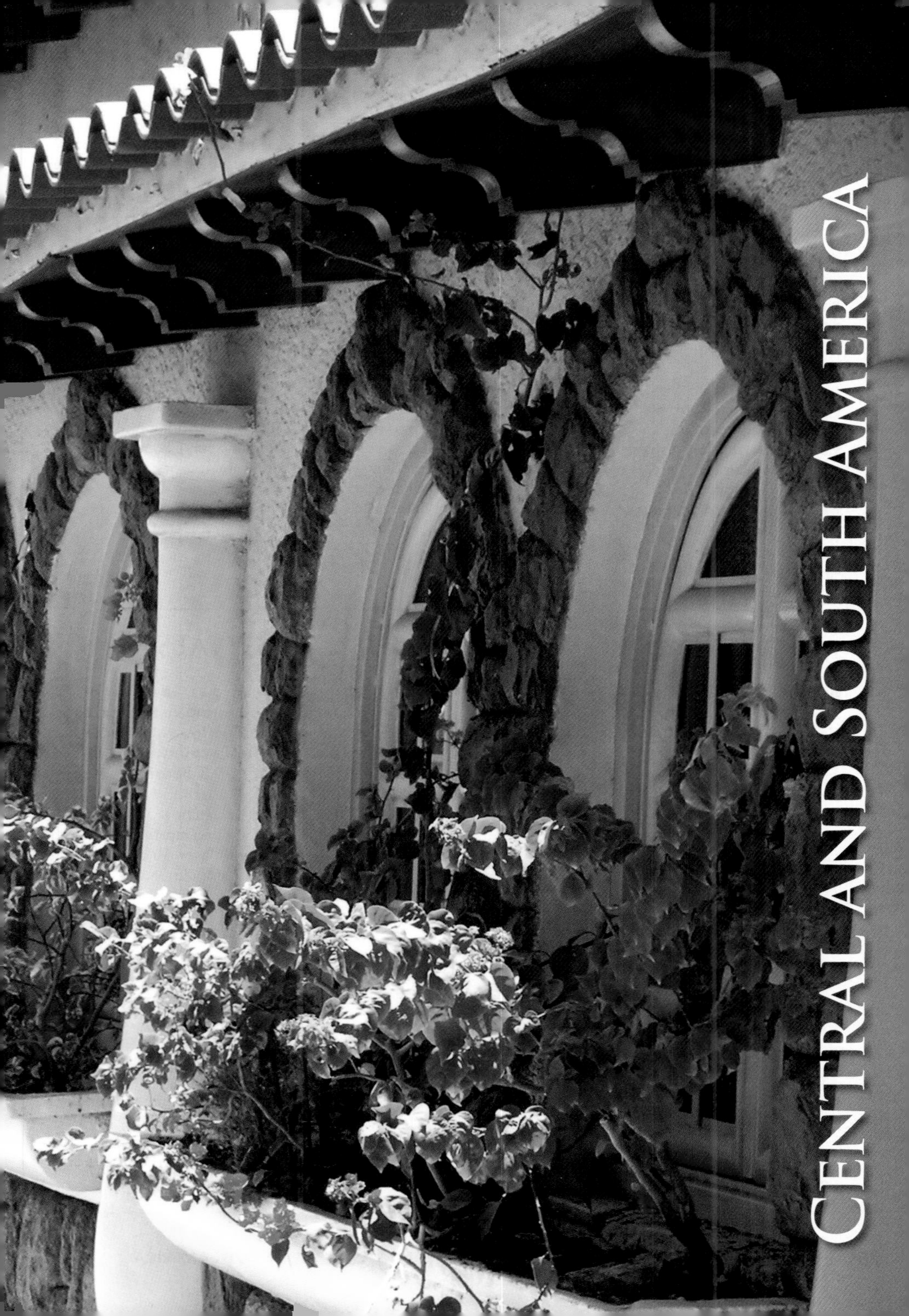

Central and South America

ARGENTINA

BANFIELD

CONSERVATORIO DE MÚSICA JULIÁN AGUIRRE

Av H Yrigoyen 7652, 1828 Banfield, Argentina
t: +54 4242 4879, also fax *e:* consaguirre@yahoo.com.ar *w:* www.consaguirre.com.ar

BUENOS AIRES

DEPARTAMENTO DE ARTES MUSICALES Y SONORAS 'CARLOS LOPEZ BUCHARDO'- IUNA

Av Córdoba 2445, C1120AAG Buenos Aires, Argentina
t: +54 4 964 5593 *f:* +54 4961 9618
e: departamento@artesmusicales.org *w:* www.artesmusicales.org

Course information Instrumental studies: piano, guitar, harp, strings, flute, recorder, oboe, clarinet, bassoon, saxophone, trumpet, horn, trombone, percussion, accordion (bandoneón); chamber music, music technology.

Admissions information *Application requirements* By audition; also aural tests. Contact academica@artesmusicales.org for further details. *Language requirements* Spanish

Facilities *Music facilities* Library with more than 40,000 titles

MUSIC FESTIVALS

International Encuentros Festival Fundacion Encuentros Internacionales de Musica Contemporanea, Santa Fe 3269-4b, 1425 Buenos Aires, Argentina *t:* +54 11 4822 1383, also fax *w:* www.aliciaterzian.com.ar Concerts, masterclasses, symposium, electronic music, experimental theatre, lectures (contemporary music only). Education forum introducing ancient and contemporary music. Annual national competition (2008: string quartet; 2009: violoncello; 2010: piano)

BRAZIL

RIO DE JANEIRO

CONSERVATÓRIO BRASILEIRO DE MÚSICA

Av Graça Aranha no 57, 12o andar Castelo, Rio de Janeiro CEP 20030-002, Brazil
t: +55 21 3478 7600 *e:* cbm@cbm-musica.org.br *w:* www.cbm-musica.org.br

Course information Undergraduate and postgraduate courses in music, music technology, music therapy; new course for music in film and TV starts in March 2010.

Admissions information *Application requirements* Online application; see website.

MUSIC FESTIVALS

Festival Amazonas de Ópera *e:* festivalamazonasdeopera@culturamazonas.am.gov.br *w:* www.amazonasfestivalopera.com

Rio International Cello Encounter (RICE) Rua Dona Mariana 133, Casa 3 Botafogo, Rio de Janeiro, CEP 22280-020, Brazil *t:* +55 212 226 5913 *e:* davidchew@terra.com.br *w:* www.riocello.com Free music festival offering masterclasses with the world's leading musicians; over 60 concerts from classical, jazz and Brazilian popular music, including Cello Dance.

CHILE

VALDIVIA

CONSERVATORIO DE MÚSICA UNIVERSIDAD AUSTRAL DE CHILE

General Lagos 1107, Valdivia, country
t: +56 63 22 19 16 *f:* +56 63 21 38 13 *e:* comusica@uach.cl; hescobar@uach.cl *w:* www.uach.cl/conservatorio

Contact Hector Escobar, conservatoire dir.

Course information 2-yr courses in instrumental studies.

Admissions information *Application requirements* Entrance exam.

Facilities *Performance opportunities* Series of concerts and recitals; chamber orchetra, youth orchestra.

COLOMBIA

BOGOTÁ

UNIVERSIDAD NACIONAL DE COLOMBIA - CONSERVATORIO DE MÚSICA
Avenida Carrera 30 no 45-03, Edificio 305, Bogota
t: +57 1 3165000 ext 12506 *e:* consermu_farbog@unal.edu.co *w:* www.facartes.unal.edu.co
Course information The music programme is currently being restructured; full details will be available on the website from Jan 2010.

MUSIC FESTIVALS

Cartagena Music Festival
w: http://cartagenamusicfestival.com

GUATEMALA

GUATEMALA CITY

UNIVERSIDAD DEL VALLE DE GUATEMALA
Departamento de Música, BA Isabel Ciudad-Real, Guatemala City, Guatemala
t: +502 2364 03 36 ext 541 *e:* isabelcr@uvg.edu.gt *w:* www.uvg.edu.gt
Course information Licenciatura (5-yr intensive BA programme) in music education.
Admissions information *Application requirements* Graduate of high school; application by personal statement and proof of exam results.

MEXICO

MEXICO CITY

CONSERVATORIO NACIONAL DE MÚSICA DE MÉXICO
Presidente Mazaryk 582, Colonia Polanco, Mexico
t: +52 80 63 47 *e:* conservatorianos@hotmail.com *w:* www.conservatorianos.com.mx
Course information Licentiates in harp, opera/concert singing, harpsichord, composition, choral/orchestral conducting, guitar, string instruments, woodwind instruments, brass instruments, organ, percussion, piano, musicology, teaching.

AMERICAS

PERU

LIMA

CONSERVATORIO NACIONAL DE MÚSICA
Jr Carabaya 421-435, Lima, Peru
t: +51 426 9677 *f:* +51 426 5658
e: informes@cnm.edu.pe *w:* www.cnm.edu.pe
Course information Professional training in performance, composition, conducting and research based study. Flexible training programmes up to a maximum of 10 semesters (5 years). *Instrumental* Woodwind, brass, strings, percussion, harp, guitar, piano all available as principal study *Vocal* Singing course *Conducting* Choral conducting available as primary option *Historical performance* Early music group *Composition* Available as a principal study or an elective *Orchestral* Brass band, symphony orchestra, wind orchestra *Chamber music* Guitar ensemble and other instrumental chamber groups *Opera* Opera studio *Choral* Mixed-voice choir *Other* Musicology; music education
Admissions information *Application requirements* Competitive auditions every Jan.

PUERTO RICO

CONSERVATORIO DE MÚSICA DE PUERTO RICO

951 Ave Ponce de León, San Juan, 00918, Puerto Rico
t: +787 751 0160 *f:* +787 763 3886
e: admisiones@cmpr.edu *w:* www.cmpr.edu
Contact Eutimia Santiago, admissions dir

Course information BMus, MMus, graduate diploma in performance. *Instrumental* Orchestral instruments, guitar, piano *Vocal* Classical singing *Orchestral* Symphony orchestra, bands, ensembles. *Chamber music* Chamber music ens. *Opera* Opera workshop *Choral* Large choir and chamber choir *Jazz/world* Jazz big band; afrocaribbean music ens.

Admissions information *Term dates* 16 Aug-10 Dec (1st semester); 18 Jan-21 May (2nd semester). *Application requirements* Music knowledge and experience is required. Specific requirements are listed at www.cmpr.edu/admisiones *Application deadline* Dec for BMus, Jan for postgraduates. Late admissions for BMus in May (subject to availability of places). *Fees* Enrolment fee $35.00 for BMus, $100.00 for postgraduate students. Full fee details on website. *No of students* Approx 400 students, 33 international. *Language requirements* Must read, write and comprehend Spanish. Individual classes can be held in English, group classes are in Spanish.

Facilities *Music facilities* New theatre under construction, soundproofed rooms, performance spaces, computers with music software. *Performance opportunities* All students participate in large and small ensembles during their studies.

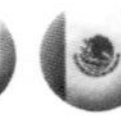

THE REST OF THE WORLD

THE REST OF THE WORLD

AUSTRALIA AND NEW ZEALAND PAGE 256

Australia's music conservatoires are all faculties of universities and are therefore fully integrated within the national higher education system, and the structure of degree programmes closely matches the anglo-saxon model (bachelors, masters, doctorate). The slight difference is that Australian institutions offer a degree after 3 years' study; successful completion of this entitles students to move to a 4th 'honours' year.

A more significant difference is that, being a southern hemisphere country with winter during the northern hemisphere's summer and conversely, the academic year is reversed. While this may cause a little difficulty for exchange programme candidates, for those looking to study at postgraduate level it would simply be a question of taking a break between the end of the bachelors degree at home and the beginning of the masters down under (beginning in February).

The same is true of New Zealand, and here also practical advanced music training is provided at universities, incorporated within traditional university academic music departments rather than specialist faculties.

Both countries support music centres dedicated to the promotion of their respective national musics: Sounz, The Centre for New Zealand Music (http://sounz.org.nz/) and the Australian Music Centre (www.australianmusiccentre.com.au).

WORLD PAGE 265

The majority of this guide has focused on institutions in western countries with a long tradition of providing music training. But as many western conservatoires are realising, the opportunities for establishing links elsewhere are great. China in particular is proving willing to build contacts in western countries (several US institutions, for instance, hold entrance auditions in China), just as it is raising the profile of classical music in the country through a programme of concert hall building and promotion of young artists.

Of course, Japan and South Korea have been particularly successful at developing their own music education systems, as evinced by the number of Japanese and Korean musicians performing on international concert stages both as soloists, orchestral members, chamber musicians and conductors. The teaching of western music in Japan, for instance, goes back to the second part of the 19th century, with Japanese educators looking to the USA for its ideas and principles. Consequently, students heading there can be assured of a thorough training to go alongside the unique cultural experiences on offer to a westerner living there.

Elsewhere – Palestine, for example, or India – the infrastructure for classical music education is only now being put in place, and you can read our special focus on music in India here. Otherwise, in the remainder of this section, we provide contact details for a selection of institutions in various locations around the world for those who are interested in venturing off the well trodden path.

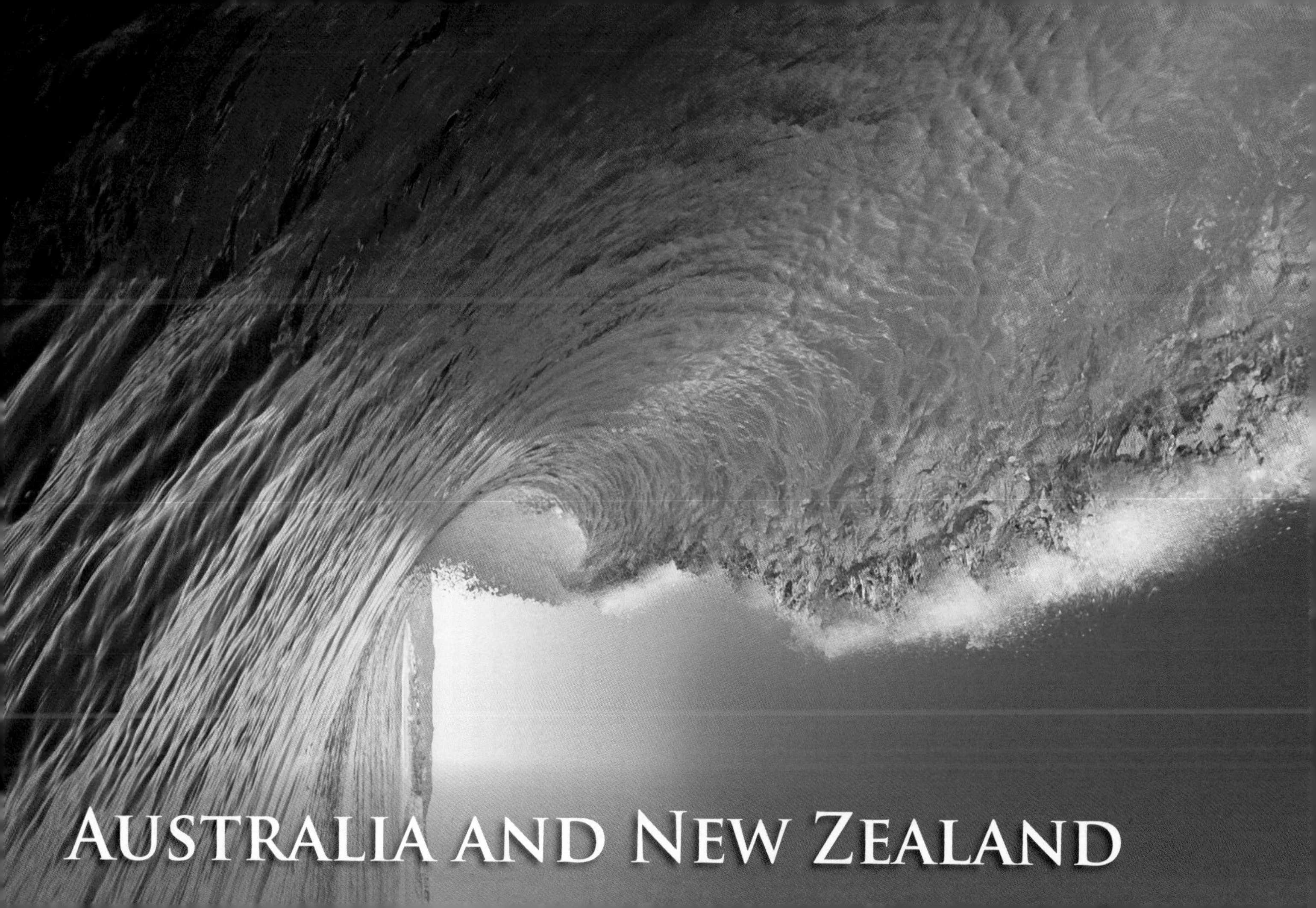
AUSTRALIA AND NEW ZEALAND

AUSTRALIA

ADELAIDE

Capital of the state of South Australia with a population of over 1 million people, the city has a reputation for being one of Australia's cultural centres. It also has a sizeable student population of over 50,000. The city is close to several national parks, not to mention some of the country's popular winemaking areas.

CLIMATE

Hottest months January and February (17-29°C), coolest month July (7-15°C). Rainfall modest for most of the year, peaking in June and July (around 80mm).

MUSICAL LIFE

The main orchestra, one of the country's biggest and busiest, is the Adelaide Symphony Orchestra which performs widely throughout the country (including Sydney Opera House)

OTHER CULTURAL INFORMATION

Art Gallery of South Australia is neighbour to the state's museum; the former includes a collection of art and artefacts from around the world and houses temporary/visiting events. The Tandanya National Aboriginal Cultural Institute promotes art, music and the culture in general of indigenous Australians. The city's arts centre is the Adelaide Festival Centre which has 4 main performance spaces: the 2000-seater main theatre, 2 smaller spaces and outdoor amphitheatre.

FESTIVALS AND EVENTS

The main festival is the biennial all-round Adelaide Festival of Arts (February-March, even numbered years), which has a strong classical music programme. There are numerous associated events and other cultural celebrations, such as the cabaret festival (June), a festival of ideas (July). The South Australian Living Artists Festival (August) focuses on local artists and features exhibitions and public art events.

TOURIST INFORMATION

www.adelaidecitycouncil.com, visitor@adelaidecitycouncil.com, +61 8 8203 7611

ELDER CONSERVATORIUM OF MUSIC

The University of Adelaide, Adelaide SA 5005, Australia
t: +61 8 8303 5995 *f:* +61 8 8303 4423
e: music@adelaide.edu.au
w: www.music.adelaide.edu.au

Course information Bachelor of music (performance; instrumental, jazz, pedagogy, music technology); bachelor of education (performance, composition, integrated studies); PG degrees; PhD, GradDip; diploma of instrumental music (2-yr part time course available to students on another undergraduate course at the university).

Admissions information *Application requirements* International students apply direct to university or through international representatives across the world. Audition process involves audition, interview, portfolio plus aural and theory test. Master of music and PhD available in performance, as well as ethnomusicology/musicology, composition, music education, music technology. Graduate diploma for performance-focused *Application deadline* 30 Sep for local and international students; auditions early Dec (some late auditions may be scheduled). *Fees* AUS $1500-3900 (commonwealth supported students); non-commonwealth students pay more. All international students must pay fees. *Scholarships* Various prizes, awards and scholarships offered by the Elder Conservatorium. University of Adelaide also offers scholarships to those who can demonstrate financial need.

Facilities *Music facilities* Elder Hall auditorium, with organ; electronic music unit; music library. *Performance opportunities* Series of lunchtime recitals featuring students; various student ensembles, orchestras, choirs and chamber groups.

BRISBANE

Capital city of the Pacific coast state, Queensland. The city's architecture shows plentiful evidence of its colonial origins but there has also been much recent development

CLIMATE

Hottest month January (21-29°C), coolest month July (10-20°C). Rainfall highest in summer (over 100mm per month November-February), dropping off for the winter months (July-September averages between 25mm and 40mm).

MUSICAL LIFE

The Queensland Orchestra is based at the concert hall in the Queensland Performing Arts Centre but also performs at the conservatoire. The Lyric Theatre at the same centre is Opera Queensland's main home – it stages 3 productions each year as well as touring.

OTHER CULTURAL INFORMATION

Performing arts centre has 2 performance spaces

besides the concert hall and lyric theatre: main Playhouse theatre (850 seats) and Cremorne Theatre, a more flexible space. Queensland Theatre Company and the state's ballet company perform there. A relatively new modern art gallery is located nearby, alongside the main state gallery, the Queensland Art Gallery. An alternative cultural venue is the Judith Wright Centre of Contemporary Arts which covers a range of performing and visual art forms and is home to a correspondingly diverse number of cultural organisations: the Institute of Modern Arts, a circus ensemble, dance company and the Australian Film Television and Radio School. The Brisbane Powerhouse is another contemporary performance centre, with a variety of types of performance space.

FESTIVALS AND EVENTS
A triennial exhibition showcases art from the Asia-Pacific area

TOURIST INFORMATION
www.visitbrisbane.com.au

QUEENSLAND CONSERVATORIUM
PO Box 3428, South Brisbane QLD 4101, Australia
t: +61 7 3735 6111 *f:* +61 7 3735 6262
e: qcgu_enquiry@griffith.edu.au
w: www.griffith.edu.au/music
Course information BMus in classical music, music technology and popular music. Graduate certificates, and diplomas in music, music technology, vocal studies and opera studies. MMus and research programmes also offered.
Admissions information *Application deadline* 1 Aug, undergraduate; 15 Oct (semester 1) or 31 May (semester 2), postgraduate. *Scholarships* Email intl-financialaid@griffith.edu.au for information on scholarships available to international students. *No of students* 650 students from over 20 countries internationally.
Facilities *Music facilities* 2 campuses (South Bank and Gold Coast). 615 seat concert hall, music technology studios and music library (South Bank); pop music studios (South Bank). Various performers in residence. *Performance opportunities* A range of outreach projects across Queensland, ensemble in residence scheme, competitions, concerts and events.

CANBERRA
Australia's capital city although far from being its largest (its population is well under half a million) or its most vibrant, located on Lake Burley Griffin and surrounded by hills.

CLIMATE
Hottest month January (13-28°C), coldest month July (0-11°C). Rainfall is more or less uniform throughout the year, ranging between 40mm and 60mm per month.

MUSICAL LIFE
City's main concert hall is at the conservatoire.

OTHER CULTURAL INFORMATION
Performing arts and entertainment at the Canberra Theatre and Playhouse. The distinctive, modern-design National Museum of Australia is located in the capital, as is the country's national library. Local exhibits on display at the Canberra Museum and Gallery.

FESTIVALS AND EVENTS
International Music Festival in May; also folk festival in April.

TOURIST INFORMATION
www.visitcanberra.com.au

CANBERRA SCHOOL OF MUSIC
The Australian National University, Building 100, Canberra ACT 0200, Australia
t: +61 2 6125 5700 *f:* +61 2 6125 9775
e: schoolofmusic@anu.edu.au
w: www.anu.edu.au/music
Course information Bachelor of arts and bachelor of music degrees; successful completion of 3-year bachelor of music gives access to 4th year specialisation. 1-year master of music in performance (including jazz), musicology or composition; graduate diploma and graduate certificate also available for students wishing to advance their technical or musical skills. School is home to university keyboard institute, focusing on keyboard-related activity in performance, teaching, research and instrument-making/restoration.
Admissions information *Application requirements* Students must either audition in their own country or submit a recording. Bachelors candidates must sit a diagnostic entrance exam at the start of the year. *Scholarships* ANU scholarships available for students in all faculties, including international students; students automatically considered for scholarships at time of audition. *Language requirements* English

Facilities *Music facilities* Llewellyn Hall, seats over 1300, is also venue for visiting professional groups; band room, seats 120; rehearsal room, seats 120. Research resources on Australian composers. *Accommodation* International students guaranteed accommodation if they accept academic offer and apply for accommodation by 21 Jan.

HOBART

Main city and port on the island of Tasmania overlooked by Mount Wellington – this, together with its waterside location, gives it a particularly natural feel. It is a major base for sailing in Australia (there is an annual yacht race on Boxing Day from Sydney to Hobart).

CLIMATE

Warmest months January and February (11-22°C), coldest month July (-3-4°C). Rainfall is relatively similar from month to month but marginally wetter in autumn.

MUSICAL LIFE

Tasmanian Symphony Orchestra is based at the Federation Concert Hall (also a recital venue.

OTHER CULTURAL INFORMATION

Theatre Royal is the main theatre, staging drama, music events, opera, comedy etc. The state museum and gallery focuses on the island's history and geography.

FESTIVALS AND EVENTS

Main arts festival is known as 10 Days on the Island, a biennial event (odd-numbered years) featuring various art forms, exhibitions etc, and not restricted to the cify.

TOURIST INFORMATION

www.welcometohobart.com.au, info@vibetasmania.co.au, +61 3 6234 4666

UNIVERSITY OF TASMANIA CONSERVATORIUM OF MUSIC

University of Tasmania, Private Bag 63, Hobart TAS 7001, Australia
t: +61 3 6226 7314 (general); +61 3 6226 7351 (international office) *f:* +61 3 6226 7333
e: international.office@utas.edu.au; conservatorium.admin@utas.edu.au *w:* www.utas.edu.au/music
Contact Anne Marie Forbes, international office.

Course information BMus is 3-year professional training degree, with option to progress to 1-year advanced honours degree by recommendation from the faculty. Bachelor of music studies degree concentrates on theory and understanding of music. Graduate certificate/diploma, 2-yr diploma, MMus and PhD offered. *Contemporary* Students can choose to focus on contemporary music during the BMus.

Admissions information *Term dates* Two intakes; Feb and Jul. *Application requirements* Written test on music theory and history, plus aural test and general writing ability; performance audition comprising 3 contrasting pieces; interview. Overseas applicants may also need to supply recording. *Fees* Undergrad music degrees AUS $15,750; masters degree, graduate diploma etc approx AUS $15,000. *Scholarships* The Tasmanian International Scholarship Scheme; UTAS offers an unlimited number of scholarships to meritorious students entering all courses (except medicine and research studies). These scholarships provide a 25% reduction in tuition fees for the duration of a course. All applicants are automatically considered for a scholarship and if successful will be notified on their course offer letter.

Facilities *Music facilities* 200 seat recital hall with 4 pianos, computer lab, recording room/digital streaming studio, DVD authoring studio, piano lab, percussion room, lecture theatre with piano, music library. *Accommodation* Accommodation is available to students a short distance away at the main Sandy Bay campus in Hobart. Students can either catch a bus or walk to the Conservatorium. Private accommodation can also be arranged with assistance from UTAS.

SYDNEY

Largest city in Australia, though not actually its capital, located on the Pacific coast in the south east state of New South Wales. It has a population of around 4.5 million people and is the country's commercial and cultural centre, not to mention a major international tourist destination. Its harbour, complete with bridge and Opera House, is a world famous landmark, and its oceanside location comes with numerous beaches. In common with all major cities, it has much to offer the visitor, and the student in particular, by way of nightlife, leisure and cultural activities.

CLIMATE

Hottest month January (18-26°C), coolest month July (8-17°C), and although summers can be much hotter, winters remain relatively mild and temperatures remain above freezing. Rainfall is high during summer and autumn (generally through storms rather than prolonged periods of rain) with over 100mm per month from January to June.

MUSICAL LIFE

Sydney Opera House is home to the Sydney Symphony Orchestra, which performs around 150 concerts a year in the concert hall there and elsewhere. Opera Australia is the home company, performing in the 1500+ seater opera theatre that is also the main stage for the Australian Ballet. The City Recital Hall is another substantial international concert venue (it opened in 2000), but intended mostly for smaller scale orchestras, chamber music and choirs. The city's town hall was, before the Opera House, the main venue for orchestral concerts and is still used now (it has a notable William Hill & Son organ). The Australian Brandenburg Orchestra is a period instrument band based in the city (but which splits its season between Sydney and Melbourne), as is the Australian Chamber Orchestra (which takes its concert programmes to various major Australian cities).

OTHER CULTURAL INFORMATION

Sydney Opera House includes various spaces for performing arts as well as opera and orchestras – the drama theatre is the base for the 1200 seater Sydney Theatre Company. Various theatres besides, such as the 2-space Wharf Theatre (a Sydney Theatre Company venue), a converted waterside commercial venue; other major venues are the Capitol Theatre, Theatre Royal and Lyric Theatre. It has the usual range of galleries and museums, including a contemporary art museum, the MCA.

FESTIVALS AND EVENTS

There are numerous cultural events throughout the year, the Sydney Festival in January being the largest, covering every form of performing art, visual art, free and open air events etc; there is also a fringe event running alongside it. Main art event is the Biennale of Sydney (even-numbered years); Sydney Film festival runs for a fortnight in June

LOCAL PUBLICATIONS

The country's main newspaper, The Sydney Morning Herald (www.smh.com.au), is published in the city.

TOURIST INFORMATION

www.sydneyaustralia.com.au

AUSTRALIAN INTERNATIONAL CONSERVATORIUM OF MUSIC

114 Victoria Rd, Rozelle, Sydney NSW 2039, Australia
t: +61 2 9637 0777 *f:* +61 2 9637 0222
e: admin@aicm.edu.au *w:* www.aicm.edu.au
Contact Katrina Quintal.

Course information Bachelor of music (perf), diploma of music (perf); master of music in association with the Wesley Institute in worship arts, music and media, performance or arts management; also perf arts high school (yrs 7-12). Jazz, classical and contemporary performance available.

Admissions information *Term dates* Mid Feb-early Jul (semester 1); end Jul-early Dec (semester 2). *Application requirements* Entrance by audition and interview. *Application deadline* 12 Feb (semester 1); 10 Jul (semester 2). *Fees* AUS $16,800 (local), AUS $19,600 (international). *Scholarships* Check website for details. *No of students* 20% of student body from overseas. *Language requirements* IELTS score 6.0 for international students.

Facilities *Music facilities* Performance hall, practice studios, classrooms, recording facilities, computers and technology, various instruments. *Accommodation* Homestay accommodation available.

SYDNEY CONSERVATORIUM OF MUSIC

The University of Sydney, Sydney NSW 2006, Australia
t: +61 2 9351 1222 *f:* +61 2 9351 1264
e: con.international@sydney.edu.au
w: http://sydney.edu.au/music
Contact Elaine Chia.

Course information Diploma of music, bachelor of music studies, bachelor of music (performance, musicology, composition, music education), advanced diploma of opera, graduate diploma of music, master of music studies (performance, pedagogy, creative sound production), master of music (performance, musicology, composition, music education), DMA, PhD.

Admissions information *Term dates* Late Feb-Jun (semester 1); Jul to end Nov (semester 2). *Application requirements* Must meet minimum university entry and pass audition and/or interview. *Application deadline* 31 Oct (for Feb entry); 30 Apr (for Jul entry). *Fees* Undergraduate from AUS $12,360 per semester; postgraduate from AUS $12,000 per semester. *Scholarships* Over AUS $1 million in scholarships awarded each year. Merit-based scholarships assessed on audition. No separate application necessary. Other university scholarships available by application. *No of* *students* 830 students, inc 80 international students. *Language requirements* English (IELTS minimum 6.5) for most degrees.

Facilities *Music facilities* 5 performance halls (inc 500-seat concert hall), 69 practice rooms, 130 teaching studios and offices, music technology and recording facilities, extensive library. Close to Sydney Opera House, in heart of Sydney's cultural precinct. *Performance opportunities* Over 400 concerts per year plus local, regional and international touring opportunities *Accommodation* On-campus accommodation at University of Sydney; accommodation service available through international office.

MUSIC FESTIVALS

Adelaide Festival of the Arts PO Box 8221, Station Arcade, Adelaide SA 5000, Australia *t:* +61 8 8216 4444 *f:* +61 8 8216 4455 *e:* info@adelaidefestival.com.au *w:* www.adelaidefestival.com.au Biennial. Multi-arts festival. Opera, dance, classical and contemporary music, theatre, visual arts, new media events, literature, outdoor, masterclasses, forums, etc

Australian Festival of Chamber Music PO Box 5871, Townsville Qld 4810, Australia *t:* +61 7 4771 4144 *f:* +61 7 4771 4122 *e:* info@afcm.com.au *w:* www.afcm.com.au Concert season of chamber music; chamber music seminar.

Australian International Music Festival Sydney World Projects, 195 Glen Cove Marina Rd, Suite 201, Vallejo, CA 94591, USA *t:* +1 707 556 5885 *f:* +1 707 556 5896 *e:* deborah-gibbs@world-projects.com *w:* www.world-projects.com Annual. Brings together best school, university, community musicians to Sydney Opera House, with opportunity to join in a wide variety of music and social activities.

International Trumpet Guild Conference ITG2010, Conference Secretariat, PO Box 601, Pyrmont, NSW 2009, Australia *t:* +61 2 951 7722 *f:* +61 2 9518 7222 *e:* itg2010@trumpetguild.org *w:* www.trumpetguild.org Festival featuring concerts and clinics by the world's finest trumpet players and teachers. Changes country each year.

ISCM World Music Days 2009 ISCM Secretariat, c/o Muziek Centrum Nederland, Rokin 111, NL-1012 KN Amsterdam, The Netherlands *t:* +31 20 3446060 *e:* info@iscm.org *w:* www.iscm.org Contemporary music concerts, meetings, symposium. Different location each year; 2010 in Sydney.

Perth International Arts Festival M418, University of Western Australia, 3 Crawley Ave, Crawley WA 6009, Australia *t:* +61 8 6488 2000 *f:* +61 8 6488 8555 *e:* festival@perthfestival.com.au *w:* www.perthfestival.com.au Oldest annual international multi-arts festival in the southern hemisphere. Offers some of the world's best theatre, music, film, visual arts, street arts, literature and free community events.

NEW ZEALAND

AUCKLAND

Major city in New Zealand's North Island. Its Pacific location (a curiosity of the city is that, being situated on a narrow strip of land, it is bounded on each side by a different sea) and natural environment, combined with the generally relaxed lifestyle of the city, make it an attractive place to live. Maritime activity is very much in evidence, the city being something of a magnet for yachtsmen.

CLIMATE

Warmest months January and February (15-24°C), coolest month July (7-15°C). Rainfall relatively high at 100mm or more per month from April to September, dropping to around 70mm in January and February).

MUSICAL LIFE

Auckland Philharmonia is the city's orchestra and one of the country's best known, performing mostly at the restored, 1500+ seater Town Hall; the building also includes a smaller room (430 seats). The New Zealand Symphony also has an office in the city and the majority of its programmes, which tour the main New Zealand cities, are performed in Auckland – it's a similar situation for New Zealand Opera.

OTHER CULTURAL INFORMATION

Major venues are the Aotea Centre housing the Herald Theatre for visiting theatre companies and a sizeable auditorium for conferences; and. The Civic, a venue for musicals and suchlike The strong presence of the indigenous Maoris in the city means that there is much evidence of traditional cultural expression.

FESTIVALS AND EVENTS

The biennial Auckland Festival (March, odd-numbered years) has performances in various art forms including music. The city is one of the locations for the annual New Zealand Film Festival (July)

TOURIST INFORMATION

www.aucklandnz.com, nz@aucklandnz.com, +64 9 307 0616

NATIONAL INSTITUTE OF CREATIVE ARTS AND INDUSTRIES

The University of Auckland, Building 520, 6 Symonds St, Auckland, New Zealand
t: +64 9 373 7599 ext 87409 *e:* info-music@auckland.ac.nz *w:* www.creative.auckland.ac.nz

Course information Bachelor of music, 3-year course in composition, history and literature of music, jazz, classical performance, popular music; available as honours degree with 1 extra year's study. Postgrad diploma and master of music both 1-year courses; master of music available in performance, composition, musicology. Doctor of music arts an advanced performance-centred programme.

Admissions information *Term dates* Classes start early March (semester 1) and mid Jul (semester 2). *Application deadline* 1 Oct (semester 1), 1 May (semester 2). *Fees* For international students: NZ $23,290 (BA), NZ $24,390 (BA honours), NZ $24,390 (MM), NZ $27,680 (doctor of musical arts); further administrative fees also apply. *Scholarships* Scholarships available for international students at both undergrad and postgrad levels. *Language requirements* English required.

Facilities *Music facilities* 155-seat music theatre used for staged productions and concerts; practice spaces, recording facilities. *Performance opportunities* School of Music students perform in public with large and small ensembles and in lunchtime concerts and 'emerging artists' series. The School of Music also facilitates hiring student musicians for various external events. *Accommodation* Student residences available in Auckland, including full-board halls of residence, self-catering university flats and private accommodation.

WELLINGTON

New Zealand's capital city lying at a natural harbour on Cook Strait on the south western end of the North Island. Is noted for its picturesque appearance, with its coastal location and surrounded by lush green hills.

CLIMATE

Warmest months January and Feburary (13-21°C), coldest month (July 6-11°C). Wettest month June (150mm), driest month February (60mm). The city's nickname is Windy Wellington.

MUSICAL LIFE

New Zealand Symphony Orchestra and New Zealand Opera both have bases in Wellington and Auckland – opera (among other events) at the Opera House, concerts are at the 2210+ seater Michael Fowler Centre. This is part of the Wellington Convention Centre which also runs the Town Hall and TSB Arena venues, both also used for music events. Royal New Zealand Ballet based in the city (it performs at the St James theatre), as is Chamber Music New Zealand, an organisation promoting concerts throughout the country.

OTHER CULTURAL INFORMATION

City Gallery runs varied art exhibitions; the Adam Art Gallery, part of Victoria University, is another interesting gallery, aiming to present stimulating exhibitions and related events. Wellington Arts Centre encompasses various forms of cultural performance and production, including some devoted to the indigenous Maori culture; this is also a key component of the collection in the Museum of New Zealand, often known as Te Papa, a shortened version of its full title. Theatres include BATS Theatre (contemporary/experimental theatre); Circa Theatre has 2 spaces as well as its own company, as does Downstage Theatre. The city is considered by many the centre of the New Zealand film industry.

FESTIVALS AND EVENTS

New Zealand Arts Festival, with theatre, dance and literature accompanying various classical concerts in its programme, takes place in the city every 2 years (even-numbered years).

TOURIST INFORMATION

www.wellingtonnz.com, bookings@wellingtonnz.com, +64 4 802 4860

TE KOKI - THE NEW ZEALAND SCHOOL OF MUSIC

PO Box 2332, Wellington, New Zealand
t: +64 4 463 5369 *f:* +64 4 463 5157
e: info@nzsm.ac.nz; philippa.scott@vuw.ac.nz
w: www.nzsm.ac.nz
Contact Philippa Scott (course enquiries)

Course information A variety of undergraduate and postgraduate courses in classical performance, musicology, ethnomusicology, instrumental/vocal composition, jazz, music studies, music therapy, musicology, sonic arts. Double majors possible; also foundation certificate in jazz.

Admissions information *Application requirements* International students apply through Victoria University of Wellington. Performance auditions. *Application deadline* Sep (auditions in Oct). *Fees* NZ $21,468, international undergrad tuition; NZ $24,236, international postgrad tuition; various non-tuition fees also apply. *Scholarships* Scholarships available but must be applied for; see website for details of prizes available, including music prizes as well as scholarships.

Facilities *Music facilities* Concert room, concert hall, small theatre; instrument collection includes period instruments (originals and copies); keyboard lab with 12 digital pianos (at Kelburn campus) and with 22 keyboards (at Mt Cook campus); practice rooms available. Artists in residence are New Zealand Piano Quartet, the New Zealand String Quartet, Chrome (period instrument group).

MUSIC FESTIVALS

Adam International Cello Festival and Competition PO Box 3770, Christchurch, New Zealand *t:* +64 3355 4054 *f:* +64 3 365 0318 *e:* catherine@adamcello.co.nz *w:* www.adamcello.co.nz Competition, daily masterclasses, concerts, recitals, workshops and finals gala concert.

New Zealand International Arts Festival PO Box 10-113, Wellington, New Zealand *t:* +64 4 473 0149 *f:* +64 4 471 1164 *e:* nzfestival@festival.co.nz *w:* www.nzfestival.co.nz

Otago Festival of the Arts PO Box 5710, Dunedin 9058, New Zealand *t:* +64 3 477 7600 *f:* +64 3 474 5431 *e:* info@otagofestival.co.nz *w:* www.otagofestival.co.nz Biennial. Festival celebrating the very best in the performing, visual and related arts.

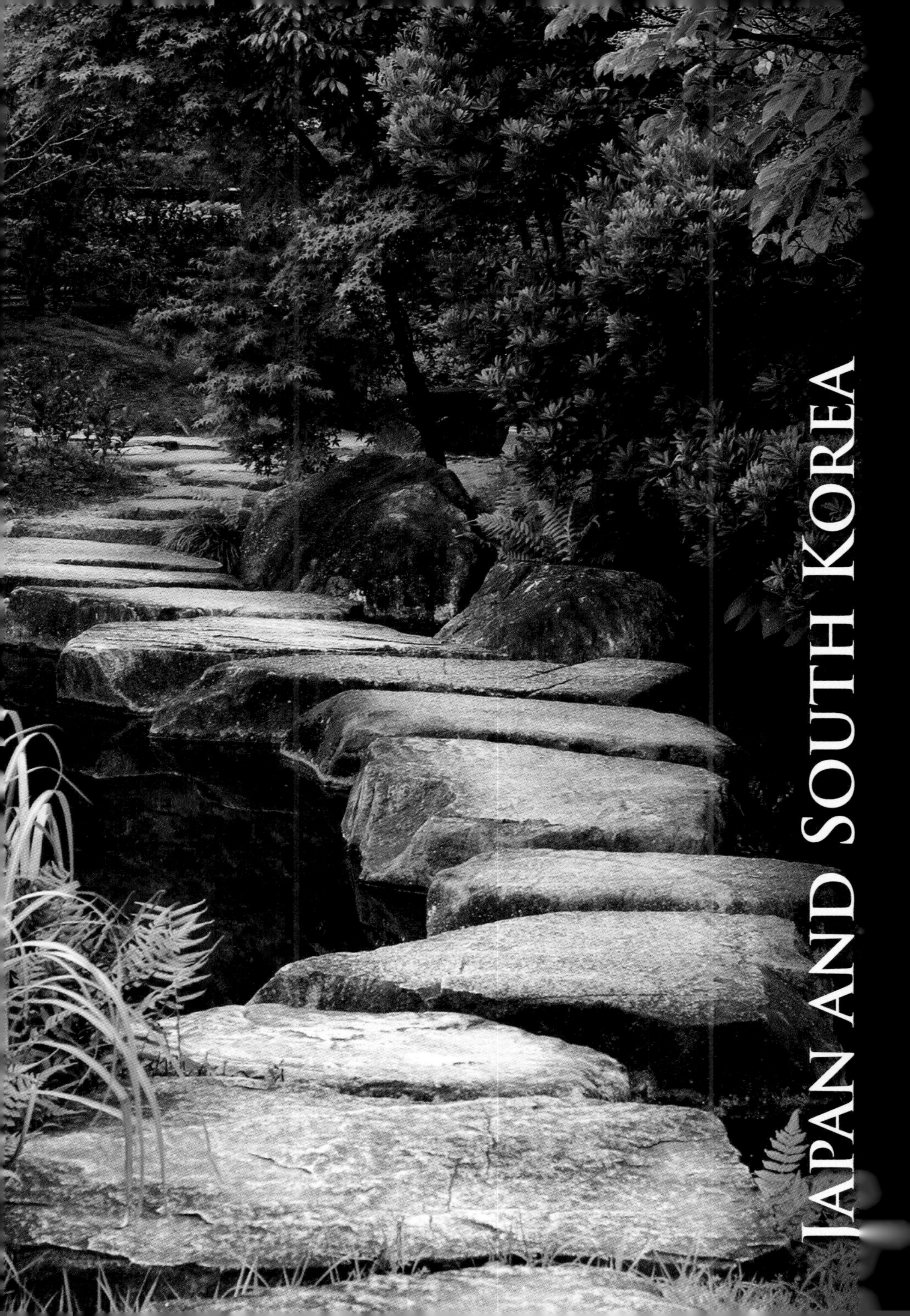
JAPAN AND SOUTH KOREA

JAPAN

NAGOYA

NAGOYA COLLEGE OF MUSIC

7-1 Inabaji-cho, Nakamura-ku, Nagoya-shi, Aichi-ken, Japan
e: shomu_on@meion.ac.jp *w:* www.meion.ac.jp

TOKYO

TOHO GAKUEN SCHOOL OF MUSIC

1-41-1 Wakaba-Cho, Chofu-shi, Tokyo 182-8510, Japan
t: +81 3 3307 4101 *f:* +81 3 3307 4354
e: exam@tohomusic.ac.jp *w:* www.tohomusic.ac.jp
Course information Bachelor of music, master of music.

TOKYO COLLEGE OF MUSIC

3-4-5 Minami-Ikebukuro, Toshima-ku, Tokyo 171-8540, Japan
t: +81 3 3982 3196 *f:* +81 3 3982 8440
e: admissions@tokyo-ondai.ac.jp *w:* www.tokyo-ondai.ac.jp
Course information 4-year degree programmes available in music education, vocal music, instrumental music, composition (including film scoring), conducting. Non-degree programmes in traditional Japanes music (instruments and composition), jazz improvisation, Indonesian gamelan.
Facilities *Music facilities* Main campus includes concert hall; 12-storey classroom/studio building with recital hall and pipe organ; practice room facility; graduate school with performance space and recording studio; 2-storey ensemble rehearsal building.

MUSIC FESTIVALS

Japan Contemporary Music Festival c/o Japan International League of Artists, 1-34-8 Shinjuku Gyoen-mae Bldg 2F, Shinjuku-ku, Tokyo, Japan *t:* +81 3 3356 4033 *f:* + 81 3 3356 5780 *e:* music@jila.co.jp *w:* www.jila.co.jp Annual. The festival features the winning works of the Tokyo International Competition for Chamber Music Composition held in November every year.

Japan International Youth Musicale in Shizuoka Tokoha Gakuen Educational Institute, 1 22 1 Sena Aoi-ku, Shizuoka City, Shizuoka Prefecture 420-0911, Japan *t:* +81 54 261 1356 *f:* +81 54 261 5601 *e:* jiym2@tokoha.ac.jp *w:* www.tokoha.ac.jp/jiym/jiym.html Triennial international youth music festival.

Kitakyushu International Music Festival 2-1-1 Chuo, Yahatahigashi-ku, Kitakyushu 802-0019, Japan *t:* +81 93 663 6567 *f:* +81 93 662 3028 *e:* info@kimfes.com *w:* www.kimfes.com

Osaka International Festival New Asahi Building, 2-3-18 Nakanoshima, Kita-ku, Osaka 530-0005, Japan *t:* +81 6 6227 1061 *f:* +81 6 6227 1262 Annual. Classical music, concertos, piano recitals, ballet, traditional Japanese music and dance.

Pacific Music Festival Sumitomo Seimei Sapporo Chuo Building 1F, 1-14 Minami 2-jo, Higashi 1-chome, Chuo-ku, Sapporo 060-0052, Japan *t:* +81 11 242 2211 *f:* +81 11 242 1687 *e:* webmaster@pmf.jp *w:* www.pmf.jp International educational music festival. Orchestra with chamber music, string quartet and composition courses.

DAEGU

KEIMYUNG UNIVERSITY COLLEGE OF MUSIC AND PERFORMING ARTS

2800 Dalgubeoldaero, Dalseo-Gu, Daegu 704-701, South Korea
e: intl@kmu.ac.kr *w:* www.kmu.ac.kr
Course information Departments of orchestral instruments, voice, composition, piano, organ.
Admissions information *Term dates* Sep-Dec (1st semester); Mar-Jun (2nd semester) *Application deadline* May
Facilities *Music facilities* Multimedia studio, acting room, film editing room, computer/MIDI studio, sound recording studio, listening room. *Accommodation* 5 halls of residence, one allocated to english speakers.

SEOUL

KOREA NATIONAL UNIVERSITY OF ARTS

Seongbuk-gu, Seoul, 136-716, South Korea
t: +82 2 7469 042 *e:* whiten58@knua.ac.kr (admissions); ir@knua.ac.kr (international relations) *w:* www.knua.ac.kr
Course information Bachelor's offered in vocal music, instrumental music, composition, conducting and musicology. 3-year artist diploma in opera, lied & oratorio, instrumental music or conducting; MA in composition, music technology or musicology. School of Korean Traditional Arts also offers BA or MA in traditional music (vocal music, instrumental music, composition) and traditional folk theatrics. Also film, TV, dance, drama, multimedia and musical theatre courses.
Admissions information *Term dates* 1 Sep-mid Jan (fall semester); 2 Mar-mid Jul (spring semester). *Language requirements* Fluency in English (IELTS 5.3 or higher) or Korean (TOPIK level 3 or higher)
Facilities *Music facilities* There are a total of 11 venues for performance, exhibition, and film-screening: Five for performance including an art theater, a small theater, KNUA Hall, a box stage, an experimental stage; two for exhibition; one movie theater; and three projection rooms. *Accommodation* Dormitories on campus.

SUMMER SCHOOLS
FINDING AN INSTRUMENTAL TEACHER
MUSIC SCHOLARSHIPS

HONG KONG, CHINA AND TAIWAN

HONG KONG

CITY OF HONG KONG

HONG KONG ACADEMY OF PERFORMING ARTS
School of Music, 1 Gloucester Road, Wanchai, Hong Kong
t: +852 2584 8554 or 2584 8579 *f:* +852 2584 8722 *e:* aso@hkapa.edu; pr@hkapa.edu
w: www.hkapa.edu
Contact Academic services officer
Course information Bachelor of music degree (3 years) provides training to professional level plus historical/theoretical knowledge. Advanced diploma (2 years) focuses on performing and performance issues. Professional diploma (usually 1 year) for post-diploma or post-degree professional training. Master of music available in performance or composition (2 years in either case). Courses provided in several departments: Chinese music; composition & electronic music; keyboard; opera & vocal studies; strings; woodwind, brass and percussion; academic studies.
Admissions information *Application requirements* 2-round audition: preliminary performance followed by audition and theory test. *Fees* Diploma, advanced diploma and professional diploma: HK$31,575.00; bachelor's: HK$42,100.00; master's: HK$78,000.00 (full-time), HK$52,000.00 (part-time) in 2010-11 *Scholarships* A significant number of scholarships are awarded by the Academy each year to both local and non-local students based on academic merit and/or financial need. These scholarships are donated by the Society of the Academy for Performing Arts, other private organisations, professional bodies and individuals. *No of students* Approx 200 students, up to 20% international. *Language requirements* Proficiency in English or Chinese must be demonstrated; requirements differ depending on course.
Facilities *Music facilities* 3 purpose-built performance venues: concert hall and recital hall at Wanchai campus, theatre at new Bethanie campus. 12 teaching rooms, 17 practice rooms. Electronic music studio, keyboard lab. Instruments include pipe organ, chamber organ, harpsichords, fortepiano, 8 concert pianos, various string instruments (including baroque). Large orchestral music collection. *Performance opportunities* Recitals, masterclasses and staged opera productions throughout the year. *Accommodation* None; students must arrange their own accommodation.

MUSIC FESTIVALS

Hong Kong Arts Festival c/o International Programme Office, 35 Little Russell St, London, United Kingdom *t:* +44 20 7637 5661 *f:* +44 20 7323 1151 *e:* joseph.seelig@easynet.co.uk *w:* www.hk.artsfestival.org Features all types of music, but mainly classical, world music and jazz.

BEIJING

CENTRAL CONSERVATORY OF MUSIC

43 Baokia Street, Xicheng District, Beijing 100031, China
t: +86 10 66425597 *e:* contactus@ccom.edu.cn
w: www.ccom.edu.cn

Course information 4 year bachelors (5 year for composition, musicology, conducting, music education, vocal/opera); 2-3 year masters, includes thesis and viva. Non-degree study programmes available.

Admissions information *Application requirements* Online application form and then competitive audition *Application deadline* Beginning of Dec; auditions in Feb *Fees* Application fee 200 yuan preliminary + 60 yuan, next round (undergrad); 900 yuan (postgrad). Tuition: 33,000 yuan (undergrad), 38,000 yuan (masters), 42,000 yuan (doctorate). *No of students* Approx 1900 students in total, of whom 40 from overseas. *Language requirements* No rigid rules on Chinese requirements for international students who apply for advanced study.

Facilities *Music facilities* Concert hall and recital hall *Accommodation* Twin rooms in halls of residence.

SHANGHAI

SHANGHAI CONSERVATORY OF MUSIC

No 20 Fenyang Road, Xuhui District, Shanghai 200031, China
t: +86 10 64370137 *f:* +86 10 64330866
w: www.shcmusic.edu.cn

SICHUAN

SICHUAN CONSERVATORY OF MUSIC

6 Xinsheng Road, Chengdu 610021, China
t: +86 28 85430297 *f:* +86 28 85430712
e: sccmws@126.com; scyyxy@mail.sc.cninfo.net
w: www.sccm.cn

Course information Courses in composition; music performance (conducting, piano, organ, accordion, woodwind, strings, traditional Chinese instruments, voice inc opera and musical theatre); arts marketing and management; musicology; music education; film & TV; piano tuning and violin-making. Undergrad degrees 4-5 years, depending on course. Also classical Chinese dance; art and design.

Admissions information *Application requirements* Entrance exam in Mar (undergrad); Jan (masters). *Fees* 21,000 yuan (undergrad); 27,000 yuan (masters) per year. *Language requirements* Entrance exam in Mandarin.

TAIWAN

TAIPEI

NATIONAL TAIWAN UNIVERSITY OF ARTS

59, Sec 1, Ta-kuan Rd, Panchiao, Taipei, Taiwan
t: +886 2 22722181 *f:* +886 2 29687563
e: pr@.ntua.edu.tw *w:* www.ntua.edu.tw

Admissions information *Application requirements* Application must include 2 letters of recommendation and health certificate. *Application deadline* 1 Feb-30 Mar. *Fees* US $60 or NT $1500 application fee. *Scholarships* Scholarships of NT $10,000 per month for outstanding international students. Also scholarships providing free tuition and smaller NT $3000 monthly living allowance. Application period for scholarships is after acceptance. *Language requirements* Instruction is mainly in Mandarin; undergrad applicants must be proficient.

TAIPEI NATIONAL UNIVERSITY OF THE ARTS - SCHOOL OF MUSIC

1 Hsuen-Yuen Road, Peitou, Taipei 112, Taiwan
t: +886 2 2893 8200 *f:* +886 2 2893 8856
e: musiccollege@www.tnua.edu.tw *w:* http://musiccollege.tnua.edu.tw

Course information Bachelor of music (composition, keyboard, voice, strings, woodwind, brass, percussion); course has core requirements for all majors (including history of Chinese music, history of Taiwanese music, traditional music, plus western music history, theory, musicianship). Master of music (composition, piano, voice, conducting). MA programme (music pedagogy or musicology). Master of music for wind, string or percussion players comes from Graduate Institute of Orchestral Instruments.

SOUTH EAST ASIA

INDIAN CLASSICAL MUSIC

Background

Literature about Indian classical music by non-Indian writers has a long history. Apart from the many musical treatises written in Persian during the six centuries of Islamic dominance of India (13th to 18th centuries), British and Eurasian commentators also began to write about Indian music from the late 18th centuries onwards. In more recent times, broadcasting and recording technology, cheap travel and the growth of Indian communities overseas have made Indian classical music accessible to thousands of new listeners around the world. Yet despite these changes and the deep interest in Indian classical music cultivated by many non-Indians, the number of non-Indian performers of Indian classical music is still very small.

There are several important reasons for this. Firstly, the traditional system for training performers in India involved living full-time with of one teacher, normally for a period of several years. This system – known as the *guru-shishya* tradition – has changed significantly since Indian independence (for example students now rarely live full-time with their *guru*), but its core values and the nature of the relationship between teacher and disciple still prevail. Secondly, there is no standardised approach to training within the *guru-shishya* system: it is predominantly an oral tradition, so doesn't fit readily into an institutional framework. This emphasis on oral training also means that working knowledge in one or more Indian languages may be required to learn with some *gurus* although nowadays many do speak at least broken English.

> "Some music students from the West who come to India find it difficult to understand the *guru-shishya* relationship. They may think that it means a total and unquestioning surrender to the *guru* – the dissolution of their own personality – but this can be dangerous. If this equation is not understood in its proper spirit, it can be exploited by one or other party, either consciously or unconsciously. The relationship should only go beyond strictly musical training if based on mutual affection, trust and respect.
>
> Dr Suvarnalata Rao
> Musician / Musicologist

Which tradition: Hindustani or Carnatic?

The serious music student interested in learning Indian classical music must first decide which tradition to pursue. The two main branches of Indian classical music – Hindustani and Carnatic – are similar in their fundamental approach to melodic and rhythmic organization (*rāga* and *tāla*), yet they are distinct traditions, distinguishable by their styles and forms, poetry and song repertories, intonation, ornamentation and instrumentation. Hindustani music is prevalent across India but particularly strong in northern Hindi-speaking states, whilst Carnatic music tends to be concentrated in the southern states of Karnataka, Andhra Pradesh, Kerala and Tamil Nadu.

Students must also choose at the outset whether to specialise in melody or percussion, with melody students training either as vocalists or instrumentalists. A teacher may assist the student's decision by testing his or her rhythmic and melodic aptitude. Depending on the specialisation selected, the teacher will then embark on a phase of training in which only the basic building-blocks of melody and rhythm are taught. The first exercises given to students in both Hindustani and Carnatic traditions are in fact very similar – the more important stylistic nuances are not introduced until the student has mastered the basics.

Opportunities for training in India

For a newcomer to either tradition, a variety of training options is available. Normally a student will not go straight to a *guru*, but will first learn with a teacher, either on a one-to-one basis or as part of a class. Many teachers in India run their own classes, but there are also numerous institutions offering full time courses in music. These include colleges and departments attached to universities as well as other centres run by the government or functioning with government recognition. As in the UK and many other countries, only universities are able to confer degrees, while the other courses lead to diplomas and place less emphasis on theory but focus more on professional training.

Entrance requirements vary from organisation to organisation, with all formal courses requiring an audition. By European standards, fees are generally not very high, however there is little standardisation in terms of syllabus options, so prospective students need to do their own careful research when comparing different courses. In addition, the aims and objectives of some institutions are not clearly articulated, the result being a mixture of individual teaching styles grouped under one roof.

Institutional training for performers

While Indian institutions offering diplomas and degrees in Hindustani and Carnatic music have created wider access to training, contributed to the spread of musicology and helped to develop new audiences for live and recorded music, aspiring professional performers still tend to follow the *guru-shishya* system.

The Sangeet Research Academy in Kolkata (Calcutta) was established in 1978 to bridge this divide between traditional and institutional approaches. The academy syllabus is modelled on the *guru-shishya* system, but framed within a modern institution that also conducts research and uses new technology to promote Hindustani music. The SRA is now recognized as one of the India's leading Hindustani music institutions and several important young artists have emerged from the academy in recent years.

Because the opportunities for learning Hindustani and Carnatic music in India are so diverse, students are advised to undertake their own thorough investigations, including visiting India in person before embarking on a long course of study. A handful of key organisations in India and overseas are listed below as possible starting-points for further research.

Ali Akbar College of Music (Switzerland), Birmannsgasse 42, CH-4055 Basel, Switzerland; *T:* +41-61-2728032; *W:* http://www.aliakbarcollege.org/

Ali Akbar College of Music (USA), 215 W End Avenue, San Rafael, CA 94901-2645, USA; *T:* +1-415-454-9396; *E:* office@aacm.org; *W:* www.aacm.org

Artists-India Gallery: http://www.artists-india.com/

Bharatiya Vidya Bhavan, Munshi Sadan, Bharatiya Vidya Bhavan Chowk, Kulapati K.M. Munshi Marg, Mumbai 400 007, India; *T:* +91-22-23631261 / 23630265 / 23634462 / 63 / 64; *E:* bhavan@bhavans.info; *W:* www.bhavans.info

Dhrupad Sansthan Bhopal Nyas, Suraj Nagar, P.O. National Judiciary Academy, Bhadbhada, Bhopal 462 044, India; *T:* +91-755-2660873; *E:* dhrupad.sansthan@gmail.com; *W:* www.dhrupad.org

Indian Council for Cultural Relations, Azad Bhavan Indraprastha Estate, New Delhi 110002, India; *T:* +91-11-23379309 / 23379310 / 23379314; *W:* www.iccrindia.org

ITC Sangeet Research Academy, 1, Netaji Subash Chandra Bose Road, Tollygunge, Kolkata 700 040, India; *T:* +91-33-24713395 / 24810559; *E:* info@itcsra.org.in; *W:* www.itcsra.org

Kalakshetra Foundation, Thiruvanmiyur, Chennai 600041, India; *T:* +91-44-24524057 / 0836; *W:* http://www.kalakshetra.in

The Music Academy, Madras, New No. 168 (Old No. 306), T.T.K. Road, Chennai - 600 014, India; *T:* +91-44-2811 2231 / 5162; *E:* music@musicacademymadras.com; *W:* www.musicacademymadras.in

National Centre for the Performing Arts, NCPA Marg, Nariman Point, Mumbai 400021, India; *T:* +91-22-22824567; *E:* suvarnarao@hotmail.com; *W:* www.ncpamumbai.com

Rotterdam World Music Academy, Kruisplein 26, 3012 CC Rotterdam, The Netherlands; *T:* T +31-10-2171100; *E:* codarts@codarts.nl; *W:* http://www.codarts.nl

Sangeet Natak Akademi, Rabindra Bhavan, Ferozeshah Road, New Delhi 110 001, India; *T:* +91-22-23387246 / 47 / 48; *E:* sangeetnatak@bol.net.in; *W:* http://sangeetnatak.org

Society for the Promotion of Indian Classical Music and Culture Amongst Youth, 41/42, Lucknow Road, Delhi 110054, India; *T:* +91-11-32594087; *E:* info@spicmacay.com; *W:*http://spicmacay.com/

SINGAPORE

SINGAPORE

YONG SIEW TOH CONSERVATORY OF MUSIC

National University of Singapore, 3 Estate Office Drive, Singapore 117485, Singapore
t: +65 6516 1167 *f:* +65 6872 6915
e: music@nus.edu.sg *w:* www.nus.edu.sg
Course information 4-year bachelor of music degree, majoring in either performance (piano or orchestral instruments) or composition; core curriculum includes theory, history, repertoire studies, conducting, music technology. 2-year graduate diploma has a limited number of places; modules to be passed include major study, large ensemble/ accompanying, chamber ensemble, recital.
Admissions information *Application requirements* Regional auditions in Singapore, Malaysia, China, Hong Kong, Taiwan, Thailand, New Zealand. Recordings acceptable for those who do not live close to audition locations; must include a spoken self-introduction on why they wish to study at the conservatoire. *Fees* S $59,520 total annual tuition for international students; additional fees also apply. *Scholarships* Partial or full scholarships may be awarded based on student's ability or on conservatoire's instrumental requirements. All students automatically considered. *Language requirements* All classes conducted in English; intensive language support available for successful non-native speaking applicants.
Facilities *Music facilities* Various performance opportunities in various concert series run by conservatoire.

THAILAND

SALAYA

MAHIDOL UNIVERSITY COLLEGE OF MUSIC

25/25 Phutthamonthon Sai 4 Rd, Salaya, Photthamonthon, Nakhonpathom, 73170, Thailand
e: mswww@mahidol.ac.th *w:* www.mahidol.ac.th
Course information Undergrad courses in 7areas: music performance,Thai and oriental music, jazz, music technology, music industry, pop music, composition; all follow courses in music theory, music history, music technology. Masters degrees in musicology, music education, music performance.
Facilities *Music facilities* 353-seat music auditorium, recital hall (approx 200 seats), outdoor performance areas; rehearsal rooms, teaching studios, audiovisual room, music library.music arboretum made up of trees used for making instruments, but is also used for special music performances. *Accommodation* Dormitories and other on-campus accommodation available.

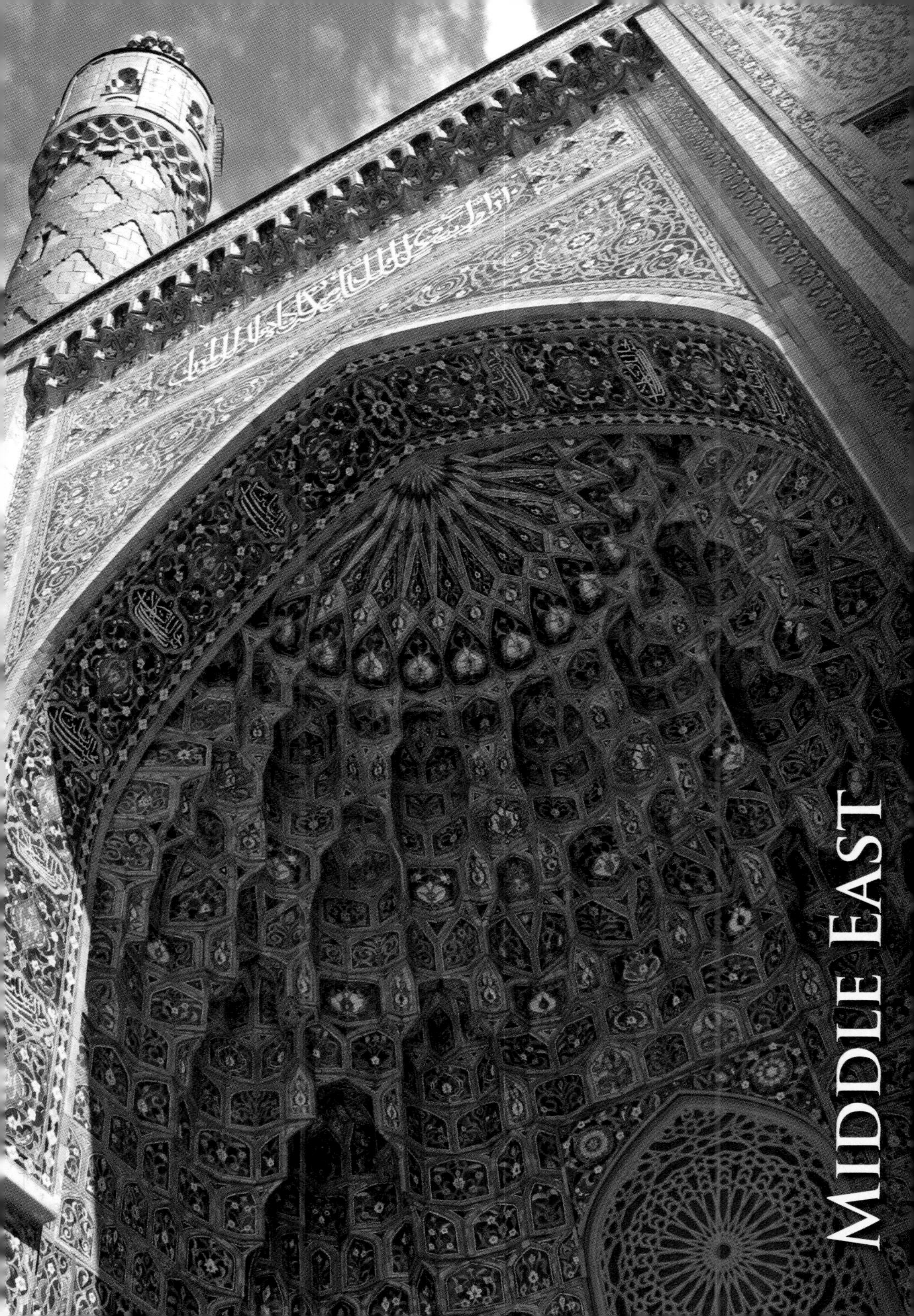

Middle East

JERUSALEM

JERUSALEM ACADEMY OF MUSIC AND DANCE, THE

Campus Givat Ram, Jerusalem,
t: +972 2675 9911 *f:* +972 2652 7713
w: www.jamd.ac.il
Course information Bachelor's and master's courses in 3 faculties: performing arts; composition, conducting and music education; dance, movement and movement notation.
Admissions information *No of students* Over 600 students in total. *Language requirements* English required.

TEL AVIV

BUCHMANN-MEHTA SCHOOL OF MUSIC

Tel Aviv University, Tel Aviv 69978, Israel
t: +972 36408415 *f:* +972 36409174
e: music1@post.tau.ac.il
w: www.tau.ac.il/arts/music
Course information Undergraduate: BMus and BA degrees; postgraduate: MMus and MA (with or without thesis) degrees, as well as artist diploma; "special status" non degree studies (for one or two years). *Instrumental* Violin, viola, cello, double bass, flute, oboe, clarinet, bassoon, french horn, trumpet, trombone, tuba, percussion, harp, piano, organ *Orchestral* Orchestral training program in collaboration with the Israel Philharmonic Orchestra
Admissions information *Term dates* 10 Oct 2010-3 Jun 2011 (semester break 14 Jan 2011- 13 Feb 2011) *Application requirements* Auditions include keyboard proficiency exam as well as live audition; applicants are recommended to attend in person (recordings may be submitted for informal assessment). Postgrad students are accepted at discretion of faculty. *Application deadline* 1 May. *Fees* No application fees. Tuition approximately NIS 16,000 per academic year. *Scholarships* Scholarships available for outstanding students and those in financial hardship; school's excellence programme pays tuition for selected students. The orchestra's work pays full tuition for these students. *Language requirements* Studies for performance majors as well as postgraduate conducting are in English. Other courses need a high level of Hebrew.
Facilities *Music facilities* 450-seat concert hall with 2 Steinway concert pianos, recording studio (connected to hall); smaller, flexible auditorium (120); baroque room with harpsichord, clavichord, fortepiano and pipe organ. *Accommodation* International students are allocated a place in the university dorms.

MUSIC FESTIVALS

Felicja Blumental International Music Festival *e:* info@blumentalfestival.com *w:* www.blumentalfestival.com Musicians from around the globe and talents from Israel. Recitals, musical spectaculars, specially commissioned ballet; lectures, films.
Israel Festival, Jerusalem Jerusalem Theatre, PO Box 4409, 91044 Jerusalem, Israel *t:* +972 2 561 1450 *f:* +972 2 566 9850 e: info@israel-festival.org.uk *w:* www.israel-festival.org.il Annual. Opera, symphonic and chamber music, contemporary and early music, recitals, theatre, ballet and contemporary dance, ethnic music, jazz, rock, multidisciplinary.
Red Sea Jazz Festival 6 Rabin Square, 64951 Tel Aviv, Israel *t:* +972 3 695 9355 *f:* +972 3 696 3528 *e:* eilam@netvision.net.il *w:* www.redseajazzeilat.com/EN Annual. 40 concerts featuring top jazz ensembles, masterclasses and evening jam sessions.
Zimriya-World Assembly of Choirs 4 Aharonowitz St, 64951 Tel Aviv, Israel *t:* +972 3 528 0233 *f:* +972 3 629 9524 e: harzimco@netvision.net.il *w:* www.zimriya.org.il Workshops, concerts, opera.

LEBANON

BEIRUT

ECOLE DE MUSIQUE GHASSAN YAMMINE

PO Box 7, Bikfaya Metn, Beirut, Lebanon
t: +961 3304455 *f:* +961 4980656 *e:* info@edmgy.com *w:* www.edmgy.com
Contact Ghassan Yammine, pres.
Course information Diplomas offered jointly with Boulogne-Billancourt Conservatoire in France. *Instrumental* Orchestral instruments, plus traditional percussion and recorder *Vocal* Vocal studies *Composition* Jazz and classical. *Choral* Children's and adult choir. *Jazz/world* Piano, guitar, electric guitar, bass guitar, flute, saxophone, trumpet, trombone, drums, voice. *Other* Music education, music technology (computerised music, studio production, DJ courses, oriental organ solution); oriental music (oud, bouzouk, kanoun, nay and singing).
Admissions information *Application deadline* All year round. *Fees* $400-1800 per year. *Scholarships* Scholarships available; link to the Ecole de Musique Supérieure de Musique de Paris allows exceptional students to continue their studies in France. *No of students* 600. *Language requirements* French or English.
Facilities *Music facilities* Four campuses across Beirut. *Accommodation* Help finding accommodation available.

MUSIC FESTIVALS

Al Bustan International Festival of Music and the Arts Mail Box 343, 56 Gloucester Rd, London, United Kingdom *f:* +44 20 7937 2633 *e:* festival@albustan.co.uk *w:* www.albustanfestival.com

PALESTINE

JERUSALEM

EDWARD SAID NATIONAL CONSERVATORY

PO Box 66676, 20 Azzahra Street, Jerusalem 91666,
t: +972 2 627 1711 *f:* +972 2 627 1710
e: info@ncm.birzeit.edu *w:* www.ncm.birzeit.edu
Course information Branches in Jerusalem, Ramallah, Bethlehem; pre-conservatoire training leading to diploma that will qualify students for entry into forthcoming university level programme at ESNCM.

APPENDIX

OPERA STUDIOS

Atelier Lyrique - Opéra National de Paris
France *t:* +33 1 40 01 17 52 *f:* +33 1 40 01 17 87 *e:* atelierlyrique@operadeparis.fr *w:* www.operadeparis.fr
Course information For singers: repertoire workshops; role study; special classes (pronunciation, diction, vocal control, theatre workshops etc); possible participation in Opéra de Paris productions and other concerts. Also opportunities for répétiteurs.
Admissions information *Course dates* Oct-Jun. *Application requirements* Applicants must be aged at least 18 and no more than 30. Auditions in Paris in Mar. *Application deadline* Mid Feb. *Scholarships* No fees; singers receive monthly stipend (EUR 1700 in 2009-10).

Bayerische Staatsoper Opernstudio
Germany *t:* +49 89 2185 1046 *f:* +49 89 2185 1003 *e:* opernstudio@st-oper.bayern.de *w:* www.staatsoper.de/opera-studio
Course information Supporting highly talented young artists and preparing them for an international career. Role studies, vocal lessons, acting and movement classes, language training and career development workshops. Artists take small roles in productions on the main stage and take part in concert projects. They also work with professional singers and conductors and have the opportunity to attend main stage rehearsals and performances.
Admissions information *Course dates* Sep-Jul *Application requirements* Singers of all nationalities at the beginning of their career may apply. Age limit 30 for women, 32 for men. Apply with CV (incl date of birth), photo and a recording of 3 arias or songs, of which one should be by Mozart and one in German. *Application deadline* 31 Dec *Scholarships* Members of the opera studio are employed through the German union contract (NV Bühne). 2009 salary amounted to EUR 1689 before tax. *No of students* 8

Cardiff International Academy of Voice
United Kingdom *t:* 02920 481753 *e:* HillJ5@cardiff.ac.uk *w:* www.cardiff.ac.uk/ciav
Course information Students train intensively for eight months. Training includes a two-week course at the Teatro dei Differenti in Barga, Tuscany.
Admissions information *Application requirements* To apply, send a CV and recording of 3 contrasting arias.

Houston Grand Opera Studio USA *t:* +1 713 546 0227 *e:* studio@houstongrandopera.org *w:* www.houstongrandopera.org
Course information A pre-professional, high-level programme for singers and pianists. Artists usually stay at HGO for two seasons, where they sing and study roles, and have weekly voice (or piano) lessons and daily coaching. Other classes include two hours of one-to-one language teaching per week, and group classes in acting, stage movement, diction, finance, etc. Most studio artists have completed a masters degree in voice (or collaborative piano), although this is not required.
Admissions information *Course dates* End Aug-end May. *Application requirements* Selection occurs as part of the Eleanor McCollum competition. Online application in Sep ($25 non-refundable application fee), preliminary auditions in Nov, followed by finals in Houston in late Jan/Early Feb. *Application deadline* Late Sep. *Fees* $27,000 stipend paid to students, plus full health insurance and other benefits. *No of students* 8-12 students.

Internationales Opernstudio Köln Germany *t:* +49 221 221 28391 *e:* rupert.burleigh@stadt-koeln.de *w:* www.operkoeln.com/die-oper/opernstudio/
Course information Programme includes coaching, language teaching, text and basic stage deportment classes. Studio members also appear on a regular basis in main roles in the Kinderoper and comprimario roles with the main opera company as well in their own studio productions.
Admissions information *Application requirements* Singers who are interested in auditioning should write to the studio at the address above. Audition by invitation only. Applicants must have completed vocal training and have stage experience. *Scholarships* Modest monthly salary, paid in part by the "Bühnen der Stadt Köln" and in part by the "Association of the Friends of the Opera" in form of a non-taxable award.

Jette Parker Young Artists Programme
United Kingdom *t:* 020 7212 9192 *f:* 020 7212 9497 *e:* youngartistsprogramme@roh.org.uk *w:* www.roh.org.uk/discover/thepeople/jpya/index.aspx
Course information The JPYAP supports the artistic development of young professional singers, conductors, directors and répétiteurs. The Young Artists are salaried company members, who work at the Royal Opera House on a full-time basis over a two-year period, receiving coaching in all opera disciplines and working on Royal Opera productions.

They give an annual performance on the main stage as well as recitals at and outside the Royal Opera House and also work regularly with the Education and Development Departments. Coaching in all opera disciplines, including music, languages, movement and acting, as well as guidance in related issues and career development, balanced with singing small roles and covering major roles for The Royal Opera.
Admissions information *course dates* Sep-Jul *Application requirements* The programme is intended for extremely gifted individuals at the start of their professional career. Singers and music staff are expected to have some performance experience and to have completed training at an established music college (though this is not an essential requirement). *Application deadline* 8 Jan 2010 (music staff), Oct 2010 (singers), Dec 2010 (directors). *Scholarships* Full time salary for 2 years, plus payment for roles sung or covered. *No of students* 10 singers, 2 staff, 1 director

National Opera Studio United Kingdom
t: +44 20 8874 8811 *f:* +44 20 8875 0404
e: info@nationaloperastudio.org.uk *w:* www.nationaloperastudio.org.uk
Course information 1-year intensive course providing opera training to singers and repetiteurs at an international level. The course adds dramatic, language and interpretative skills to trainess, preparing them for a professional career in opera. 10-15 coaching sessions per week with music, language,movement and stagecraft coaches. Trainees perform concerts throughout the year directed by internationally renowned directors, and normally attend residencies with 2 of the 6 main British opera companies during the 2nd term. For each of the trainees awarded a place on the course, tuition fees are fully covered by grants and scholarships.
Admissions information *Course dates* Sep-Dec, Jan-Mar, Apr-Jun. *Application requirements* Audition. *Application deadline* Dec. *Fees* Audition fee. All other fees paid for through donations to NOS and ACE funding. *Scholarships* Tuition fees are fully covered by grants and scholarships. *No of students* 15 trainees.

Opéra National du Rhin France *t:* +33 388 75 48 04 *f:* +33 388 24 09 34
e: cdefreminville@onr.fr *w:* www.operanationaldurhin.eu/en--auditions.html
Course information 2 years of intense operatic training
Admissions information *Application requirements* Applicants must be under 32 years of age. *Application deadline* Auditions every two years - next round not until end 2011. *No of students* 8 singers and 2 repetiteurs.

Opera Studio Nederland Netherlands *t:* +31 20 420 05 62 *f:* +31 20 42 25 05 *e:* info@operastudio.nl *w:* www.operastudio.nl
Course information Programme bridges gap between conservatoire training and professional stage. Maximum of 8 singers; Dutch candidates given priority. See website for full course details, application procedure and deadlines.
Admissions information *Scholarships* Singers receive monthly grant.

Oper Frankfurt Opera Studio Germany
e: opernstudio@buehnen-frankfurt.de *w:* www.oper-frankfurt.com
Course information Professional tuition in learning new roles, acting, language coaching, phonetics lessons, dialogue, improvisation, make-up. Masterclasses with renowned singers, plus opportunity to perform in small roles in the opera house.
Admissions information *Application requirements* Applicants must have completed singing studies; age limit 30 or younger for women, 32 or younger for men. *Application deadline* End of February.
Portland Opera Studio USA *t:* +1 503 241 1407 *f:* +1 503 241 4212 *e:* music@portlandopera.org *w:* www.portlandopera.org
Course information Vocal coaching, language training, acting classes, masterclasses. Students feature in their own production as well as in supporting roles for mainstage season.
Admissions information *Application requirements* Auditions in New York. *Application deadline* Applications open late summer for entry into subsequent year's programme.

Royal Northern College of Music Opera Studio country *t:* +44 161 907 5200 *e:* info@rncm.ac.uk *w:* www.rncm.ac.uk
Course information New course leading to RNCM international artist diploma. Students perform principal roles in RNCM operas; other performance opportunities.
Admissions information *Course dates* Sep-Apr (2 terms). *Application requirements* Applicants must have completed undergrad and postgrad vocal and opera studies, plus stage experience.

OPERA STUDIOS

San Francisco Opera Center USA *t:* +1 415 861 4008 *e:* merolaauditions@sfopera.com *w:* http://sfopera.com/operacenter.asp
Course information Adler fellowships for advanced singers and répétiteurs offer intensive training and roles in SFO's main stage season.
Admissions information *Application requirements* Applicants must have attended Merola Opera Program, 11-week summer training programme. National auditions held in Oct-Nov.

Staatsoper Unter den Linden - Opernstudio Germany *t:* +49 30 20354635 *f:* +49 30 20354668 *e:* b.anifantakis@staatsoper-berlin.de *w:* www.staatsoper-berlin.de/en_EN/content/opera_artist_opernstudio
Course information 2-year programme. Students learn supporting roles for main stage. Language and voice teaching, acting lessons, training in movement and improvisation, musical coaching and m/classes with guests and members of Staatsoper Unter den Linden.
Admissions information *Application requirements* Age limit 32; application by CV with repertoire list, photo and recording of three arias. *Application deadline* 01 Sep-15 Nov *Scholarships* Monthly scholarship plus salary of EUR 1800 *No of students* 6

Swiss Opera Studio Switzerland *t:* +41 32 322 84 13 *f:* +41 32 322 84 34 *e:* opernstudio@hkb.bfh.ch *w:* www.hkb.bfh.ch
Course information 2-yr MA in Specialised Music Performance: Opera
Admissions information *Course dates* Course begins in Autumn 2010 *Application requirements* Open to those studying at Swiss conservatoires. Students remain registered as voice students at their home institution and take classes at the Swiss Opera Studio. *Application deadline* 15/03/2010 *Fees* CHF 600 per semester. Students should expect to pay for excursions, concerts and course materials on top of tuition fees. *No of students* 24 students in total.

Zurich Opera House - International Opera Studio Switzerland *t:* +41 44 268 66 01 *f:* +41 44 268 64 37 *e:* ios@opernhaus.ch *w:* www.opernhaus.ch
Course information Prepares exceptionally talented young singers and pianists for an international operatic career. Training includes musical interpretation, acting, style, ensemble singing, vocal interpretation, diction. Students are given small parts in Zurich Opera productions, attend performances, workshops and masterclasses. Also course for répétiteurs.
Admissions information *course dates* Academic year Sep-mid July. *Application requirements* Age limit 30 (women), 31 (men). See website for details and application form. *Scholarships* All students receive monthly scholarship. Grants are funded by various organisations and charities.

Association Européenne de Conservatoires, Académies de Musique et Musikhochschulen (AEC) PO Box 805, NL-3500 AV Utrecht, The Netherlands. *t:* +31 30 2361242 *f:* +31 30 2361290 *e:* aecinfo@aecinfo.org *w:* www.aecinfo.org European cultural and educational network with 238 member institutions in professional music training in 55 countries. Aims to stimulate and support international collaboration; represents the interests of the professional music training sector on national, European and international level.

British Council *t:* +44 161 957 7755 *f:* +44 161 957 7762 *e:* general.enquiries@britishcouncil.org *w:* www.britishcouncil.org The UK's international organisation for cultural relations and educational opportunities. UK offices in London, Manchester, Edinburgh, Cardiff, Belfast; overseas offices in 110 countries.

Conservatoires UK Admissions Service (CUKAS) Rosehill, New Barn Lane, Cheltenham GL52 3LZ, United Kingdom *t:* +44 871 468 0470 *w:* www.cukas.ac.uk Provides facilities to research and apply for practice-based music courses at the following UK conservatoires: Birmingham Conservatoire, Leeds College of Music, Royal College of Music, Royal Northern College of Music, Royal Scottish Academy of Music and Drama, Royal Welsh College of Music and Drama, Trinity College of Music.

European League of Institutes of the Arts (ELIA) Keizersgracht 105, NL-1015 CH Amsterdam, The Netherlands. *t:* +31 877 875 244 *f:* +31 877 875 344 *e:* elia@elia-artschools.org *w:* www.eila-artschools.org Independent network of approx 315 arts educations institutes covering all arts disciplines (dance, design, theatre, fine art, music, media arts, architectures) from 47 countries.

European Music School Union Postbus 265, NL-3500 AJ Utrecht, Netherlands. *t:* +31 30 2303740 *f:* +31 30 2303749 *e:* office@musicschoolunion.eu *w:* www.musicschoolunion.eu Umbrella organisation of national music school associations with 26 countries affiliated. Non-governmental and non-profit organisation.

International Association of Music Information Centres Steentstraat 25, B-1000 Brussels, Belgium. *t:* +32 2 504 90 90 *f:* +32 2 502 81 03 *e:* iamic@iamic.net *w:* www.iamic.net Worldwide network of organisations promoting new music; 41 member organisations in 38 countries.

Jeunesses Musicales International Palais des Beaux-Arts, rue Baron Horta 13, B-1000 Bruxelles, Belgium. *t:* +32 2 513 97 74 *f:* +32 2 514 4755 *e:* mail@jmi.net *w:* www.jmi.net Set up in 1945 to enable young people to develop through music across all boundaries. Member organisations in 45 countries.

Mundus Musicalis - Study Music in Europe AEC, PO Box 805, NL-3500 AV Utrecht, Netherlands. *t:* +31 30 2361242 *f:* +31 30 2361290 *e:* aecinfo@aecinfo.org *w:* www.studymusicineurope.org Information website for students (particularly those from outside EU) wishing to study music in Europe.

National Association of Schools of Music 11250 Roger Bacon Drive, Suite 21, Reston, VA 20190-5248, USA. *t:* +1 703 437 0700 *f:* +1 703 437 6312 *e:* info@arts-accredit.org *w:* http://nasm.arts-accredit.org Organisation of schools, conservatoires, colleges and universities in USA. Establishes national standards, provides information to potential students and parents.

Project Visa *w:* http://projectvisa.com/ Information on visa requirements around the world; also details of embassies.

UK Erasmus Council UK Erasmus National Agency, British Council, 28 Park Place, Cardiff CF10 3QE, United Kingdom *t:* +44 29 2039 7405 *f:* +44 29 2023 7494 European Commission exchange programme that enables students in 31 countries to study for part of their degree in another Incorporated into the Socrates programme which covers education from school to university to lifelong learning.

Unesco International Music Council 1 rue Miollis, F-75732 Paris Cedex 15, France. *t:* +33 1 45 68 48 50 *f:* +33 1 45 68 48 66 *w:* www.unesco.org/imc Global network of expert organisations and individuals working in the field of music.

DIRECTORY OF ADVERTISERS

CONSERVATOIRES

Birmingham Conservatoire (p 32) Paradise Place, Birmingham B3 3HG, United Kingdom t: +44 121 331 5901 f: +44 121 331 5906 e: conservatoire@bcu.ac.uk w: www.conservatoire@bcu.ac.uk

CIT Cork School of Music (p 63) Union Quay, Cork, Ireland t: +353 21 480 7310 f: +353 21 454 7601 e: bmus@cit.ie w: www.cit.ie

Guildhall School of Music (p 37) Silk St, London EC2Y 8DT, United Kingdom t: +44 20 7628 2571 f: +44 20 7256 9438 e: music@gsmd.ac.uk w: www.gsmd.ac.uk

Royal Academy of Music (inside front cover) Marylebone Rd, London NW1H 5HT, United Kingdom t: +44 20 7873 7373 f: +44 20 7873 7374 e: registry@ram.ac.uk w: www.ram.ac.uk

Royal Northern College of Music (p 42) 124 Oxford Rd, Manchester M13 9RD t: +44 161 907 5200 f: +44 161 273 7611 e: admissions@rncm.ac.uk w: www.rncm.ac.uk

Royal Scottish Academy of Music (p 35) 100 Renfrew St, Glasgow G2 3DB, United Kingdom t: +44 141 332 4101 f: +44 141 332 8909 e: registry@rsamd.ac.uk w: www.rsamd.ac.uk

Trinity College of Music (p 40-41) King Charles Court, Old Royal Naval College, London SE10 9JF, United Kingdom t: +44 20 8305 4444 f: +44 20 8305 9444 e: enquiries@tcm.ac.uk w: www.tcm.ac.uk

COMPETITIONS

The John Kerr English Song Competition (p 60) Clifton Coach House, Camden Park, Tunbridge Wells TN2 5AA, United Kingdom t: +44 1892 530049 e: maureen.lyle@googlemail.com w: www.johnkerraward.org.uk

DIARY & ANSWERING SERVICES

Morgensterns Diary Service (inside back cover) PO Box 3027, South Croydon CR2 6ZN, United Kingdom t: +44 20 8681 0555 f: +20 8649 7464 e: teleteam@morgensterns.com w: www.morgensterns.com

INSTRUMENTS & ACCESSORIES

Affourtit Bows (p 32) Kastellaan 28, NL-1628 KP Hoorn, The Netherlands t: +31 229 503193 f: +31 6 51127566 e: Pieter@affourtit-bowmaker.com w: www.affourtit-bowmaker.com

Florian Leonhard Fine Violins (p 66) 3 Frognal Lane, London NW3 7DY, United Kingdom t: +44 20 78113 3307 f: +44 20 7813 3308 e: violins@florianleonhard.com w: www.florianleonhard.com

Savarez SA (p 70) 5 ave Barthélemy Thimonnier, BP 133, F-69643 Caluire Cedex, France t: +33 4 37 40 32 00 f: +33 4 37 40 62 10 e: contact@savarez.fr w: www.savarez.fr

Tom Woods Instruments Ltd (p 4 and outside back cover) t: +44 20 7362 1812 e: tom@tomwoodscellos.com w: www.tomwoodscellos.com

Top Wind (p 35) 2 Lower Marsh, London SE1 7RJ, United Kingdom t: +44 20 7401 8787 f: +44 20 7401 8788 e: enquiries@topwind.com w: www.topwind.com

SUMMER SCHOOLS & FESTIVALS

Chetham's International Summer School (p 48) Chetham's School of Music, Long Millgate, Manchester M3 1SB, United Kingdom t:+44 1625 266899, also fax e: info@pianosummerschool.com w: www.pianosummerschool.com

Walnut Hill School (p 213) 12 Highland Street, Natick MA 01760, USA e: jyournell@walnuthillarts.org w: www.walnuthillarts.org

WEB RESOURCES

Piano Street (p 23) w: www.pianostreet.com

OUR OTHER DIRECTORIES

BRITISH & INTERNATIONAL MUSIC YEARBOOK 2010

Thousands of promoters, performing musicians, composers and organisations choose the music yearbook to promote their services and skills through its listings. Hundreds take advantage of Rhinegold's range of advertising opportunities, making it the one-stop shop for the UK classical music industry with around 600 pages of listings covering every aspect of the business.

BRITISH MUSIC EDUCATION YEARBOOK 2010

A complete guide to music education institutions, organisations and services, local authority music contacts, suppliers, and individual performers and performing organisations with educational programmes. It provides information for music students, parents and teachers from primary school to adult and continuing education level.

BRITISH PERFORMING ARTS YEARBOOK 2009/2010

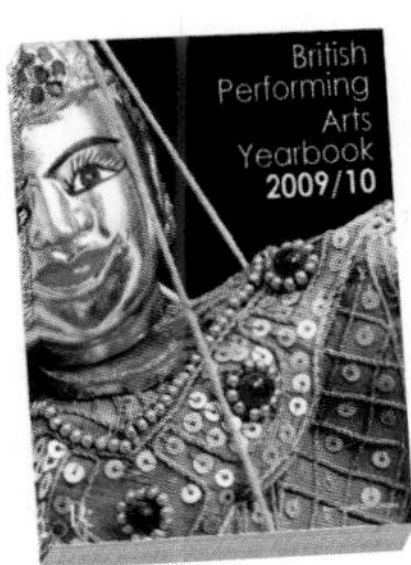

A directory of the UK performing arts industry with essential information for anyone working in it, whether creatively or in the administrative and support sectors. Theatre, dance, opera, circus and all manner of performing arts companies.